PARADIGM
COLLEGE
ACCOUNTING

FOURTH EDITION REVISED

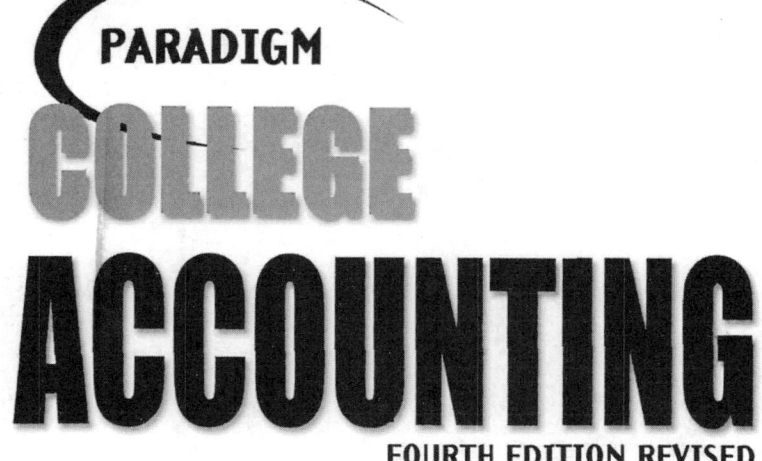

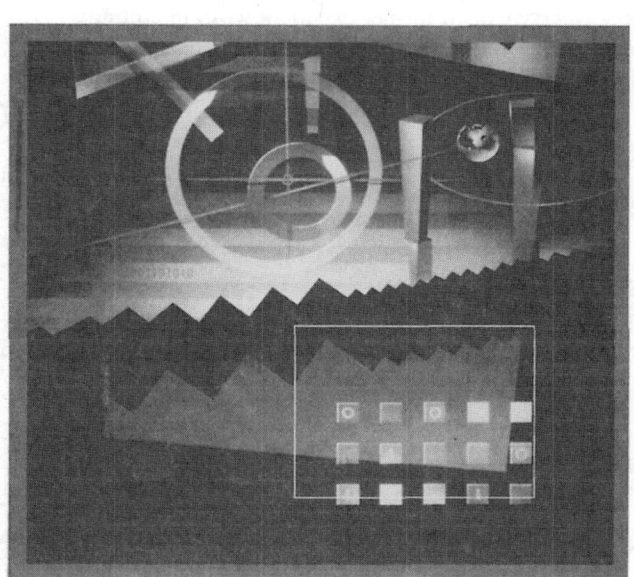

STUDY GUIDE AND WORKING PAPERS
Chapters 1–18

Robert L. Dansby, Ph.D.
Columbus Technical College • Columbus, Georgia

Burton S. Kaliski, Ed.D.
Southern New Hampshire University • Manchester, New Hampshire

Michael D. Lawrence, MBA, CPA, CMA
Portland Community College • Portland, Oregon

EMCParadigm
PUBLISHING

ACKNOWLEDGMENT

The authors and publisher wish to thank Sherry Cohen for her excellent work in editing the chapter summaries and practice tests.

Cover Image: Roy Weinman, Image Bank.

ISBN: 0-7638-2003-2
C/N: 27610

Printed in the United States of America.
10 9 8 7 6

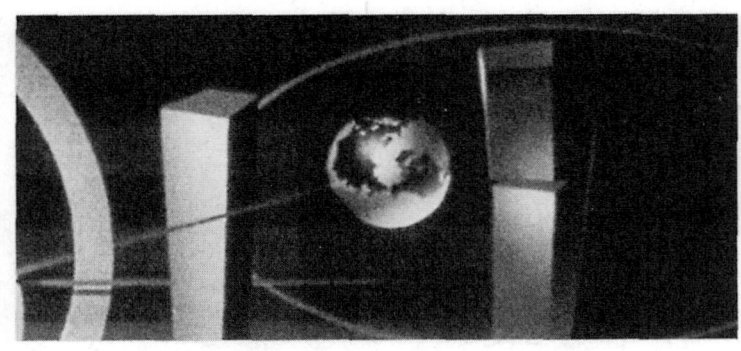

CONTENTS

The Nature of Accounting

CHAPTER SUMMARY

Every individual involved in any kind of work practices **accounting**, which is the process of recording, summarizing, analyzing, and interpreting financial activities to permit organizations and individuals to make informed judgments and decisions.

Organizations need accounting in order to measure success (or failure). One form of organization is the private **business**, which is organized with the objective of earning a profit. Three common forms of business are the **service business**, the **merchandising business**, and the **manufacturing business**.

Users of accounting information include owners, managers, investors, lenders, and the government. Ownership of business can be in the form of a **sole proprietorship** (owned by one person), a **partnership** (owned by two or more persons), or a **corporation** (owned by stockholders). In financial terms, accounting is used to communicate to those who have a need or legal right to know about the financial activities of a particular business. Thus, accounting has been called "the language of business."

The **business entity concept** states that the owner of a business and the business are two separate accounting units. Personal items of the owner should be excluded from all business documents and records.

The accounting system that we use today is deeply rooted in history and is based on three elements: assets, liabilities, and owner's equity. **Assets** are items with money value that are owned by a business. Common examples of assets include cash, accounts receivable, equipment, and supplies. Equipment and supplies are **tangible**, or physical, assets. **Liabilities** are debts owed to creditors. Accounts payable is the major type of liability, and another is notes payable. **Owner's equity** is the dollar value of the financial claim of the owner to the assets of the business. The accounting elements are combined into the **accounting equation**: Assets = Liabilities + Owner's Equity, or A = L + OE.

The value of the accounting elements changes constantly as transactions take place. A **transaction** is any event or condition that changes the value of a firm's assets, liabilities, or owner's equity. The **cost principle** is used to value assets.

All business transactions affect one or more of the basic accounting elements. The effect of business transactions can be stated in terms of increases and decreases in the accounting elements. To maintain the accounting equation in balance, all transactions are recorded as having a **dual effect** on the accounting elements. One type of transaction involves a **shift of assets**, in which one asset increases and another asset decreases. Other transactions affect two accounting elements, such as an increase in an asset and an increase in a liability.

There are two ways to increase owner's equity: (1) an owner investment of cash or other assets into the business and (2) **revenue**—income from carrying out the major activity of a firm. The **realization principle** states that revenue should be recorded when it is earned. There are two ways to decrease owner's equity: (1) an owner withdrawal of cash or other assets from the business and (2) **expenses** incurred in operating a business. Expenses are the costs of operating a business.

The summarizing function of the accountant is shown by the preparation of **financial statements** at the end of an accounting period. An **accounting period** is a period of time, usually a year, for which accounting records are kept. The **income statement** summarizes revenues and expenses, showing **net income** or **net loss** for an accounting period. When revenues exceed expenses, there is a net income. On the other hand, when expenses exceed revenues, there is a net loss. The **statement of owner's equity** shows changes that have occurred in owner's equity during an accounting period. The **balance sheet** is a list of assets, liabilities, and owner's equity on a specific date, usually the last day of an accounting period.

PRACTICE TEST

PART 1 TRUE/FALSE

Please circle the correct answer.

T F 1. Recording means making written records of events.

T F 2. Accounting is a narrow, specialized field that serves only a small part of society.

T F 3. Accounting is often called "the language of business."

T F 4. A merchandising business is one that performs services for customers in order to earn a profit.

T F 5. The three accounting elements are assets, liabilities, and owner's equity.

T F 6. An account payable is usually an informal debt that is based on a spoken promise made to a creditor.

T F 7. The cost principle states that, when purchased, all assets are recorded at their actual cost regardless of market value.

T F 8. The effect of every business transaction can be stated in terms of increases or decreases (or both) in the basic elements of the accounting equation.

T F 9. When business transactions are recorded, the accounting equation must always be left in balance.

T F 10. Owner's equity is increased by revenues and expenses and decreased by owner withdrawals and investments.

T F 11. An accounting period is usually one year, but it can be any length of time.

T F 12. In determining net income, withdrawals by the owner of the business are deducted as business expenses.

T F 13. Other names for the income statement include operating statement, earnings statement, and profit and loss statement.

T F 14. A statement of owner's equity is a listing of all the assets, liabilities, and owner's equity of a business.

T F 15. A balance sheet is rather like a financial snapshot of a business because it shows the firm's financial position at a specific point in time.

PART II MATCHING

Please match each of the following terms with its definition.

a. accounting
b. accounts payable
c. accounts receivable
d. assets
e. balance sheet
f. business entity concept
g. cash
h. creditor
i. equipment
j. expenses

k. financial statements
l. income statement
m. liabilities
n. net income
o. note payable
p. owner's equity
q. revenue
r. supplies
s. transaction
t. withdrawal

_____ 1. The asset that includes currency, coins, checks, and money orders made payable to the business.

_____ 2. The asset that includes physical items such as copy paper, staples, pencils, and other items needed to run the business.

_____ 3. The process of recording, summarizing, analyzing, and interpreting financial activities to permit individuals and organizations to make informed judgments and decisions.

_____ 4. Debts owed by the business.

_____ 5. Any activity that changes the value of a firm's assets, liabilities, or owner's equity.

_____ 6. Costs of operating a business that do not provide future benefit to the business.

_____ 7. A summary of the revenues and expenses of a business for a period of time, such as a month or a year.

_____ 8. A listing of the firm's assets, liabilities, and owner's equity at a specific point in time.

_____ 9. A removal of business assets for personal use by the owner.

_____ 10. The liability that results from purchasing goods or services on credit.

_____ 11. The principle that a business is separate from its owner and other businesses.

_____ 12. Summaries of financial activities that are prepared on a regular basis at the end of each accounting period.

_____ 13. The excess of assets over liabilities.

_____ 14. Income that comes from carrying out the major activity of a firm.

_____ 15. The excess of revenue over expenses.

_____ 16. The physical assets, such as typewriters, desks, and computers, needed by a business in order to operate.

_____ 17. Items with money value that are owned by a business.

_____ 18. A formal written promise to pay a specified amount at a definite future date.

_____ 19. A person or business to whom an account payable is owed.

_____ 20. An asset arising from selling goods or services on credit to customers.

PART III FILL IN THE BLANKS

Please complete each sentence with the correct word or words.

1. A(n) _____ is an organization that operates with the objective of earning a profit.

2. A(n) _____ is a business owned by one person.

3. A(n) _____ purchases goods produced by others and then sells them to customers in order to earn a profit.

4. _____ means examining reports by breaking them down in order to determine financial success or failure.

5. Combining written records into reports at regular intervals is the process of _____.

6. A business owned by more than one person is a(n) _____.

7. A(n) _____ is a business owned by stockholders.

8. _____ are items with money value that are owned by a business.

9. The asset arising from selling goods or services on credit to customers is called _____.

10. The liability that results from purchasing goods and services on credit is called _____.

11. The difference between assets and liabilities is the part of the business that the owner can claim. It is called _____.

12. The accounting equation can be stated as _____ equals _____ plus _____.

13. The purchase of supplies for cash is a transaction in which a(n) _____ occurs.

14. In order to maintain the balance of the accounting equation, it is necessary to record transactions as having a(n) _____ on the basic accounting elements.

15. When expenses are greater than revenues, a(n) _____ results.

PART IV MULTIPLE CHOICE

Please circle the correct answer.

1. The term *accounting* includes which of the following activities:
    a. recording
    b. summarizing
    c. analyzing
    d. interpreting
    e. all of the above

2. A form of business that is owned by investors (called stockholders) is a
    a. sole proprietorship.
    b. partnership.
    c. corporation.
    d. none of the above.

3. The items with money value that are owned by a business are its
    a. liabilities.
    b. assets.
    c. expenses.
    d. revenues.

4. The debts owed by a business are its
   a. liabilities.
   b. assets.
   c. expenses.
   d. revenues.

5. Examples of assets include
   a. cash, accounts receivable, accounts payable.
   b. accounts receivable, equipment, supplies.
   c. equipment, accounts payable.
   d. none of the above.

6. Owner's equity is defined as
   a. the things owned by a business.
   b. the revenues produced by a business.
   c. the difference between assets and liabilities.
   d. cash.

7. If a business has assets of $50,000 and liabilities of $15,000, the owner's equity is
   a. $65,000.
   b. $35,000.
   c. impossible to determine. There is not enough information given.

8. Which of the following transactions would affect only the assets of the business?
   a. The purchase of supplies for cash
   b. The purchase of a computer on credit
   c. The investment of cash by the owner
   d. The withdrawal of cash by the owner

9. Which of the following transactions would affect both the assets and liabilities of the business?
   a. The purchase of supplies for cash
   b. The purchase of a computer on credit
   c. The investment of cash by the owner
   d. The withdrawal of cash by the owner

10. The business entity concept states that, for purposes of accounting, the owner of a business and the business itself are
    a. the same.
    b. separate only if the business is a corporation.
    c. two separate units.
    d. none of the above.

11. The statement that shows a summary of a firm's revenues and expenses for a specific period of time is the
    a. statement of owner's equity.
    b. balance sheet.
    c. financial statement.
    d. income statement.

12. Which of the following statements are called "period" statements?
    a. Income statement and statement of owner's equity
    b. Income statement and balance sheet
    c. Balance sheet and statement of owner's equity
    d. All are period statements.

13. What is the equation for the balance sheet?
    a. Revenue minus expenses equals net income.
    b. Beginning capital plus investment plus net income minus withdrawals equals ending capital.
    c. Assets equals liabilities plus owner's equity.
    d. None of the above

14. In which order should the financial statements be prepared?
    a. Balance sheet, statement of owner's equity, income statement
    b. Statement of owner's equity, income statement, balance sheet
    c. Income statement, statement of owner's equity, balance sheet
    d. Preparation order does not matter.

15. If the statement of owner's equity is prepared before the income statement, what information will be missing from the statement of owner's equity?
    a. Revenue
    b. Beginning capital
    c. Investment
    d. Net income

PART V WRITING/SHORT ANSWER

1. **Reflect** Make a list, in words or simple phrases, of the most important and meaningful points in this chapter.

2. **Question** Think about the most confusing points or the material you do not understand in this chapter. Write down two or three questions that remain unanswered.

3. **Connect** Explain, in one or two sentences, the connection between the main points of this chapter and the major goals of the entire course.

4. **Summarize** Review this chapter's Joining the Pieces visual summary and explain the concept(s) illustrated in a few sentences.

This page intentionally left blank.

WORKING PAPERS

SKILLS REVIEW

EXERCISE 1-1

(a) _____

(b) _____

(c) _____

(d) _____

(e) _____

(f) _____

EXERCISE 1-2

	A	=	L	+	OE
+	**−**	**−**	**+**	**−**	**+**
(a)					
(b)					
(c)					
(d)					
(e)					
(f)					
(g)					
(h)					

EXERCISE 1-3

	Assets				= Liabilities +		Owner's Equity		
	Cash	+ Accounts Receivable	+ Supplies	+ Equipment	= Accounts Payable	+ J. Walker, Cap.	+ Revenue	− Expenses	
(a)									
(b)									
(c)									
(d)									
(e)									
(f)									
(g)									
(h)									

EXERCISE 1-4

EXERCISE 1-5

EXERCISE 1-6

1. _____   5. _____

2. _____   6. _____

3. _____   7. _____

4. _____   8. _____

EXERCISE 1-8

1. _____
   _____
   _____

2. _____
   _____
   _____

3. _____
   _____
   _____

4. _____
   _____
   _____

5. _____
   _____
   _____

6. _____
   _____
   _____

CASE PROBLEMS

PROBLEM 1-1A OR 1-1B

	Assets				**= Liabilities +**			**Owner's Equity**		
	Cash	+	Office Supplies	+	Office Equipment =	Accounts Payable	+	Capital, +	Revenue	− Expenses
(a)										
(b)										
Bal.										
(c)										
Bal.										
(d)										
Bal.										
(e)										
Bal.										
(f)										
Bal.										
(g)										
Bal.										
(h)										
Bal.										
(i)										
Bal.										
(j)										
Bal.										
(k)										
Bal.										

This page intentionally left blank.

	Assets				= Liabilities +		Owner's Equity		
	Cash	+ Accounts Receivable +	Supplies	+ Equipment =	Accounts Payable	+ Capital	+ Revenue	– Expenses
(a)								
(b)								
Bal.								
(c)								
Bal.								
(d)								
Bal.								
(e)								
Bal.								
(f)								
Bal.								
(g)								
Bal.								
(h)								
Bal.								
(i)								
Bal.								
(j)								
Bal.								
(k)								
Bal.								
(l)								
Bal.								

This page intentionally left blank.

PROBLEM 1-3A OR 1-3B

		Assets			= Liabilities +		Owner's Equity		
Cash	+ Accounts Receivable +	Office Supplies +	Store Supplies +	Equipment =	Accounts Payable +	Dee Ann Dill, Capital	+ Revenue	– Expenses
(a)									
(b)									
Bal.									
(c)									
Bal.									
(d)									
Bal.									
(e)									
Bal.									
(f)									
Bal.									
(g)									
Bal.									
(h)									
Bal.									
(i)									
Bal.									
(j)									
Bal.									
(k)									
Bal.									

This page intentionally left blank.

1.

2.

3.

1.

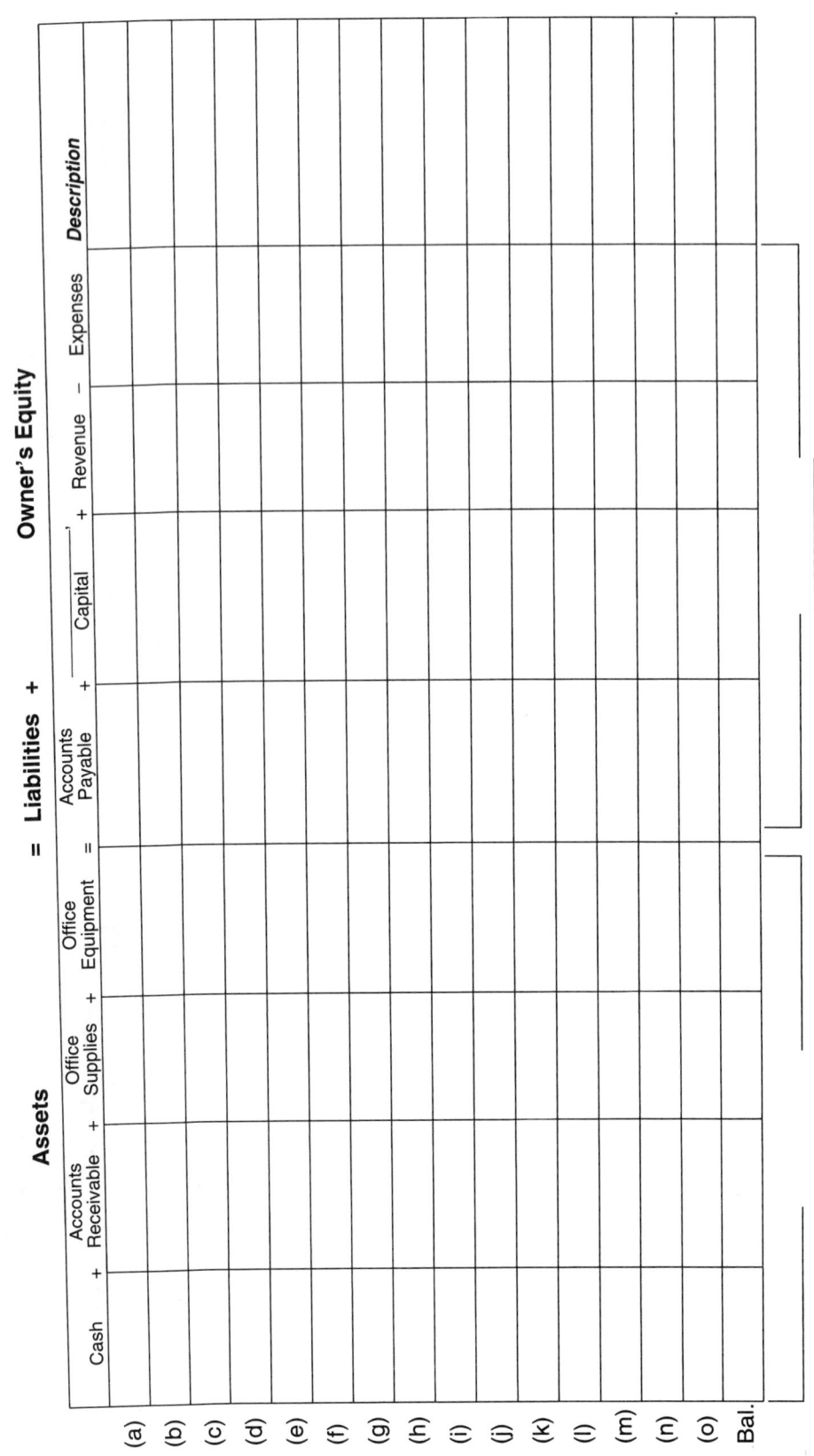

2.

3.

PROBLEM 1-5A OR 1-5B (continued)

4.

This page intentionally left blank.

PROBLEM SOLVING

1., 2., 3.

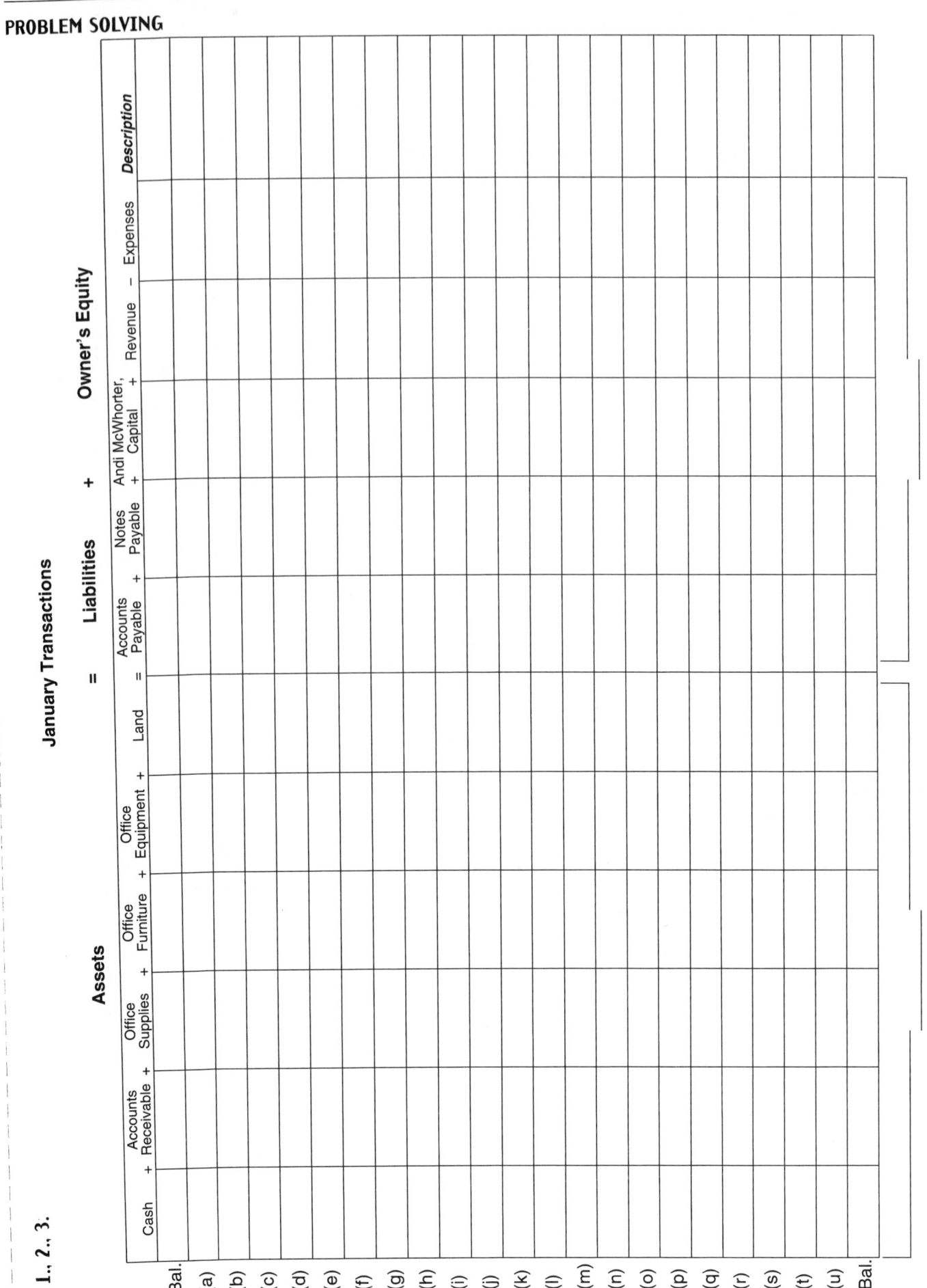

January Transactions

	Assets						=	Liabilities	+	Owner's Equity			
	Cash +	Accounts Receivable +	Office Supplies +	Office Furniture +	Office Equipment +	Land	=	Accounts Payable +	Notes Payable +	Andi McWhorter, Capital +	Revenue –	Expenses	Description
Bal.													
(a)													
(b)													
(c)													
(d)													
(e)													
(f)													
(g)													
(h)													
(i)													
(j)													
(k)													
(l)													
(m)													
(n)													
(o)													
(p)													
(q)													
(r)													
(s)													
(t)													
(u)													
Bal.													

4.

5.

February Transactions

	Assets						=	Liabilities		+	Owner's Equity			
	Cash +	Accounts Receivable +	Office Supplies +	Office Furniture +	Office Equipment +	Land	=	Accounts Payable +	Notes Payable +		Andi McWhorter, Capital +	Revenue –	Expenses	Description
Bal.														
(a)														
(b)														
(c)														
(d)														
(e)														
(f)														
(g)														
(h)														
(i)														
(j)														
(k)														
(l)														
(m)														
(n)														
(o)														
(p)														
(q)														
(r)														
(s)														
Bal.														

6.

COMMUNICATIONS

_____

_____

_____

_____

_____

_____

_____

_____

_____

_____

_____

_____

_____

_____

_____

ETHICS

_____

_____

_____

_____

_____

_____

_____

_____

_____

_____

_____

_____

_____

_____

_____

_____

_____

_____

This page intentionally left blank.

PRACTICE TEST ANSWERS

PART I

1. T
2. F
3. T
4. F
5. T
6. T
7. T
8. T
9. T
10. F
11. T
12. F
13. T
14. F
15. T

PART II

1. g
2. r
3. a
4. m
5. s
6. j
7. l
8. e
9. t
10. b
11. f
12. k
13. p
14. q
15. n
16. i
17. d
18. o
19. h
20. c

PART III

1. business
2. sole proprietorship
3. merchandising business
4. Analyzing
5. summarizing
6. partnership
7. corporation
8. Assets
9. accounts receivable
10. accounts payable
11. owner's equity
12. assets, liabilities, owners' equity
13. shift in assets
14. dual effect
15. net loss

PART IV

1. e
2. c
3. b
4. a
5. b
6. c
7. b
8. a
9. b
10. c
11. d
12. a
13. c
14. c
15. d

PART V

Answers will vary. Please discuss questions with your instructor. You can also discuss issues related to this chapter by logging onto the Paradigm Accounting Web Site at www.emcp.com and clicking on the discussion section.

Recording Business Transactions

CHAPTER SUMMARY

Every business transaction has at least two effects on the elements of the accounting equation. Since there are at least two effects, this has come to be called the *dual effect*. Recording both effects of a transaction is called **double-entry accounting**. Double-entry accounting is the foundation of modern accounting.

The dual effect of a transaction can be recorded in terms of changes in the accounting equation. However, it is considered a better practice to have an individual form to record and store financial information concerning each component of the accounting elements. An **account** is an individual form or record used to show changes in each asset, liability, and owner's equity item. There are various types of accounts. Usually, accounts are bound together in book form, are kept in loose-leaf binders, or are part of a computer system. Such a grouping of accounts is called a **ledger**.

The **standard form of account** is a basic account form with two amount (or money) columns. A **T account** is a skeleton version of the standard form of account. The left side of an account is the **debit** side. The right side of an account is the **credit** side. **To debit** an account means to enter an amount on the left, or debit, side. **To credit** an account means to enter an amount on the right, or credit, side.

Changes in the various accounts are recorded by entering debits and credits. A debit can signify *either* an increase or a decrease, depending on the type of account. Likewise, a credit can signify *either* an increase or a decrease, depending on the type of account. Asset accounts are increased on the debit side and decreased on the credit side. Liability accounts and the owner's capital account are increased on the credit side and decreased on the debit side. Having opposite increase and decrease sides for accounts on the left side of the equation (assets) and accounts on the right side of the equation (liabilities and owner's equity) maintains the accounting equation in balance.

Revenue increases owner's equity. Expenses and owner withdrawals decrease owner's equity. These changes in owner's equity could be recorded directly in the owner's capital account, but this would clutter the account and make it necessary to analyze the owner's capital account in order to determine the amount of net income or net loss for an accounting period. Thus, increases in owner's equity due to revenue are recorded in revenue accounts; decreases in owner's equity due to expenses and owner withdrawals are recorded in expense accounts and an owner's drawing account.

The rules of debit and credit are applied to revenue, expense, and drawing accounts based on their relationship to owner's equity. Because revenue increases owner's equity, increases in revenue accounts are recorded on the same side that shows increases in owner's equity—the credit side. Because expenses and owner withdrawals decrease owner's equity, increases in these accounts are recorded on the same side that shows decreases in owner's equity—the debit side.

At the end of an accounting period, the balances of all revenue accounts, expense accounts, and the owner's drawing account are transferred to the owner's capital account. Therefore, these accounts are referred to as **temporary owner's equity accounts**.

There are customarily more increases in an account than decreases. For this reason, the **normal balance** of an account is always on the increase side. Thus, asset and expense accounts and the owner's drawing account have normal debit balances because these accounts are increased on the debit side. Liability and revenue accounts and the owner's capital account have normal credit balances because these accounts are increased on the credit side.

In a double-entry accounting system, total debits must always equal total credits. To check this equality, a **trial balance** is periodically taken of accounts in the ledger. A trial balance is a listing of all ledger accounts with their balances. A trial balance is usually prepared at the end of each month.

The **balance** of an account is determined by adding (**footing**) the debit side, adding the credit side, and calculating the difference between the two sides. A **debit balance** occurs when the debit side is larger; a **credit balance** occurs when the credit side is larger.

We can summarize the rules in this chapter as follows:

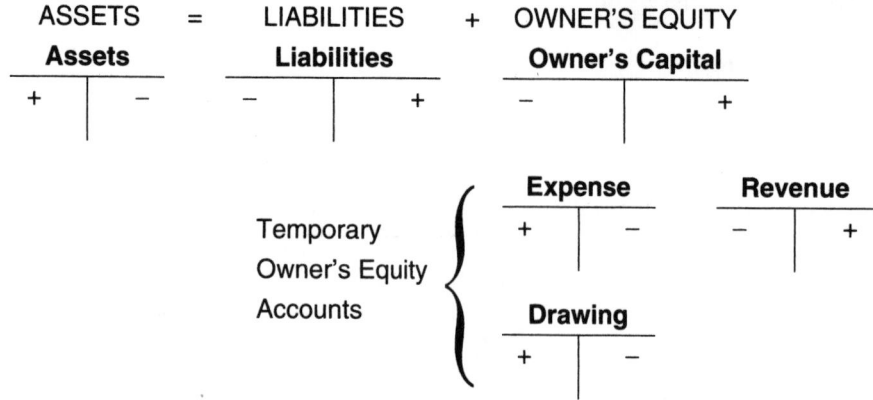

PRACTICE TEST

PART I TRUE/FALSE

Please circle the correct answer.

T F 1. Double-entry accounting means that each transaction has at least two effects, both of which are recorded.

T F 2. In double-entry accounting, each transaction is recorded twice.

T F 3. An account is a separate form or record used to record and summarize information related to each asset, each liability, and each component of owner's equity.

T F 4. Debit is the name given to the right side of an account.

T F 5. Credit is the name given to the right side of an account.

T F 6. A grouping of accounts is called a journal.

T F 7. The word *charge* is sometimes used as a synonym for debit.

T F 8. When we debit an account, we make an entry on the left side of the account.

T F 9. When an account is credited, it is decreased.

T F 10. Asset accounts are increased with debits and decreased with credits.

T F 11. Liability accounts are increased with credits and decreased with debits.

T F 12. Entering equal debits and credits keeps the accounting equation in balance.

T F 13. Revenue and expense accounts are temporary owner's equity accounts.

T F 14. Revenues and expenses are increased with credits and decreased with debits.

T F 15. The trial balance is one of the formal financial statements.

PART II MATCHING

Please match each of the following terms with its definition.

a. account
b. balance
c. credit
d. credit balance
e. debit
f. debit balance
g. double-entry accounting

h. drawing account
i. footing
j. ledger
k. normal balance
l. T account
m. temporary owner's equity accounts
n. trial balance

ledger   1. A collective grouping of accounts.

Credit   2. An entry on the right side of an account.

Trial   3. A listing of all ledger accounts with their balances.

_____   4. The balance that one expects to find in an account; the balance on the side that increases an account.

_____   5. The balance that occurs when the debit side of an account is larger.

_____   6. Recording both effects of a transaction on the accounting elements.

_____   7. A skeleton form of the standard form of account.

_____   8. The expense and revenue accounts and the owner's drawing account.

_____   9. An amount determined by footing the debit and credit sides of an account and calculating the difference.

_____   10. The total of the debit or credit column of an account.

_____   11. An entry on the left side of an account.

_____   12. A separate form or record used to record and summarize information related to each asset, each liability, and each aspect of owner's equity.

_____   13. The account used when the owner withdraws cash or other assets from the business for personal use.

_____   14. The balance that occurs when the credit side of an account is larger.

PART III FILL IN THE BLANKS

Please complete each sentence with the correct word or words.

1. To _____ an account means to enter an amount on the left side.

2. To _____ an account means to make an entry on the right side.

3. The terms *debit* and *credit* do not mean _____ or _____.

4. Debit and credit can each mean either _____ or _____, depending on the type of account.

5. If Pam Jones invests $10,000 cash in a new travel agency, both the _____ account and the _____ account will be increased.

6. If Pam Jones purchases supplies for cash, the _____ account will be decreased and the _____ account will be increased.

7. Revenue and expense accounts are subdivisions of _____.

8. Revenue accounts are increased on the _____ side.

9. Expense accounts are increased on the _____ side.

10. Withdrawals decrease _____; therefore, the drawing account is increased on the _____ side.

11. In analyzing a transaction, we must decide which _____ are affected by the transaction.

12. A(n) _____ is a listing, as of a certain date, of all ledger accounts with their balances.

13. The first step in preparing a trial balance is to find the _____ of each account.

14. Footing means _____ the debit and credit columns of each account.

15. The normal balance of an account is on the _____ side.

PART IV MULTIPLE CHOICE

Please circle the correct answer.

1. A grouping of accounts is called a
   a. journal.
   b. ledger.
   c. book.
   d. file.

2. To debit an account means to
   a. increase the account.
   b. decrease the account.
   c. make an entry on the left side of the account.
   d. make an entry on the right side of the account.

3. To credit an account means to
   a. increase the account.
   b. decrease the account.
   c. make an entry on the left side of the account.
   d. make an entry on the right side of the account.

4. An asset account is decreased by
   a. debiting the account.
   b. crediting the account.

5. The owner's capital account is increased by
   a. debiting the account.
   b. crediting the account.

6. In order to make a proper entry for each transaction, a careful analysis is made to determine
   a. the titles of the accounts affected.
   b. whether the accounts affected are increased or decreased.
   c. how to record the increase or decrease.
   d. all of the above.

7. The purchase of equipment on account would be recorded as a
   a. debit to Equipment and a credit to Accounts Payable.
   b. debit to Equipment and a credit to Cash.
   c. debit to Accounts Payable and a credit to Equipment.
   d. debit to Equipment only.

8. Owner's equity is increased by
   a. revenues and expenses.
   b. revenues and investments.
   c. expenses and withdrawals.
   d. revenues and withdrawals.

9. Owner's equity is decreased by
   a. revenues and expenses.
   b. revenues and investments.
   c. expenses and withdrawals.
   d. revenues and withdrawals.

10. An expense account is increased by
    a. debiting the account.
    b. crediting the account.

11. A revenue account is increased by
    a. debiting the account.
    b. crediting the account.

12. If Pam Jones' Travel Agency pays rent on office space for the month,
    a. Rent Expense is debited and Pam Jones, Capital is credited.
    b. Cash is debited and Rent Expense is credited.
    c. Rent Expense is debited and Cash is credited.
    d. none of the above.

13. If Pam Jones collects revenue for services performed,
    a. Revenue is debited and Cash is credited.
    b. Cash is debited and Revenue is credited.
    c. Cash is debited and Pam Jones, Capital is credited.
    d. none of the above.

14. If Pam Jones withdraws cash for personal use,
    a. Personal Expense is debited and Cash is credited.
    b. Pam Jones, Capital is debited and Cash is credited.
    c. Cash is debited and Pam Jones, Drawing is credited.
    d. Pam Jones, Drawing is debited and Cash is credited.

15. The first step in preparing the trial balance is to
    a. put the heading at the top of the page.
    b. list all accounts in the ledger with their balances.
    c. determine the balance of each account.
    d. foot the trial balance and check for equality of debits and credits.

PART V WRITING/SHORT ANSWER

1. **Reflect** Make a list, in words or simple phrases, of the most important and meaningful points in this chapter.

2. **Question** Think about the most confusing points or the material you do not understand in this chapter. Write down two or three questions that remain unanswered.

3. **Connect** Explain, in one or two sentences, the connection between the main points of this chapter and the major goals of the entire course.

4. **Summarize** Review this chapter's Joining the Pieces visual summary and explain the concept(s) illustrated in a few sentences.

WORKING PAPERS

SKILLS REVIEW

EXERCISE 2-1

	Type of Account	Increase Side	Decrease Side	Normal Balance
Cash	Asset	Debit	Credit	Debit
Equipment				
Joe King, Drawing				
Accounts Payable				
Service Revenue				
Accounts Receivable				
Joe King, Capital				
Taxes Payable				
Fees Earned				
Rent Expense				

EXERCISE 2-2

	Recorded on Debit Side	Recorded on Credit Side
(b)	X	
(c)		
(d)		
(e)		
(f)		
(g)		

EXERCISE 2-3

Equipment	Accounts Payable

Cash	Service Revenue

Rent Expense

EXERCISE 2-4

(a) _____

_____

_____

_____

_____

_____

_____

_____

_____

_____

(b) _____

_____

_____

_____

_____

_____

_____

_____

_____

_____

EXERCISE 2-4 (continued)

(c) _____

(d) _____

(e) _____

EXERCISE 2-4 (continued)

(f) _____

(g) _____

(h) _____

(i)

(j)

EXERCISE 2-5

Cash

Accounts Receivable

Supplies

Equipment

Accounts Payable

Tom Anderson, Capital

Tom Anderson, Drawing

Revenue from Commissions

Rent Expense

Utilities Expense

EXERCISE 2-6

ACCOUNT TITLE	DEBIT	CREDIT

This page intentionally left blank.

PROBLEM 2-1A OR 2-1B

1., 2., 3.

Cash	
a. 14,500	c. 625
~~b. 8000~~	d. 575
f. 150	i. 550
K. 200	J. 225
	L 315
19285 22,850	m 75
14850	n 625
	o 575
= 11285	3,565
	3565

Accounts Receivable	
G. 350	K. 200
	150

Office Supplies	
d 575	d. 575

Truck Supplies	
h. ~~150~~ 125	

Equipment	
	e. 4000

Truck	
b. 8000	

Accounts Payable	
m. 75	e. 4000
	h. 125
	~~m. 75~~
	4,200

John Distas Capital	
	a. 14,500
	~~f. 150~~
	G. 350
	K. 200 15,200
	b. 8000

, Drawing	
n. 625	

Cleaning Fees	
	f. 150

Rent Expense	
c. 625	

Salaries Expense	
i. 550	
o. 575	
1,125	

Truck Expense	
h. 125	
J. 225	
350	

Utilities Expense	
L. 315	

3.

John Distasio Trial Balance May 5, 20X1													
ACCOUNT TITLE		DEBIT					CREDIT						
CASH	11295	1	4	5	0	0							
Acct Receivable	150		3	5	0	00							
Truck	8000	8	0	0	0	00							
office supplies	575		5	7	5	00							
Equipment	4000	4	0	0	0								
Acct Payable	4050						4	2	0	0			
John Distasio, Capital	22.500						1	5	2	0	0		
John Distasio, drawing	625			6	2	5				4050			
Rent expense				6	2	5				22,500			
Salaries expense			1	1	2	5							
Truck expense	2290			3	5	0				500			
Utilities expense				3	1	5							
		2	7	0	5	0	2	7	050				

19400

PROBLEM 2-2A OR 2-2B

(a) _____

_____

(b) _____

_____

(c) _____

_____

(d) _____

_____

(e) _____

_____

(f) _____

_____

(g) _____

_____

(h) _____

_____

(i) _____

_____

(j) _____

_____

(k) _____

_____

This page intentionally left blank.

PROBLEM 2-3A OR 2-3B

1., 2., 3.

Cash	
a. 14,000	b. 450
g. 400	d. 1,100
n. 200	e. 600
	f. 170
14,600	J. 350
	K. 160
10,166	l. 299
	m. 180
	o. 700
	P. 75
	Q. 350
	4,434

Accounts Receivable	
i. 425	

Office Supplies	
b. 450	
K. 160	

Office Equipment	
C. 3,900	
h. 600	
~~K. 160~~	
4,660	

Accounts Payable	
d. 1,100	C. 3,900
	h. 600
	4,500
	d. 3,100

MACK , Capital	
	a. 14,000

MACK , Drawing	
o. 700	

Revenue from Fees	
	g. 400
	i. 425
	n. 200
	10,025

Rent Expense	
e. 600	

Salaries Expense	
J. 350	

Advertising Expense	
f. 170	

Telephone Expense	
M. 180	

Utilities Expense	
l. 299	

Miscellaneous Expense	
P. 75	

3.

DAVID MACK TRIAL BALANCE June 1, 20X1											
ACCOUNT TITLE			**DEBIT**				**CREDIT**				
CASH	~~1200~~		10	1	6	6					
Account Recievable	225			4	2	5					
Office Supplies	610			A	5	0					
Office Equipment	8700		4	6	6	0					
Account Payable	7600							4	5	0	0
MACK, capital								14	0	0	0
Mack, drawing				7	0	0		10	0	2	5
Revenue	825							10	0	2	5
Rent expense				6	0	0					
Salaries expense				3	5	0					
advertizing expense				1	7	0					
Telephone expense				1	8	0					
Utilities expense				2	2	9					
miscellaneous expense					7	5					
Miscellaneous expense											
			22425				22425				

1., 2., 3.

+ Cash −			− Accounts Receivable +		+ Office Supplies −
a. 28,000	b. 375		i. 450		b. 375
h. 110	d. 8,500		k. 410		
28,110	e. 6,000		1,060		
= 9065	f. 90				
	g. 800		**+ Office Equipment −**		**+ Automobile −**
	j. 75		c. 3,200		d. 8,500
	l. 925				
	m. 125				
	n. 205				
	o. 800				
	p. 75				
	q. 575				
	r. 500				
	19,045				

+ Trucks −		− Accounts Payable +		Georg Lawson, Capital +	
e. 6,000		q. 575	c. 3,200	? p. 75	a. 28,000
		r. 500			
		1,075	= 2,125		27,925

+ Lawson, Drawing −		− Service Revenue +		+ Rent Expense	
o. 800			h. 110	g. 800	
			i. 450		
			k. 610		
			1,170		

+ Salaries Expense		+ Gasoline and Oil Expense		+ Telephone Expense	
L. 925		f. 90		m. 125	

+ Utilities Expense		+ Miscellaneous Expense	
n. 205		j. 75	

3.

ACCOUNT TITLE		DEBIT	CREDIT
CASH	9 515	9065	
Acct Receivable	610	1060	
Office supplies	375	375	
" Equipment	3 200	3200	
Automobile		8500	
Trucks	24,600	6000	
Acct Payable	20 725	→	2125
LAWSON, CAPITAL	28000	→	27925
Drawing	875	875	8800
Service Revenue			1170
Rent expense		800	
Salaries expense		925	
Gasoline + Oil expense		90	
Tephone expense		125	
Utilities expense		205	
		49895	49895

GEORGE LAWSON
TRIAL BALANCE
MARCH 1, 20X1

?

MOGREN Company
Trial Balance
July 31, 20X2

ACCOUNT TITLE	DEBIT	CREDIT
CASH	11500	
Acct Receivable	3000	
Building	43000	
Equipment	30500	
Acct Payable		9000
Linda Mogren, capital ?		67750
Linda Mogren, Drawing	13500	
Revenue from service		39900
Rent expense	7000	
Salaries Expense	2850	
Telephone Expense	1000	
Utilities Expense	4300	
	116,650	48,900

1st 116,650
− 48900
_____
67,750

This page intentionally left blank.

CHALLENGE PROBLEMS

PROBLEM SOLVING

1., 2., 3.

Cash	Accounts Receivable	Office Supplies

	Truck Supplies	Equipment

Truck	Accounts Payable	Notes Payable

David Payne, Capital	David Payne, Drawing	Delivery Revenue

Rent Expense	Salaries Expense	Gasoline and Oil Expense

PROBLEM SOLVING (continued)

Utilities Expense Telephone Expense Repair Expense

Miscellaneous Expense

3.

ACCOUNT TITLE	DEBIT	CREDIT

4.

5.

6.

COMMUNICATIONS

ETHICS

This page intentionally left blank.

PRACTICE TEST ANSWERS

PART I

1. T
2. F
3. T
4. F
5. T
6. F
7. T
8. T
9. F
10. T
11. T
12. T
13. T
14. F
15. F

PART II

1. j
2. c
3. n
4. k
5. f
6. g
7. l
8. m
9. b
10. i
11. e
12. a
13. h
14. d

PART III

1. debit
2. credit

3. increase, decrease
4. increase, decrease
5. Cash, Pam Jones, Capital
6. Cash, Supplies
7. owner's capital
8. credit
9. debit
10. owner's equity, debit
11. accounts
12. trial balance
13. balance
14. adding
15. increase

PART IV

1. b
2. c
3. d
4. b
5. b
6. d
7. a
8. b
9. c
10. a
11. b
12. c
13. b
14. d
15. c

PART V

Answers will vary. Please discuss questions with your instructor. You can also discuss issues related to this chapter by logging onto the Paradigm Accounting Web Site at www.emcp.com and clicking on the discussion section.

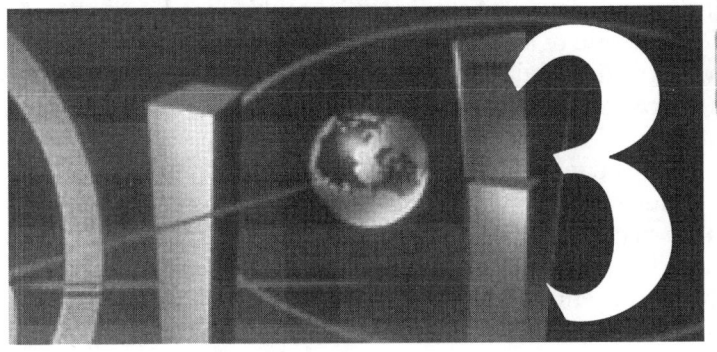

3 Starting the Accounting Cycle for a Service Business

CHAPTER SUMMARY

The **accounting cycle** for a service business consists of the steps involved in the recording and summarizing processes of accounting. The first four steps in the accounting cycle for a service business are the following:

1. Analyze transactions from source documents.
2. Record transactions in a journal.
3. Post from the journal to the ledger.
4. Prepare a trial balance of the ledger.

Source documents are various types of business papers used as a basis for recording business transactions. Examples of source documents include checks received, bills received, receipts, check stubs, and invoices. The accounting **principle of objective evidence** states that source documents should form the foundation for recording business transactions.

A **journal** is a form in which transactions are recorded in chronological order (by order of date). Since the journal is the first place in which transactions are formally recorded, it is referred to as the **book of original entry**. There are many forms of journals in use today. The most basic form of journal has two money (or amount) columns and is referred to as the **general journal**.

The process of recording transactions in a journal is called **journalizing**. Recording transactions in a journal follows the same analysis, and uses the same account titles, as recording transactions in T accounts. Recording transactions in a journal, however, is considered to be a better practice because both the debit and credit parts of an entry are shown together in the same record.

Most journal entries involve only one debit and one credit. Occasionally, however, more than one debit or credit will be needed to record an entry. An entry requiring more than one debit and/or credit is called a **compound entry**.

The journal provides a complete record of each transaction in chronological order. However, the ledger is still needed to provide a summary of data relating to each account. Entries in the journal are transferred to the ledger on a regular basis, usually at the end of the month. The process of transferring amounts from the journal to the ledger is called **posting**. The ledger is usually called the **book of final entry**. After all postings have been made to the ledger accounts, the equality of debits and credits is proved by preparing a trial balance.

Since most businesses have many accounts in their ledger, a directory of the accounts available in the ledger is needed. A directory of the accounts in the ledger is called a **chart of accounts**. The numbering system for the chart of accounts depends *on the needs* of the individual business. In this chapter, we used a three-digit, five-category plan, with the first digit indicating the category of an account and the second and third digits indicating the position of the individual account within its particular classification. Journal page numbers and account numbers are used as a **cross reference** after posting.

We also showed a more functional form of ledger account called the **balance form of account**. The four-column account form resembles the standard form of account; however, balance columns are added that display the balance of the account after each posting.

A trial balance that does not balance is said to be "out of balance." An unbalanced trial balance means that there is an error somewhere in the system. Errors are of three types: math, recording, and posting. **Math errors** result from incorrect addition or subtraction and are corrected, if made in pencil, by erasure and recalculation. If made in ink, math errors are corrected by lining out the wrong figure, initialing the correction, and entering the correct figure in ink.

Recording errors are errors made in journal entries. If the recording error is discovered before it has been posted to the ledger, a correction can be made by lining out the incorrect information and entering the correct information. If the recording error has been posted to the ledger, a **correcting entry** is needed. A good technique for making correcting entries is to set up two sets of T accounts. One set shows the incorrect entry that was made. The other set shows the correct entry that should have been made. By analyzing the two sets of T accounts, a proper correcting entry can be made.

Posting errors result from incorrect transfers from the journal to an account or from the ledger to the trial balance. Posting errors should never be corrected by erasure. Instead, such errors are corrected by lining out the incorrect information and inserting the correct information. For future reference, the correction should be initialed by the person who made the correction.

Common posting errors include transpositions and slides. A **transposition** is the reversal of digits, such as entering 240 for 420. A **slide** is an entry with an incorrectly placed decimal point, such as entering 100 for 1,000 or 24.50 for 245.

Some errors that are very small in amount may not be corrected. This follows the **principle of materiality**, which states that proper accounting procedures have to be strictly followed only for events and transactions that would have a material effect on a business's financial statements. A material effect is an effect that involves a significant dollar amount.

PRACTICE TEST

PART I TRUE/FALSE

Please circle the correct answer.

T F 1. The sequence of steps or procedures used by a business to record and summarize accounting data is known as the accounting cycle.

T **F** 2. The first step in the accounting cycle is to record transactions in the journal.

T F 3. A source document is a business paper such as a check or a sales slip.

T F 4. The journal is referred to as the book of original entry.

T **F** 5. The process of recording transactions in the journal is called posting.

T F 6. When a transaction is recorded in the general journal, the name of the account to be debited is written on the first line at the extreme left of the Account Title column.

T F 7. A compound entry is a journal entry requiring more than one debit or one credit.

T **F** 8. The ledger provides a chronological record of the transactions of a business.

T F 9. A journal entry records all of the important information about a transaction in one place.

T **F** 10. The process of transferring entries from the journal to the ledger is called journalizing.

T F 11. The chart of accounts is a directory of all the accounts in the ledger.

T F 12. Posting reference numbers make it easier to trace an item in the ledger back to the journal entry in which the transaction was originally recorded.

T F 13. The trial balance shows that debit balances equal credit balances in the ledger.

T **F** 14. Recording a transaction twice will cause the trial balance to be out of balance.

T **F** 15. Failure to record a transaction will cause the trial balance to be out of balance.

PART II MATCHING

Please match each of the following terms with its definition.

a. accounting cycle
b. book of original entry
c. chart of accounts
d. compound entry
e. correcting entry
f. general journal
g. journal
h. journalizing

i. posting
j. posting errors
k. principle of materiality
l. principle of objective evidence
m. recording errors
n. slide
o. source documents
p. transposition

_o_ 1. Various types of business papers used as a basis for recording business transactions.

_g_ 2. A form in which transactions are recorded in chronological order (order by date).

_d_ 3. An entry requiring more than one debit and/or credit.

_l_ 4. The principle that states that source documents should form the foundation for recording business transactions.

_p_ 5. A reversal of digits, such as entering 480 for 840.

_c_ 6. A directory of the accounts in the ledger.

_b_ 7. The journal.

_m_ 8. Errors made in journal entries.

_f_ 9. The basic form of journal.

_i_ 10. The process of transferring entries from the journal to the ledger.

_n_ 11. An entry with an incorrectly placed decimal point, such as entering 10.5 for 105.

_j_ 12. Errors resulting from incorrect transfers from the journal to an account or from the ledger to the trial balance.

_h_ 13. The process of recording transactions in the journal.

_k_ 14. The principle that states that proper accounting procedures have to be strictly followed only for events and transactions that would have a significant effect on a business's financial statements.

_e_ 15. An entry used if a recording error has been posted to the ledger.

_a_ 16. The steps involved in the recording and summarizing processes of accounting.

PART III FILL IN THE BLANKS

Please complete each sentence with the correct word or words.

1. The third step in the accounting cycle is to ____post____ from the journal to the ledger.

2. The accounting principle of __objective evidence__ states that source documents should be used as a basis for recording transactions.

3. The journal in which any business transaction can be recorded is called the __General Journal__.

4. __Journalizing__ is the process of recording transactions in the journal.

5. If Sue Smith invested $5,000 to begin a new business, the Cash account would be debited and the __Capital__ account would be credited.

6. When transactions are recorded in the general journal, the name of the account being credited is written on the line below the debit entry and is __Indented__ one-fourth to one-half inch.

7. If Sue Smith purchased office supplies for cash, the __Office Supplies__ account would be debited and the __Cash__ account would be credited.

8. The journal provides a(n) __Chronological__ record of transactions; it is a diary of the company's transactions.

9. Transferring information from the journal to the ledger is called __Posting__.

10. The order of accounts in the ledger usually follows the order of accounts on the financial statements, beginning with the __asset__ accounts.

PART IV MULTIPLE CHOICE

Please circle the correct answer.

1. The first step in the accounting cycle is to
   a. record transactions in the journal.
   b. take a trial balance.
   c. analyze transactions from source documents.
   d. post to the ledger.

2. Which of the following is *not* found in a journal?
   a. A Date column
   b. An account for each asset, liability, revenue, and expense of the company
   c. An Account Title column
   d. Two money columns

3. If Sue Smith paid rent for one month on her office, the transaction would be recorded as
   a. a debit to Rent Expense and a credit to Cash.
   b. a debit to Cash and a credit to Rent Expense.
   c. a debit to Sue Smith, Capital and a credit to Cash.
   d. a debit to Cash and a credit to Sue Smith, Capital.

4. Which of the following are advantages of using a journal?
   a. The journal provides a chronological record of the transactions of the company.
   b. The journal provides a place to record an explanation of the entry.
   c. The journal decreases the possibility of recording errors.
   d. All of the above are advantages.

5. The second step in the accounting cycle is to
   a. journalize the transactions.
   b. post from the journal to the ledger.
   c. take a trial balance.
   d. foot the accounts.

6. The chart of accounts provides a directory or table of contents of the ledger. Which of the following types of information is **not** found in the chart of accounts?
   a. Account titles
   b. Account numbers
   c. Page numbers where the accounts are located
   d. Categories of accounts

7. The posting reference recorded in the journal after posting an entry to a ledger account is
   a. the account name.
   b. the account number.
   c. the journal code and page number.
   d. none of the above.

8. The posting reference recorded in the account during the posting process is
   a. the account name.
   b. the account number.
   c. the journal code and page number.
   d. none of the above.

9. The first step in preparing a trial balance is to
   a. write the name of the company, "Trial Balance," and the date at the top of the trial balance form.
   b. write the account titles and balances on the form.
   c. determine the balance of each account in the ledger.
   d. foot the debit and credit columns and check for equality.

10. When is it proper to erase an error?
    a. When the error is written in pencil
    b. When the error is written in ink
    c. When the error has been posted
    d. It is never proper to erase an error.

11. What is the proper procedure to follow when correcting an incorrect amount posted to the correct account?
    a. Use white-out to cover the error and write over it.
    b. Make a new journal entry and post.
    c. Line out the incorrect amount, initial it, and write in the correct amount in ink.
    d. None of the above is correct.

12. Which of the following errors would require a correcting journal entry?
    a. A $200 debit to Cash posted as a credit to Cash instead
    b. A debit of $255 posted as $225
    c. A credit of $15.00 posted as $1.50
    d. A debit to Supplies recorded in the journal as a debit to Salaries Expense and posted

13. Sue Smith purchased supplies for $200 cash and recorded the debit to Salaries Expense by mistake. The error was posted. What correcting entry must be made?
    a. Debit Supplies and credit Salaries Expense for $200
    b. Debit Salaries Expense and credit Cash for $200
    c. Debit Cash and credit Salaries Expense for $200
    d. No correcting entry is needed

14. Which of the following errors would cause the trial balance to be out of balance?
    a. Failure to record a transaction
    b. Failure to post an entire entry
    c. Posting the wrong amount to both the debit and credit sides of the correct accounts
    d. Posting a debit or credit to the wrong account
    e. None of the above

15. The principle that states that proper accounting procedures have to be strictly followed only for events and transactions that would have a significant effect on a business's financial statements is the principle of
    a. objective evidence.
    b. materiality.
    c. accounting.
    d. cost.

PART V WRITING/SHORT ANSWER

1. **Reflect** Make a list, in words or simple phrases, of the most important and meaningful points in this chapter.

2. **Question** Think about the most confusing points or the material you do not understand in this chapter. Write down two or three questions that remain unanswered.

3. **Connect** Explain, in one or two sentences, the connection between the main points of this chapter and the major goals of the entire course.

4. **Summarize** Review this chapter's Joining the Pieces visual summary and explain the concept(s) illustrated in a few sentences.

This page intentionally left blank.

SKILLS REVIEW

EXERCISE 3-1

General Journal   Page 1

	Date	Account Title	P.R.	Debit	Credit	
1						1
2						2
3						3
4						4
5						5
6						6
7						7
8						8
9						9
10						10
11						11
12						12
13						13
14						14
15						15
16						16
17						17
18						18
19						19
20						20
21						21
22						22
23						23
24						24
25						25
26						26
27						27
28						28
29						29
30						30
31						31
32						32

General Journal

	Date	Account Title	P.R.	Debit	Credit	
1						1
2						2
3						3
4						4
5						5
6						6
7						7
8						8
9						9
10						10
11						11
12						12
13						13
14						14
15						15
16						16
17						17
18						18
19						19
20						20
21						21
22						22
23						23
24						24
25						25
26						26
27						27
28						28
29						29
30						30
31						31
32						32

EXERCISE 3-2

General Journal

Page 1

	Date	Account Title	P.R.	Debit	Credit	
1						1
2						2
3						3
4						4
5						5
6						6
7						7
8						8
9						9
10						10
11						11
12						12
13						13
14						14
15						15
16						16

EXERCISE 3-3

Account Title	Normal Balance Dr.	Normal Balance Cr.	Increase Side Dr.	Increase Side Cr.
1. Supplies				
2. Owner, Drawing				
3. Accounts Receivable				
4. Truck				
5. Service Revenue				
6. Payroll Taxes Payable				
7. Owner, Capital				
8. Accounts Payable				
9. Miscellaneous Expense				
10. Office Equipment				
11. Rent Expense				
12. Fees Earned				
13. Cash				
14. Rental Revenue				
15. Utilities Expense				

EXERCISE 3-4

	Date	Account Title	P.R.	Debit	Credit	
1						1
2						2
3						3
4						4
5						5
6						6
7						7
8						8
9						9
10						10
11						11
12						12
13						13
14						14
15						15
16						16
17						17
18						18
19						19
20						20
21						21
22						22
23						23
24						24
25						25
26						26
27						27
28						28
29						29
30						30
31						31
32						32

EXERCISE 3-4 (continued)

ACCOUNT **Cash**   ACCOUNT NO. 111

DATE		ITEM	P.R.	DEBIT	CREDIT	BALANCE	
						DEBIT	CREDIT

ACCOUNT **Supplies**   ACCOUNT NO. 112

DATE		ITEM	P.R.	DEBIT	CREDIT	BALANCE	
						DEBIT	CREDIT

ACCOUNT **Equipment**   ACCOUNT NO. 115

DATE		ITEM	P.R.	DEBIT	CREDIT	BALANCE	
						DEBIT	CREDIT

ACCOUNT **Accounts Payable**   ACCOUNT NO. 211

DATE		ITEM	P.R.	DEBIT	CREDIT	BALANCE	
						DEBIT	CREDIT

EXERCISE 3-4 (continued)

ACCOUNT Edgar Lester, Capital   ACCOUNT NO. 311

DATE	ITEM	P.R.	DEBIT	CREDIT	BALANCE	
					DEBIT	CREDIT

EXERCISE 3-5

ACCOUNT TITLE	DEBIT	CREDIT

EXERCISE 3-6

General Journal

Page 1

	Date		Account Title	P.R.	Debit	Credit	
1							1
2							2
3							3
4							4
5							5
6							6
7							7
8							8
9							9
10							10
11							11
12							12
13							13
14							14
15							15
16							16

EXERCISE 3-7

	Trial Balance Will Balance	Trial Balance Will NOT Balance
1.		
2.		
3.		
4.		
5.		

This page intentionally left blank.

CASE PROBLEMS

PROBLEM 3-1A OR 3-1B

General Journal   Page 1

	Date		Account Title	P.R.	Debit	Credit	
1							1
2							2
3							3
4							4
5							5
6							6
7							7
8							8
9							9
10							10
11							11
12							12
13							13
14							14
15							15
16							16
17							17
18							18
19							19
20							20
21							21
22							22
23							23
24							24
25							25
26							26
27							27
28							28
29							29
30							30
31							31
32							32

General Journal

	Date		Account Title	P.R.	Debit	Credit	
1							1
2							2
3							3
4							4
5							5
6							6
7							7
8							8
9							9
10							10
11							11
12							12
13							13
14							14
15							15
16							16
17							17
18							18
19							19
20							20
21							21
22							22
23							23
24							24
25							25
26							26
27							27
28							28
29							29
30							30
31							31
32							32

PROBLEM 3-2A OR 3-2B

General Journal

Page 1

	Date		Account Title	P.R.	Debit	Credit	
1							1
2							2
3							3
4							4
5							5
6							6
7							7
8							8
9							9
10							10
11							11
12							12
13							13
14							14
15							15
16							16
17							17
18							18
19							19
20							20
21							21
22							22
23							23
24							24
25							25
26							26
27							27
28							28
29							29
30							30
31							31
32							32

General Journal

	Date		Account Title	P.R.	Debit	Credit	
1							1
2							2
3							3
4							4
5							5
6							6
7							7
8							8
9							9
10							10
11							11
12							12
13							13
14							14
15							15
16							16
17							17
18							18
19							19
20							20
21							21
22							22
23							23
24							24
25							25
26							26
27							27
28							28
29							29
30							30
31							31
32							32

PROBLEM 3-3A OR 3-3B

2.

General Journal

	Date		Account Title	P.R.	Debit	Credit	
1	20X2 June	1	CASH	111	2700		1
2			Office supplies	113	600		2
3			Office equipment	118	16500		3
4			Lori Lawson, Capital	311		19800	4
5			Invest Asst to start business.				5
6		1	rent expense cash		775	775	6
7		3	Office supplies	113	225		7
8			CASH Revenue.			225	8
9			Purchased office supply 4 CASH.				9
10							10
11		5	Desk + chair		2700		11
12			Cash revenue			600	12
13			note Payable			2100	13
14			Purchased Truck, Paying				14
15			$600. Down.				15
16							16
17		8	Cash		3200		17
18			Service Revenue			3200	18
19			Performed Service for Cash.				19
20							20
21		11	Lawson, Drawing		200		21
22			CASH			200	22
23			Withdrew cash for personal use.				23
24							24
25		14	Account Receivable		2100		25
26			Service revenue Acct fees earned			2100	26
27			Performed Service on Acct.				27
28							28
29		17	Acct Payable		2100		29
30			Cash			2100	30
31			made payment on acct june 5.				31
32					31,100	31,100	32

Compound entry

General Journal

	Date		Account Title	P.R.	Debit	Credit	
1	20X2 June	20	Utilities expense		550		1
2			Cash			550	2
3			Paid Utility bill.				3
4							4
5		22	Repair equipment Expense		75		5
6			cash			75	6
7			repair equipment.				7
8							8
9		25	Office supplies		375		9
10			Cash	1000		375	10
11			Buy additional Off supplies.				11
12							12
13		27	A/R Cash		35	35	13
14			Revenue office Supplies		35	35	14
15			returned defect supplies.				15
16		27	Acct Receivable		1300		16
17		29	Acct. Receivable		1300	1300	17
18			Service Revenue			1300	18
19			Received cash on Acct.				19
20		30					20
21		30	Salary Expense		1050		21
22			cash			1050	22
23			paid salaries.				23
24							24
25		30	telephone expense		195		25
26			cash			195	26
27			paid telephone expense.				27
28							28
29		30	Miscellaneous expense		175		29
30			Cash			175	30
31			paid Miscellaneous Expens				31
32							32

34,855   34,855

1., 3.

ACCOUNT Cash ACCOUNT NO. 111

DATE		ITEM	P.R.	DEBIT	CREDIT	BALANCE DEBIT	BALANCE CREDIT
20X June	1		GJ1	2 700 18 800		18 800	
	3				7 25	18 075	
	5				2 700	16 875	
	8			3 200			
	11				200	16 675	
	14			2 100			
	17				2 100	14 575	
	20				5 50	14 025	
	22				75	13 950	
	25				375	13 575	
	27				35	13 540	
	29			1 300			
	30				1 050	12 490	
	30				195	12 295	
	36				175	12 120	

ACCOUNT Accounts Receivable ACCOUNT NO. 112

DATE		ITEM	P.R.	DEBIT	CREDIT	BALANCE DEBIT	BALANCE CREDIT
20X2 June	14		GJ1	2 100		2 100	
	29		GJ2	1 300		800	

ACCOUNT Office Supplies ACCOUNT NO. 113

DATE		ITEM	P.R.	DEBIT	CREDIT	BALANCE DEBIT	BALANCE CREDIT
20X2 June	1		GJ1	600		600	
	3		GJ1	2 25		8 25	
	25		GJ2	375		1 200	
	27		GJ2	35	35	1 165	

ACCOUNT **Office Equipment**   ACCOUNT NO. **118**

DATE		ITEM	P.R.	DEBIT	CREDIT	BALANCE	
						DEBIT	CREDIT
20X june	1		GJ1	16000		16000	
	5						

ACCOUNT **Accounts Payable**   ACCOUNT NO. **211**

DATE		ITEM	P.R.	DEBIT	CREDIT	BALANCE	
						DEBIT	CREDIT
20X june	5				2100		2100
	17			2100			

ACCOUNT _LORI LAWSON_, Capital   ACCOUNT NO. **311**

DATE		ITEM	P.R.	DEBIT	CREDIT	BALANCE	
						DEBIT	CREDIT
20X2 june	1				19800		19800

ACCOUNT _LAWSON_, Drawing   ACCOUNT NO. **312**

DATE		ITEM	P.R.	DEBIT	CREDIT	BALANCE	
						DEBIT	CREDIT
20X2 june	11			200		200	

Study Guide and Working Papers • Chapter 3

ACCOUNT **Accounting Fees Earned** ACCOUNT NO. 411

DATE		ITEM	P.R.	DEBIT	CREDIT	BALANCE DEBIT	BALANCE CREDIT
20X2 June	14		GJ1	2 100		2 100	
	29			1 300		3 400	

ACCOUNT **Rent Expense** ACCOUNT NO. 511

DATE		ITEM	P.R.	DEBIT	CREDIT	BALANCE DEBIT	BALANCE CREDIT
20X2 June	1			775		775	

ACCOUNT **Salaries Expense** ACCOUNT NO. 512

DATE		ITEM	P.R.	DEBIT	CREDIT	BALANCE DEBIT	BALANCE CREDIT
20X2 June	30			1 050		1 050	

ACCOUNT **Utilities Expense** ACCOUNT NO. 513

DATE		ITEM	P.R.	DEBIT	CREDIT	BALANCE DEBIT	BALANCE CREDIT
20X2 June	20		GJ2	550		550	

ACCOUNT Telephone Expense   ACCOUNT NO. 514

DATE	ITEM	P.R.	DEBIT	CREDIT	BALANCE DEBIT	BALANCE CREDIT
20X2 June 30		GJ2	1 95		1 95	

ACCOUNT Repairs Expense – Equipment   ACCOUNT NO. 515

DATE	ITEM	P.R.	DEBIT	CREDIT	BALANCE DEBIT	BALANCE CREDIT
20X2 June 22		GJ2	75		75	

ACCOUNT Miscellaneous Expense   ACCOUNT NO. 516

DATE	ITEM	P.R.	DEBIT	CREDIT	BALANCE DEBIT	BALANCE CREDIT
20X2 June 30			1 75		1 75	

4.

ACCOUNT TITLE	DEBIT	CREDIT
LORI LAWSON		
Trial Balance		
June 1, 20X2		
111 CASH		
112 Acct Receivable	3 4 0 0	
113 office supplies	1 2 3 5	
118 office Equipment	16 0 0 0	2 1 0 0
211 Acct Payable		
311 Lori Lawson, capital		19 8 0 0
312 Lori Lawson, drawing	2 0 0	
411 Acct fees earned	3 4 0 0	5 3 0 0
511 Rent expense	7 7 5	
512 Salaries Expens	1 0 5 0	
513 Utilities expense	5 5 0	
514 Telephone expense	1 9 5	
515 Repair expense	7 5	
516 Miscellaneous Expense	1 7 5	
		21 400

This page intentionally left blank.

General Journal

Page 1

	Date		Account Title	P.R.	Debit	Credit	
1		1	Store supplies		700		1
2			office Supplies			700	2
3			To correct error in				3
4			which store supplies				4
5			had been debit to				5
6			office supplies				6
7							7
8		2	Store supplies		1000		8
9			Account Payable			1000	9
10			To correct Purchase that				10
11			was debit instead of				11
12			credit				12
13							13
14		3	Turner, draw		95		14
15			utility expense			95	15
16			To correct the payment				16
17			credited to Utility Expense				17
18			instead of Turner's draw				18
19					ar 1500	ar	19
20		4	Equipment		15000	1500	20
21			Account Payable			15000	21
22							22
23		5	A/R		500		23
24			Cash + Fees			500	24
25			correct error that was				25
26			debit to cash +				26
27			fees				27
28							28
29							29
30							30
31							31
32							32

This page intentionally left blank.

PROBLEM 3-5A OR 3-5B

2. **General Journal** Page 17

	Date		Account Title	P.R.	Debit	Credit	
1							1
2							2
3							3
4							4
5							5
6							6
7							7
8							8
9							9
10							10
11							11
12							12
13							13
14							14
15							15
16							16
17							17
18							18
19							19
20							20
21							21
22							22
23							23
24							24
25							25
26							26
27							27
28							28
29							29
30							30
31							31
32							32

PROBLEM 3-5A OR 3-5B (continued)

	Date		Account Title	P.R.	Debit	Credit	
1							1
2							2
3							3
4							4
5							5
6							6
7							7
8							8
9							9
10							10
11							11
12							12
13							13
14							14
15							15
16							16
17							17
18							18
19							19
20							20
21							21
22							22
23							23
24							24
25							25
26							26
27							27
28							28
29							29
30							30
31							31
32							32

General Journal   Page 19

	Date	Account Title	P.R.	Debit	Credit	
1						1
2						2
3						3
4						4
5						5
6						6
7						7
8						8
9						9
10						10
11						11
12						12
13						13

1., 3.

ACCOUNT Cash   ACCOUNT NO. 111

DATE	ITEM	P.R.	DEBIT	CREDIT	BALANCE DEBIT	BALANCE CREDIT

ACCOUNT **Accounts Receivable**   ACCOUNT NO. 112

DATE		ITEM	P.R.	DEBIT	CREDIT	BALANCE	
						DEBIT	CREDIT

ACCOUNT **Office Supplies**   ACCOUNT NO. 113

DATE		ITEM	P.R.	DEBIT	CREDIT	BALANCE	
						DEBIT	CREDIT

ACCOUNT **Medical Supplies**   ACCOUNT NO. 114

DATE		ITEM	P.R.	DEBIT	CREDIT	BALANCE	
						DEBIT	CREDIT

ACCOUNT **Office Equipment**   ACCOUNT NO. 117

DATE		ITEM	P.R.	DEBIT	CREDIT	BALANCE	
						DEBIT	CREDIT

ACCOUNT **Medical Equipment**   ACCOUNT NO. 118

DATE	ITEM	P.R.	DEBIT	CREDIT	BALANCE DEBIT	BALANCE CREDIT

ACCOUNT **Accounts Payable**   ACCOUNT NO. 211

DATE	ITEM	P.R.	DEBIT	CREDIT	BALANCE DEBIT	BALANCE CREDIT

ACCOUNT _____, **Capital**   ACCOUNT NO. 311

DATE	ITEM	P.R.	DEBIT	CREDIT	BALANCE DEBIT	BALANCE CREDIT

ACCOUNT _____, **Drawing**   ACCOUNT NO. 312

DATE	ITEM	P.R.	DEBIT	CREDIT	BALANCE DEBIT	BALANCE CREDIT

ACCOUNT Medical Fees Earned

DATE	ITEM	P.R.	DEBIT	CREDIT	BALANCE DEBIT	BALANCE CREDIT

ACCOUNT Salaries Expense

DATE	ITEM	P.R.	DEBIT	CREDIT	BALANCE DEBIT	BALANCE CREDIT

ACCOUNT Rent Expense

DATE	ITEM	P.R.	DEBIT	CREDIT	BALANCE DEBIT	BALANCE CREDIT

ACCOUNT Utilities Expense

DATE	ITEM	P.R.	DEBIT	CREDIT	BALANCE DEBIT	BALANCE CREDIT

ACCOUNT Laboratory Fees Expense   ACCOUNT NO. 514

DATE	ITEM	P.R.	DEBIT	CREDIT	BALANCE	
					DEBIT	CREDIT

ACCOUNT Miscellaneous Expense   ACCOUNT NO. 515

DATE	ITEM	P.R.	DEBIT	CREDIT	BALANCE	
					DEBIT	CREDIT

4.

ACCOUNT TITLE	DEBIT	CREDIT

PROBLEM SOLVING

1.

Georgian Theater

Chart of Accounts

Assets   **Owner's Equity**

____ _____

____ _____

____ _____

____ _____

Revenue

____ _____

____ _____

____ _____

____ _____

____ _____

____ _____

Expenses

Liabilities

____ _____

____ _____

____ _____

____ _____

____ _____

____ _____

____ _____

____ _____

____ _____

____ _____

____ _____

3.   **General Journal**   Page 1

	Date		Account Title	P.R.	Debit	Credit	
1							1
2							2
3							3
4							4
5							5
6							6
7							7
8							8
9							9
10							10
11							11
12							12
13							13
14							14
15							15
16							16
17							17
18							18
19							19
20							20
21							21
22							22
23							23
24							24
25							25
26							26
27							27
28							28
29							29
30							30
31							31
32							32

General Journal

	Date	Account Title	P.R.	Debit	Credit	
1						1
2						2
3						3
4						4
5						5
6						6
7						7
8						8
9						9
10						10
11						11
12						12
13						13
14						14
15						15
16						16
17						17
18						18
19						19
20						20
21						21
22						22
23						23
24						24
25						25
26						26
27						27
28						28
29						29
30						30
31						31
32						32

PROBLEM SOLVING (continued)

General Journal

	Date		Account Title	P.R.	Debit	Credit	
1							1
2							2
3							3
4							4
5							5
6							6
7							7
8							8
9							9
10							10
11							11
12							12
13							13
14							14
15							15
16							16
17							17
18							18
19							19
20							20
21							21
22							22
23							23
24							24
25							25
26							26
27							27
28							28
29							29
30							30
31							31
32							32

General Journal

	Date		Account Title	P.R.	Debit	Credit	
1							1
2							2
3							3
4							4
5							5
6							6
7							7
8							8
9							9
10							10
11							11
12							12
13							13
14							14
15							15
16							16
17							17
18							18
19							19
20							20
21							21
22							22
23							23
24							24
25							25
26							26
27							27
28							28
29							29
30							30
31							31
32							32

PROBLEM SOLVING (continued)

2., 4.

ACCOUNT _____ ACCOUNT NO. _____

DATE	ITEM	P.R.	DEBIT	CREDIT	BALANCE	
					DEBIT	CREDIT

ACCOUNT _____ ACCOUNT NO. _____

DATE	ITEM	P.R.	DEBIT	CREDIT	BALANCE	
					DEBIT	CREDIT

PROBLEM SOLVING (continued)

ACCOUNT _____   ACCOUNT NO. _____

DATE		ITEM	P.R.	DEBIT	CREDIT	BALANCE	
						DEBIT	CREDIT

ACCOUNT _____   ACCOUNT NO. _____

DATE		ITEM	P.R.	DEBIT	CREDIT	BALANCE	
						DEBIT	CREDIT

ACCOUNT _____   ACCOUNT NO. _____

DATE		ITEM	P.R.	DEBIT	CREDIT	BALANCE	
						DEBIT	CREDIT

ACCOUNT _____   ACCOUNT NO. _____

DATE		ITEM	P.R.	DEBIT	CREDIT	BALANCE	
						DEBIT	CREDIT

PROBLEM SOLVING (continued)

ACCOUNT _____ ACCOUNT NO. _____

DATE	ITEM	P.R.	DEBIT	CREDIT	BALANCE	
					DEBIT	CREDIT

ACCOUNT _____ ACCOUNT NO. _____

DATE	ITEM	P.R.	DEBIT	CREDIT	BALANCE	
					DEBIT	CREDIT

ACCOUNT _____ ACCOUNT NO. _____

DATE	ITEM	P.R.	DEBIT	CREDIT	BALANCE	
					DEBIT	CREDIT

ACCOUNT _____ ACCOUNT NO. _____

DATE	ITEM	P.R.	DEBIT	CREDIT	BALANCE	
					DEBIT	CREDIT

PROBLEM SOLVING (continued)

ACCOUNT _____ ACCOUNT NO. _____

DATE		ITEM	P.R.	DEBIT	CREDIT	BALANCE	
						DEBIT	CREDIT

ACCOUNT _____ ACCOUNT NO. _____

DATE		ITEM	P.R.	DEBIT	CREDIT	BALANCE	
						DEBIT	CREDIT

ACCOUNT _____ ACCOUNT NO. _____

DATE		ITEM	P.R.	DEBIT	CREDIT	BALANCE	
						DEBIT	CREDIT

ACCOUNT _____ ACCOUNT NO. _____

DATE		ITEM	P.R.	DEBIT	CREDIT	BALANCE	
						DEBIT	CREDIT

ACCOUNT _____   ACCOUNT NO. _____

DATE		ITEM	P.R.	DEBIT	CREDIT	BALANCE	
						DEBIT	CREDIT

ACCOUNT _____   ACCOUNT NO. _____

DATE		ITEM	P.R.	DEBIT	CREDIT	BALANCE	
						DEBIT	CREDIT

ACCOUNT _____   ACCOUNT NO. _____

DATE		ITEM	P.R.	DEBIT	CREDIT	BALANCE	
						DEBIT	CREDIT

ACCOUNT _____   ACCOUNT NO. _____

DATE		ITEM	P.R.	DEBIT	CREDIT	BALANCE	
						DEBIT	CREDIT

PROBLEM SOLVING (continued)

ACCOUNT _____ ACCOUNT NO. _____

DATE		ITEM	P.R.	DEBIT	CREDIT	BALANCE	
						DEBIT	CREDIT

ACCOUNT _____ ACCOUNT NO. _____

DATE		ITEM	P.R.	DEBIT	CREDIT	BALANCE	
						DEBIT	CREDIT

ACCOUNT _____ ACCOUNT NO. _____

DATE		ITEM	P.R.	DEBIT	CREDIT	BALANCE	
						DEBIT	CREDIT

ACCOUNT _____ ACCOUNT NO. _____

DATE		ITEM	P.R.	DEBIT	CREDIT	BALANCE	
						DEBIT	CREDIT

PROBLEM SOLVING (continued)

ACCOUNT _____ ACCOUNT NO. _____

DATE	ITEM	P.R.	DEBIT	CREDIT	BALANCE	
					DEBIT	CREDIT

ACCOUNT _____ ACCOUNT NO. _____

DATE	ITEM	P.R.	DEBIT	CREDIT	BALANCE	
					DEBIT	CREDIT

5.

ACCOUNT TITLE	DEBIT	CREDIT

6.

COMMUNICATIONS

ETHICS

This page intentionally left blank.

PRACTICE TEST ANSWERS

PART I

1. T
2. F
3. T
4. T
5. F
6. T
7. T
8. F
9. T
10. F
11. T
12. T
13. T
14. F
15. F

PART II

1. o
2. g
3. d
4. l
5. p
6. c
7. b
8. m
9. f
10. i
11. n
12. j
13. h
14. k
15. e
16. a

PART III

1. post
2. objective evidence
3. general journal
4. Journalizing
5. Sue Smith, Capital
6. indented
7. Office Supplies, Cash
8. chronological
9. posting
10. asset

PART IV

1. c
2. b
3. a
4. d
5. a
6. c
7. b
8. c
9. c
10. a
11. c
12. d
13. a
14. e
15. b

PART V

Answers will vary. Please discuss questions with your instructor. You can also discuss issues related to this chapter by logging onto the Paradigm Accounting Web Site at www.emcp.com and clicking on the discussion section.

4 The Accounting Cycle Continued—Work Sheet, Financial Statements, and Adjusting Entries

CHAPTER SUMMARY

Chapter 3 presented the first four steps in the accounting cycle for a service business. Chapter 4 continued the study of the accounting cycle for a service business.

At the end of an accounting period, there are usually some accounts that are not up to date. This happens because changes in the nature of certain accounts occur as time passes, and it is usually not practical to attempt to keep up with the changes as they occur. For example, supplies (and other prepaid items) are consumed constantly. In most businesses, it would be an enormously time-consuming task for the accountant or bookkeeper to make an entry each time supply items are used, so no regular recording for supplies used is made during the accounting period. Instead, the accounting for supplies used is postponed until the end of the accounting period. The balance of the Supplies account is then adjusted to reflect the cost of supplies used during the period. An **adjusting entry** is an entry made at the end of an accounting period to show up-to-date or accurate amounts in certain accounts. Adjusting entries record **internal transactions** (transactions that involve no outside parties).

The portion of a prepaid asset that has been used no longer provides a future benefit to the business; therefore, it becomes an expense. The expense for supplies used is recognized by debiting the Supplies Expense account and crediting the Supplies account. Other adjustments typically needed by a service business include those for insurance expired, depreciation of long-term assets, and liability for unpaid salaries.

Insurance paid in advance is considered to be an asset because it has money value and will provide a service that will benefit the business in the future. Insurance paid in advance is debited to an asset account entitled Prepaid Insurance. The adjustment for insurance expired is determined by dividing the amount of the prepayment of the **premium** by the number of months prepaid. The resulting amount is then multiplied by the number of months in the accounting period that the policy was prepaid. The adjusting entry involves a debit to the Insurance Expense account and a credit to the Prepaid Insurance account.

With the exception of land, all long-term physical assets used by a business are said to depreciate. **Depreciation** is an allocation process in which the cost of an asset is divided up over the periods the asset is used to produce revenue. The amount of depreciation can be calculated in various ways. This chapter uses the **straight-line method**, a method that yields the same amount of depreciation for each full period in which the asset is used. Depreciation is recorded by debiting a depreciation expense account and crediting an accumulated depreciation account. The accumulated depreciation account is an example of a **contra account**. A contra account's balance is opposite to the balance of the account to which it relates. Thus, accumulated depreciation accounts have credit balances that are opposite to the debit balances of asset accounts. The difference between the balance of the asset account and the balance of the accumulated depreciation account is the asset's **book value**.

Unpaid salaries occur when the accounting period ends on a date different from the end of the payroll period. Unpaid salaries have been earned by the employees and, thus, are an expense to the business. However, they have not yet been paid by the employer. The adjustment for unpaid salaries involves a debit to the Salaries Expense account and a credit to the Salaries Payable account.

Adjusting entries are based on the **matching principle** of accounting. This principle states that revenue earned during an accounting period should be offset by the expenses that were necessary to produce the revenue, and the difference should be reported as the net income or net loss of the period.

A **work sheet** is an informal working paper used by the accountant to organize data and lessen the possibility of overlooking an adjustment. The exact form of work sheet varies with the needs of the business. In this chapter, we worked with a ten-column work sheet in completing the accounting cycle for Taylor and Associates.

Data for the preparation of the financial statements are taken directly from the financial statement columns of the work sheet. The income statement shows the revenues, expenses, and net income or net loss for the accounting period and is prepared from the Income Statement columns. The statement of owner's equity shows changes that have occurred in the owner's equity during the accounting period. It is prepared by adding the net income or subtracting the net loss and subtracting the owner's withdrawals from the beginning balance of the owner's capital. The resulting amount is the ending balance of the owner's capital. The balance sheet is a statement of assets, liabilities, and owner's equity as of the last day of the accounting period. Data for preparation of the balance sheet come from the Balance Sheet columns of the work sheet. In addition, the balance sheet needs an updated amount for the owner's capital. The statement of owner's equity supplies this figure.

After financial statements are prepared, the next step in the accounting cycle is to journalize adjusting entries. After the adjusting entries are journalized and posted, the ledger will be up to date and will agree with the amounts reported on the financial statements.

PRACTICE TEST

PART I TRUE/FALSE

Please circle the correct answer.

T   F   1. The fifth step in the accounting cycle is to determine needed adjustments.

T   F   2. Adjustments are needed to correct any mistakes made during the accounting period.

T   F   3. Adjusting entries are needed at the end of an accounting period to bring certain accounts up to date.

T   F   4. Adjusting entries record internal transactions.

T   F   5. Depreciation is an allocation process in which the cost of an asset is spread over its useful life.

T   F   6. Depreciation is very exact.

T   F   7. When depreciation is recorded on equipment used by a company, the Equipment account is credited.

T   F   8. An accumulated depreciation account is an example of a contra account.

T   F   9. Depreciation is recorded on all assets that will last for more than one year.

T   F   10. When the end of the accounting period differs from the last day of the pay period, unpaid salaries must be recorded.

T   F   11. If expenses are greater than revenues, the difference is reported as net income.

T   F   12. Unrecorded expenses result in an understatement of net income.

T   F   13. A work sheet is often called the accountant's scratch pad.

T   F   14. When a work sheet is used, there is no need to prepare financial statements.

T   F   15. When a work sheet is used, everything necessary for preparation of the financial statements is placed on one page.

T   F   16. After the financial statements are prepared, the adjustments must be journalized and posted.

T   F   17. Journalizing adjusting entries is unnecessary when a work sheet is used.

T   F   18. There is usually no rush to prepare financial statements at the end of an accounting period.

T   F   19. The work sheet is not a formal financial statement.

T   F   20. A ten-column work sheet has a special set of columns for statement of owner's equity items.

PART II MATCHING

Please match each of the following terms with its definition.

a. adjusting entry
b. Accumulated Depreciation
c. contra asset
d. depreciation
e. internal transactions

f. journalizing
g. matching principle
h. Prepaid Insurance
i. straight-line method
j. work sheet

_____ 1. A depreciation method that records the same amount of depreciation for every full period that the asset is used.

_____ 2. An entry made at the end of an accounting period to show up-to-date or accurate amounts in certain accounts.

_____ 3. An account whose balance is opposite to the balance of the asset account to which it relates.

_____ 4. An informal working paper used by the accountant to organize data and lessen the possibility of overlooking an adjustment.

_____ 5. The process of recording transactions in the journal.

_____ 6. An allocation process in which the cost of an asset is divided up over the periods the asset is used in the production of revenue.

_____ 7. The account used to record insurance that is paid in advance.

_____ 8. The contra asset account that summarizes the depreciation taken on an asset during its useful life.

_____ 9. The principle that states that revenue earned during an accounting period should be offset by the expenses that were necessary to produce the revenue.

_____ 10. Transactions, recorded by adjusting entries, that occur within a company and do not affect parties outside the company.

PART III FILL IN THE BLANKS

Please complete each sentence with the correct word or words.

1. The sixth step in the accounting cycle is to prepare a(n) _____.

2. _____ are prepared from the completed work sheet.

3. When insurance is paid in advance for a period of time, the _____ account is debited and the _____ account is credited.

4. At the end of the accounting period, insurance that has expired must be removed from the asset account by debiting _____ and crediting _____.

5. Adjusting entries record _____ transactions.

6. Depreciation is a way of _____ the cost of equipment and other assets with long lives over the period of time that they will be used in the production of revenue.

7. The amount of depreciation is a(n) _____.

8. One common method of depreciation is the _____ method.

9. Depreciation is recorded by debiting a depreciation expense account and crediting a(n) _____ account.

10. Recording depreciation in a separate account allows the original _____ of the asset to be shown in the asset account.

11. Generally accepted accounting principles do not allow depreciation to be taken on the asset _____.

12. When an adjustment is made to record unpaid salaries at the end of the accounting period, the _____ account is debited and the _____ account is credited.

13. Adjusting entries are _____ caused by errors; they are a(n) _____ part of the accounting cycle.

14. The _____ states that revenue earned during an accounting period should be offset by the expenses that were necessary to produce the revenue.

15. Without adjusting entries, some _____ would be unrecorded and some _____ would be overvalued.

16. The first pair of money columns on the work sheet is for the _____.

17. After the trial balance is entered on the work sheet, the _____ are recorded.

18. The Income Statement columns of a work sheet contain the balances of the _____ and _____ accounts.

19. The _____ or _____ for the accounting period is the figure needed to balance the Income Statement and Balance Sheet columns.

20. After the financial statements are prepared, the adjustments must be _____ and _____.

PART IV MULTIPLE CHOICE

Please circle the correct answer.

1. Adjusting entries are necessary at the end of the accounting period because
   a. errors have been made that need to be corrected.
   b. certain internal transactions have not been recorded.
   c. certain external transactions have not been recorded.
   d. all of the above.

2. If the Supplies account has a balance of $200, and a count of supplies show $50 on hand, the adjusting entry needed to record supplies used would be
   a. a debit to Supplies and a credit to Supplies Expense for $50.
   b. a debit to Supplies Expense and a credit to Supplies for $200.
   c. a debit to Supplies Expense and a credit to Supplies for $150.
   d. a debit to Supplies and a credit to Supplies Expense for $150.

3. If a company has a printer that costs $600 and the printer is expected to last five years, what is the depreciation per month using the straight-line method?
   a. $120
   b. $600
   c. $10
   d. none of the above

4. When recording depreciation for the period, which account is credited?
   a. the accumulated depreciation account
   b. the depreciation expense account
   c. the asset account
   d. none of the above

5. Examples of assets that are depreciated are
   a. trucks, automobiles, and office supplies.
   b. buildings, furniture, and prepaid insurance.
   c. cash registers, computers, and printers.
   d. accounts receivable and accounts payable.

6. Which asset cannot be depreciated according to GAAP?
   a. trucks
   b. computers
   c. carpeting
   d. land

7. If adjusting entries are not made, which of the following problems will result?
   a. Certain assets will be overvalued.
   b. Certain expenses will be understated.
   c. Net income will be overstated.
   d. All of the above will result.

8. The Balance Sheet columns of the work sheet contain which of the following accounts?
   a. assets, liabilities, and owner's equity
   b. revenues and expenses
   c. assets, revenues, and expenses
   d. assets, liabilities, and expenses

9. Which account balances are used in preparing the financial statements?
   a. the balances from the original trial balance on the work sheet
   b. the amounts from the adjustment columns
   c. the balances determined by taking the original balances in the trial balance columns and adding or subtracting any adjustments
   d. the balances from the ledger accounts

10. The eighth step in the accounting cycle is to
    a. prepare the work sheet.
    b. enter adjustments on the work sheet.
    c. prepare financial statements.
    d. journalize and post the adjusting entries.

PART V WRITING/SHORT ANSWER

1. **Reflect** Make a list, in words or simple phrases, of the most important and meaningful points in this chapter.

2. **Question** Think about the most confusing points or the material you do not understand in this chapter. Write down two or three questions that remain unanswered.

3. **Connect** Explain, in one or two sentences, the connection between the main points of this chapter and the major goals of the entire course.

4. **Summarize** Review this chapter's Joining the Pieces visual summary and explain the concept(s) illustrated in a few sentences.

SKILLS REVIEW

EXERCISE 4-1

(a)

(b)

(c)

(d)

(e)

EXERCISE 4-2

Account Title	Trial Balance		Adjustments	
	Dr.	Cr.	Dr.	Cr.

EXERCISE 4-2 (continued)

	Adjusted Trial Balance		Income Statement		Balance Sheet	
	Dr.	Cr.	Dr.	Cr.	Dr.	Cr.

EXERCISE 4-3

General Journal

Page 1

	Date		Account Title	P.R.	Debit	Credit	
1							1
2							2
3							3
4							4
5							5
6							6
7							7
8							8
9							9
10							10
11							11
12							12
13							13

EXERCISE 4-4

General Journal

Page 1

	Date		Account Title	P.R.	Debit	Credit	
1							1
2							2
3							3
4							4
5							5
6							6
7							7
8							8
9							9
10							10
11							11
12							12
13							13
14							14
15							15
16							16

EXERCISE 4-5

General Journal Page 1

	Date		Account Title	P.R.	Debit	Credit	
1							1
2							2
3							3
4							4
5							5
6							6
7							7
8							8
9							9
10							10
11							11
12							12
13							13
14							14
15							15
16							16

EXERCISE 4-6

1. _____

2. _____

3. _____

4. _____

5. _____

EXERCISE 4-7

1.

2.

3.

This page intentionally left blank.

PROBLEM 4-1A OR 4-1B

General Journal   Page 1

	Date		Account Title	P.R.	Debit		Credit		
1			Adjusting Entries						1
2									2
3	20X2 Jan	1	Supplies Expense		3 5 5				3
4			Supplies				3 5 5		4
5									5
6	March	1	Prepaid expence		5 8 5 0				6
7			prepaid				5 8 5 0		7
8									8
9	20X1 Jan	1	Depreciate Expense - Equipment		5 5 56				9
10			Accumulated Dep - Equnt				5 5 56		10
11									11
12	DEC	31	Salary Expense		22 8 0 0				12
13			Salary Payable				22 8 0 0		13
14									14
15									15
16									16
17									17

This page intentionally left blank.

This page intentionally left blank.

Account Title	Trial Balance		Adjustments	
	Dr.	Cr.	Dr.	Cr.

	Adjusted Trial Balance		Income Statement		Balance Sheet	
	Dr.	Cr.	Dr.	Cr.	Dr.	Cr.

This page intentionally left blank.

PROBLEM 4-3A OR 4-3B

1.

2.

3.

1.

Power Group					
Income Statement					
For Yr Ended June 30 20X2					
Revenue					
fees earned	153 0 0 0		153 0 0 0	
Expenses					
auto supplies expense	1 6 2 0			
Dep. expense – auto	1 2 0 0			
Insurance exp	3 2 0 0			
off supply exp	9 2 1 0			
Rent expense	4 8 0 0			
Repair expense	5 7 5			
Salaries Expense	104 0 0 0			
Total expense			124 6 0 5	
Net income			28 3 9 5	

2.

Power Group					
Statement of owner's equity					
For Year ended June 30, 20X2					
Capital, June 30, 20X2			60 5 8 0	
Net income for the Year 6 months	22 1 9 5		28 3 9 5	
Qm w/ withdrawals	26 0 0 0			
Decrease in Capital			3 8 0 5	
Capital June 30, 20X2			151 9 5 0	

3.

NO Expenses on few

			POWER Group											
			BALANCE Sheet											
			JUNE 30, 20X2											
ASSETS														
Cash						12	7	0	0					
supplies (auto)						2	5	7	5					
A/c						10	0	0	0					
Auto						35	0	0	0					
Acc. Dep - Auto	13	5	0	0										
Acc. Dep - office Equip	4	5	0	0		9	0	0	0					
Total asset											75	4	2	5
Liabilities														
A/P						16	6	5	0					
Salaries Payable						2	0	0	0					
Total liabilities											18	6	5	0
Owners Equity														
Hugh Power, capital											56	7	7	5
Total liabilities + owners equity											75	4	2	5

This page intentionally left blank.

1.

Account Title	Trial Balance		Adjustments	
	Dr.	Cr.	Dr.	Cr.

	Adjusted Trial Balance		Income Statement		Balance Sheet	
	Dr.	Cr.	Dr.	Cr.	Dr.	Cr.

PROBLEM 4-5A OR 4-5B (continued)

2.

3.

4.

5.

General Journal

	Date		Account Title	P.R.	Debit	Credit	
1							1
2							2
3							3
4							4
5							5
6							6
7							7
8							8
9							9
10							10
11							11
12							12
13							13
14							14
15							15
16							16
17							17
18							18
19							19
20							20
21							21
22							22
23							23
24							24
25							25
26							26
27							27
28							28
29							29
30							30
31							31
32							32

CHALLENGE PROBLEMS

PROBLEM SOLVING

2.

General Journal

Page 17

	Date	Account Title	P.R.	Debit	Credit	
1						1
2						2
3						3
4						4
5						5
6						6
7						7
8						8
9						9
10						10
11						11
12						12
13						13
14						14
15						15
16						16
17						17
18						18
19						19
20						20
21						21
22						22
23						23
24						24
25						25
26						26
27						27
28						28
29						29
30						30
31						31
32						32

General Journal

	Date	Account Title	P.R.	Debit	Credit	
1						1
2						2
3						3
4						4
5						5
6						6
7						7
8						8
9						9
10						10
11						11
12						12
13						13
14						14
15						15
16						16
17						17
18						18
19						19
20						20
21						21
22						22
23						23
24						24
25						25
26						26
27						27
28						28
29						29
30						30
31						31
32						32

General Journal

	Date		Account Title	P.R.	Debit	Credit	
1							1
2							2
3							3
4							4
5							5
6							6
7							7
8							8
9							9
10							10
11							11
12							12
13							13
14							14
15							15
16							16
17							17
18							18
19							19
20							20
21							21
22							22
23							23
24							24
25							25
26							26
27							27
28							28
29							29
30							30
31							31
32							32

9.   **General Journal**   Page 20

	Date		Account Title	P.R.	Debit	Credit	
1							1
2							2
3							3
4							4
5							5
6							6
7							7
8							8
9							9
10							10
11							11
12							12
13							13
14							14
15							15
16							16
17							17
18							18
19							19
20							20
21							21
22							22
23							23
24							24
25							25
26							26
27							27
28							28
29							29
30							30
31							31
32							32

This page intentionally left blank.

4., 5.

Account Title	Trial Balance		Adjustments	
	Dr.	Cr.	Dr.	Cr.

	Adjusted Trial Balance		Income Statement		Balance Sheet	
	Dr.	Cr.	Dr.	Cr.	Dr.	Cr.

1., 3., 9.

ACCOUNT

ACCOUNT NO.

DATE	ITEM	P.R.	DEBIT	CREDIT	BALANCE	
					DEBIT	CREDIT

PROBLEM SOLVING (continued)

ACCOUNT _____ ACCOUNT NO. _____

DATE		ITEM	P.R.	DEBIT	CREDIT	BALANCE	
						DEBIT	CREDIT

ACCOUNT _____ ACCOUNT NO. _____

DATE		ITEM	P.R.	DEBIT	CREDIT	BALANCE	
						DEBIT	CREDIT

ACCOUNT _____ ACCOUNT NO. _____

DATE		ITEM	P.R.	DEBIT	CREDIT	BALANCE	
						DEBIT	CREDIT

ACCOUNT _____ ACCOUNT NO. _____

DATE		ITEM	P.R.	DEBIT	CREDIT	BALANCE	
						DEBIT	CREDIT

PROBLEM SOLVING (continued)

ACCOUNT _____ ACCOUNT NO. _____

DATE		ITEM	P.R.	DEBIT	CREDIT	BALANCE	
						DEBIT	CREDIT

ACCOUNT _____ ACCOUNT NO. _____

DATE		ITEM	P.R.	DEBIT	CREDIT	BALANCE	
						DEBIT	CREDIT

ACCOUNT _____ ACCOUNT NO. _____

DATE		ITEM	P.R.	DEBIT	CREDIT	BALANCE	
						DEBIT	CREDIT

ACCOUNT _____ ACCOUNT NO. _____

DATE		ITEM	P.R.	DEBIT	CREDIT	BALANCE	
						DEBIT	CREDIT

PROBLEM SOLVING (continued)

ACCOUNT _____   ACCOUNT NO. _____

DATE	ITEM	P.R.	DEBIT	CREDIT	BALANCE DEBIT	BALANCE CREDIT

ACCOUNT _____   ACCOUNT NO. _____

DATE	ITEM	P.R.	DEBIT	CREDIT	BALANCE DEBIT	BALANCE CREDIT

ACCOUNT _____   ACCOUNT NO. _____

DATE	ITEM	P.R.	DEBIT	CREDIT	BALANCE DEBIT	BALANCE CREDIT

ACCOUNT _____   ACCOUNT NO. _____

DATE	ITEM	P.R.	DEBIT	CREDIT	BALANCE DEBIT	BALANCE CREDIT

PROBLEM SOLVING (continued)

ACCOUNT _____ ACCOUNT NO. _____

DATE		ITEM	P.R.	DEBIT	CREDIT	BALANCE	
						DEBIT	CREDIT

ACCOUNT _____ ACCOUNT NO. _____

DATE		ITEM	P.R.	DEBIT	CREDIT	BALANCE	
						DEBIT	CREDIT

ACCOUNT _____ ACCOUNT NO. _____

DATE		ITEM	P.R.	DEBIT	CREDIT	BALANCE	
						DEBIT	CREDIT

ACCOUNT _____ ACCOUNT NO. _____

DATE	ITEM	P.R.	DEBIT	CREDIT	BALANCE	
					DEBIT	CREDIT

ACCOUNT _____ ACCOUNT NO. _____

DATE	ITEM	P.R.	DEBIT	CREDIT	BALANCE	
					DEBIT	CREDIT

ACCOUNT _____ ACCOUNT NO. _____

DATE	ITEM	P.R.	DEBIT	CREDIT	BALANCE	
					DEBIT	CREDIT

PROBLEM SOLVING (continued)

ACCOUNT _____   ACCOUNT NO. _____

DATE	ITEM	P.R.	DEBIT	CREDIT	BALANCE	
					DEBIT	CREDIT

ACCOUNT _____   ACCOUNT NO. _____

DATE	ITEM	P.R.	DEBIT	CREDIT	BALANCE	
					DEBIT	CREDIT

ACCOUNT _____   ACCOUNT NO. _____

DATE	ITEM	P.R.	DEBIT	CREDIT	BALANCE	
					DEBIT	CREDIT

ACCOUNT _____   ACCOUNT NO. _____

DATE	ITEM	P.R.	DEBIT	CREDIT	BALANCE	
					DEBIT	CREDIT

PROBLEM SOLVING (continued)

ACCOUNT _____ ACCOUNT NO. _____

DATE	ITEM	P.R.	DEBIT	CREDIT	BALANCE	
					DEBIT	CREDIT

ACCOUNT _____ ACCOUNT NO. _____

DATE	ITEM	P.R.	DEBIT	CREDIT	BALANCE	
					DEBIT	CREDIT

ACCOUNT _____ ACCOUNT NO. _____

DATE	ITEM	P.R.	DEBIT	CREDIT	BALANCE	
					DEBIT	CREDIT

ACCOUNT _____ ACCOUNT NO. _____

DATE	ITEM	P.R.	DEBIT	CREDIT	BALANCE	
					DEBIT	CREDIT

6.

7.

8.

This page intentionally left blank.

COMMUNICATIONS

ETHICS

This page intentionally left blank.

PRACTICE TEST ANSWERS

PART I

1. T
2. F
3. T
4. T
5. T
6. F
7. F
8. T
9. F
10. T
11. F
12. F
13. T
14. F
15. T
16. T
17. F
18. F
19. T
20. F

PART II

1. i
2. a
3. c
4. j
5. f
6. d
7. h
8. b
9. g
10. e

PART III

1. work sheet
2. Financial statements
3. Prepaid Insurance, Cash
4. Insurance Expense, Prepaid Insurance
5. internal
6. allocating (dividing)
7. estimate
8. straight-line
9. accumulated depreciation
10. cost
11. land
12. Salaries Expense, Salaries Payable
13. not, planned
14. matching principle
15. expenses, assets
16. trial balance
17. adjustments
18. revenue, expense
19. net income, net loss
20. journalized, posted

PART IV

1. b
2. c
3. c
4. a
5. c
6. d
7. d
8. a
9. c
10. d

PART V

Answers will vary. Please discuss questions with your instructor. You can also discuss issues related to this chapter by logging onto the Paradigm Accounting Web Site at www.emcp.com and clicking on the discussion section.

5

Completing the Accounting Cycle for a Service Business— Closing Entries and the Post-Closing Trial Balance

CHAPTER SUMMARY

Closing entries are entries made at the end of an accounting period to transfer the balances of temporary accounts to the owner's capital account. The **temporary accounts** are revenues, expenses, and drawing. Revenue and expense accounts are closed to a clearing account entitled **Income Summary**. The Income Summary account is then closed to the owner's capital account. The owner's drawing account, not being part of the net income calculation, is closed directly to the owner's capital account. All of these entries are part of the **closing process**.

A temporary account is closed by making an entry that will balance out the account. Since revenue accounts have credit balances, a revenue account is closed by making an equal debit entry in the account and a credit entry in the Income Summary account. Expense accounts, having debit balances, are closed by crediting each expense account for its balance and making a compound debit to Income Summary. The balance of Income Summary, representing the net income or net loss, is then transferred to the owner's capital account. The owner's drawing account, with a debit balance, is closed by making an equal credit entry in the account and a debit entry in the owner's capital account.

After closing entries are posted, the balances of the **permanent accounts** (assets, liabilities, and owner's capital) will be up to date. The balances of the temporary accounts will be reduced to zero and will be ready for entries in the next accounting period. To ensure that the ledger is still in balance after closing entries are posted, a **post-closing trial balance** is taken. Only the balances of the permanent accounts will appear on the post-closing trial balance.

The ten steps in the accounting cycle for a service business can be summarized as follows:

1. Analyze transactions from source documents.
2. Record transactions in a journal.
3. Post entries to the ledger.
4. Prepare a trial balance of the ledger.
5. Determine needed adjustments.
6. Prepare a work sheet.
7. Prepare financial statements.
8. Journalize and post adjusting entries.
9. Journalize and post closing entries.
10. Prepare a post-closing trial balance.

A **fiscal period** is the span of time covering the accounting cycle. A **fiscal year** is a fiscal period covering 12 months. The fiscal year does not necessarily coincide with the calendar year. Many businesses have adopted a fiscal year that parallels their **natural business year**. That is, they end their fiscal year at the lowest point of activity in their operating cycle.

Adjusting entries are based on the *matching principle* of accounting, which states that revenue for a period should be offset by the expenses necessary to generate that revenue. To apply the matching principle, most accounting systems operate on the **accrual basis**. This basis requires that revenue be recorded when it is earned, no matter when cash is received; and expenses be recorded when they are incurred, no matter when cash is paid out. Revenue is considered to be earned when services have been satisfactorily performed or when goods have been properly delivered, and a legal claim to the revenue results. Expenses are recorded when a legal obligation to pay for goods or services used in operating the business is incurred, or when the cost of assets consumed in the business is recognized.

Another basis of accounting is referred to as the **cash basis**. Under this basis, revenue is recorded only when cash is received, and expenses are recorded only when cash is paid out. The cash basis may not result in a proper matching of revenue and expenses because, under this method, revenue and expense transactions are recorded only when cash changes hands.

The **modified cash basis**, a combination of the cash basis and the accrual basis, is used by many professional and service businesses today. Under this basis, revenue and expenses are recorded only when cash is received and paid out. However, adjustments are made for depreciation, expired insurance, and supplies used (if large amounts of supplies are purchased).

PRACTICE TEST

PART I TRUE/FALSE

Please circle the correct answer.

T   F   1. Revenue and expense accounts and the owner's drawing account are called permanent accounts.

T   F   2. When the accounting period is over, the balances of all temporary accounts are reduced to zero.

T   F   3. At the end of the accounting period, the balances of the temporary accounts are transferred to Income Summary and then the net income or net loss is transferred to the owner's capital account.

T   F   4. The entries necessary to close the temporary accounts are called adjusting entries.

T   F   5. The first step in the closing process is to close the balance of each expense account to the Income Summary account.

T   F   6. The owner's drawing account is closed to Income Summary.

T   F   7. The Income Summary account is used as a clearing account.

T   F   8. The Income Summary account is closed to the owner's capital account.

T   F   9. The balance in the Income Summary account before it is closed represents the revenue of the company minus expenses and withdrawals.

T   F   10. An account with a debit balance is closed by crediting the account for the amount of its balance.

T   F   11. A revenue account is closed by debiting the account and crediting Income Summary.

T   F   12. Information needed for the closing process can be found on the work sheet.

T   F   13. Temporary accounts are closed before the adjusting process.

T   F   14. The balance in the Income Summary account before it is closed will be the net income or net loss for the period.

T   F   15. The owner's drawing account is closed directly to the owner's capital account.

T   F   16. Closing entries are not journalized or posted.

T   F   17. The purpose of the post-closing trial balance is to assure that the ledger is in balance to begin the new accounting period.

T   F   18. A fiscal year is always the same as the calendar year.

T   F   19. A fiscal year ending at the lowest point of business activity is called a natural business year.

T   F   20. The adjusting and closing processes must be done on the last day of the fiscal period.

PART II MATCHING

Please match each of the following terms with its definition.

a. cash basis of accounting
b. calendar year
c. closing entries
d. closing process
e. fiscal period

f. Income Summary account
g. natural business year
h. permanent accounts
i. post-closing trial balance
j. temporary accounts

_____ 1. Assets, liabilities, and the owner's capital account.

_____ 2. Entries made at the end of an accounting period to transfer the balances of the temporary accounts to Income Summary and transfer the net income or net loss to the owner's capital account.

_____ 3. Revenue, expense, and drawing accounts.

_____ 4. A trial balance that includes only the balances of the permanent accounts.

_____ 5. A fiscal year that ends at the lowest point of business activity.

_____ 6. The span of time covering the accounting cycle.

_____ 7. The year that begins January 1 and ends December 31.

_____ 8. A clearing account used to summarize the balances of revenue and expense accounts.

_____ 9. The process of transferring the balances of the temporary accounts to Income Summary and transferring the net income or net loss to the owner's capital account.

_____ 10. The basis of accounting in which revenues and expenses are recorded only when cash is received or paid out.

PART III FILL IN THE BLANKS

Please complete each sentence with the correct word or words.

1. The ninth step in the accounting cycle is to journalize and post the _____.

2. Revenue and expense accounts and the owner's drawing account are called _____ accounts.

3. The process of transferring the balances of the temporary accounts to Income Summary and transferring the net income or net loss to the owner's capital account is called the _____ process.

4. One purpose of the closing process is to reduce the balances of the temporary accounts to _____.

5. The first step in the closing process is to transfer the balance of each revenue account to the _____ account.

6. The second step in the closing process is to transfer the balance of each _____ account to the _____ account.

7. The Income Summary account is closed to the owner's _____ account.

8. The owner's drawing account is closed to the _____ account.

9. The balance in the Income Summary account before it is closed represents the _____ or _____ for the period.

10. The temporary accounts are closed _____ the adjusting process.

11. A revenue account is closed by _____ the account for the amount of its balance.

12. An expense account is closed by _____ the account for the amount of its balance.

13. Information needed for the closing entries is taken from the _____.

14. After the closing entries are posted, all _____ accounts will have zero balances.

15. A(n) _____ is prepared to assure that the ledger is in balance to begin the new accounting period.

16. A(n) _____ trial balance will contain only the balances of the _____ accounts.

17. The _____ accounts are assets, liabilities, and the owner's capital account.

18. A fiscal period 12 months in length is called a(n) _____.

19. When a fiscal year ends at the lowest point in business activity, it is called a(n) _____.

20. In accrual basis accounting, revenue is recorded when _____, no matter when cash is received; and _____ are recorded when incurred, no matter when cash is paid out.

PART IV MULTIPLE CHOICE

Please circle the correct answer.

1. Revenue and expense accounts and the owner's drawing account are called
   a. permanent accounts.
   b. real accounts.
   c. temporary accounts.
   d. balance sheet accounts.

2. The third step in the closing process is to
   a. close the balance of each revenue account to Income Summary.
   b. close the balance of Income Summary to the owner's capital account.
   c. close the balance of each expense account to Income Summary.
   d. close the balance of the owner's drawing account to the owner's capital account.

3. Information for the closing process is taken from the
   a. work sheet.
   b. ledger.
   c. journal.
   d. trial balance.

4. The balance in the Income Summary account before it is closed is equal to the
   a. total assets of the firm.
   b. total liabilities of the firm.
   c. owner's equity of the firm.
   d. net income or net loss for the period.

5. The balance in the owner's drawing account is closed to the
   a. Cash account.
   b. Income Summary account.
   c. owner's capital account.
   d. The owner's drawing account is not closed.

6. The post-closing trial balance contains the balances of the following accounts:
   a. assets, liabilities, and owner's capital.
   b. revenues and expenses.
   c. assets, liabilities, and revenues.
   d. revenues, expenses, and owner's drawing.

7. A fiscal period is
   a. a month.
   b. a year.
   c. the period of time covering the accounting cycle.
   d. none of the above.

8. The steps necessary to complete the accounting cycle are performed
   a. as of the last day of the accounting period.
   b. during the last month of the accounting period.
   c. on the last day of the accounting period.
   d. none of the above.

9. Of the ten steps in the accounting cycle, most are performed only at the end or when financial statements are needed. These are
   a. steps 1 through 4.
   b. steps 3 through 10.
   c. steps 5 through 10.
   d. steps 8 through 10.

10. The accounting basis in which revenue and expenses are recognized only when cash is received or paid out is the
    a. matching basis.
    b. accrual basis.
    c. cash basis.
    d. cost basis.

PART V WRITING/SHORT ANSWER

1. **Reflect** Make a list, in words or simple phrases, of the most important and meaningful points in this chapter.

2. **Question** Think about the most confusing points or the material you do not understand in this chapter. Write down two or three questions that remain unanswered.

3. **Connect** Explain, in one or two sentences, the connection between the main points of this chapter and the major goals of the entire course.

4. **Summarize** Review this chapter's Joining the Pieces visual summary and explain the concept(s) illustrated in a few sentences.

WORKING PAPERS

SKILLS REVIEW

EXERCISE 5-1

Account Title	Permanent	Temporary	Closed	Reported On Balance Sheet	Reported On Income Statement
Salaries Payable					
Accumulated Depreciation					
Fees Earned					
Accounts Receivable					
Supplies Expense					
Owner, Capital					
Accounts Payable					
Rent Expense					
Supplies					
Equipment					

EXERCISE 5-2

General Journal   Page 1

	Date	Account Title	P.R.	Debit	Credit	
1						1
2						2
3						3
4						4
5						5
6						6
7						7
8						8
9						9
10						10
11						11
12						12
13						13
14						14
15						15
16						16
17						17
18						18

EXERCISE 5-3

General Journal

	Date	Account Title	P.R.	Debit	Credit	
1						1
2						2
3						3
4						4
5						5
6						6
7						7
8						8
9						9
10						10
11						11
12						12
13						13
14						14
15						15
16						16
17						17
18						18
19						19
20						20

EXERCISE 5-4

1.

General Journal

Page 1

	Date	Account Title	P.R.	Debit	Credit	
1						1
2						2
3						3
4						4

2. _____

3. _____

4. _____

EXERCISE 5-5

General Journal

	Date		Account Title	P.R.	Debit	Credit	
1							1
2							2
3							3
4							4
5							5
6							6
7							7
8							8
9							9
10							10
11							11
12							12
13							13
14							14
15							15
16							16
17							17
18							18
19							19
20							20
21							21
22							22
23							23
24							24
25							25
26							26
27							27
28							28
29							29
30							30
31							31
32							32

EXERCISE 5-6

	Date	Account Title	P.R.	Debit	Credit	
1						1
2						2
3						3
4						4
5						5
6						6
7						7
8						8
9						9
10						10
11						11
12						12
13						13
14						14
15						15
16						16
17						17
18						18
19						19
20						20
21						21
22						22
23						23
24						24
25						25
26						26
27						27
28						28
29						29
30						30
31						31
32						32

EXERCISE 5-7

Accounts That Will Appear
on Post-Closing Trial Balance

_____

_____

_____

_____

_____

_____

_____

_____

_____

_____

EXERCISE 5-8

Proper Sequence of Steps
in Accounting Cycle

_____

_____

_____

_____

_____

_____

_____

_____

_____

_____

This page intentionally left blank.

CASE PROBLEMS

PROBLEM 5-1A OR 5-1B

General Journal

	Date		Account Title	P.R.	Debit	Credit	
1							1
2							2
3							3
4							4
5							5
6							6
7							7
8							8
9							9
10							10
11							11
12							12
13							13
14							14
15							15
16							16
17							17
18							18
19							19
20							20
21							21
22							22
23							23
24							24
25							25
26							26
27							27
28							28
29							29
30							30
31							31
32							32

This page intentionally left blank.

1.   **General Journal**   Page 1

	Date	Account Title	P.R.	Debit	Credit	
1						1
2						2
3						3
4						4
5						5
6						6
7						7
8						8
9						9
10						10
11						11
12						12
13						13
14						14
15						15
16						16
17						17
18						18
19						19
20						20
21						21
22						22

2. _____

_____

_____

_____

This page intentionally left blank.

This page intentionally left blank.

1.

Account Title	Trial Balance		Adjustments	
	Dr.	Cr.	Dr.	Cr.

	Adjusted Trial Balance		Income Statement		Balance Sheet	
	Dr.	Cr.	Dr.	Cr.	Dr.	Cr.

2.

General Journal

	Date		Account Title	P.R.	Debit	Credit	
1							1
2							2
3							3
4							4
5							5
6							6
7							7
8							8
9							9
10							10
11							11
12							12
13							13
14							14
15							15
16							16
17							17
18							18
19							19
20							20
21							21
22							22
23							23
24							24
25							25
26							26
27							27
28							28
29							29
30							30
31							31
32							32

3.

General Journal

	Date		Account Title	P.R.	Debit	Credit	
1							1
2							2
3							3
4							4
5							5
6							6
7							7
8							8
9							9
10							10
11							11
12							12
13							13
14							14
15							15
16							16
17							17
18							18
19							19
20							20
21							21
22							22
23							23
24							24
25							25
26							26
27							27
28							28
29							29
30							30
31							31
32							32

This page intentionally left blank.

This page intentionally left blank.

Comprehensive Management Services
Work Sheet
For Year Ended December 31, 20X2

Account Title	Trial Balance Dr.	Trial Balance Cr.	Adjustments Dr.	Adjustments Cr.
Cash	9 0 0 0 00			
Office Supplies	1 7 0 0 00			(a) 1 4 0 0 00
Prepaid Insurance	1 2 0 0 00			(b) 5 0 0 00
Office Equipment	20 0 0 0 00			
Accum. Depr.—Office Equipment		5 0 0 0 00		(c) 2 0 0 0 00
Accounts Payable		2 2 0 0 00		
Salaries Payable		—		(d) 3 0 0 00
J.B. Smith, Capital		19 8 5 0 00		
J.B. Smith, Drawing	32 0 0 0 00			
Fees Earned		74 0 0 0 00		
Salaries Expense	29 0 0 0 00		(d) 3 0 0 00	
Rent Expense	3 9 0 0 00			
Advertising Expense	2 7 0 0 00			
Telephone Expense	1 1 0 0 00			
Office Supplies Expense	—		(a) 1 4 0 0 00	
Insurance Expense	—		(b) 5 0 0 00	
Depr. Expense—Office Equipment	—		(c) 2 0 0 0 00	
Miscellaneous Expense	4 5 0 00			
	101 0 5 0 00	101 0 5 0 00	4 2 0 0 00	4 2 0 0 00
Net Income				

PROBLEM 5-4A (continued)

	Adjusted Trial Balance		Income Statement		Balance Sheet	
	Dr.	Cr.	Dr.	Cr.	Dr.	Cr.
	9 0 0 0 00				9 0 0 0 00	
	3 0 0 00				3 0 0 00	
	7 0 0 00				7 0 0 00	
	20 0 0 0 00				20 0 0 0 00	
		7 0 0 0 00				7 0 0 0 00
		2 2 0 0 00				2 2 0 0 00
		3 0 0 00				3 0 0 00
		19 8 5 0 00				19 8 5 0 00
	32 0 0 0 00				32 0 0 0 00	
		74 0 0 0 00		74 0 0 0 00		
	29 3 0 0 00		29 3 0 0 00			
	3 9 0 0 00		3 9 0 0 00			
	2 7 0 0 00		2 7 0 0 00			
	1 1 0 0 00		1 1 0 0 00			
	1 4 0 0 00		1 4 0 0 00			
	5 0 0 00		5 0 0 00			
	2 0 0 0 00		2 0 0 0 00			
	4 5 0 00		4 5 0 00			
	103 3 5 0 00	103 3 5 0 00	41 3 5 0 00	74 0 0 0 00	62 0 0 0 00	29 3 5 0 00
			32 6 5 0 00			32 6 5 0 00
			74 0 0 0 00	74 0 0 0 00	62 0 0 0 00	62 0 0 0 00

DataPlus Bookkeeping Service
Work Sheet
For Year Ended December 31, 20X2

Account Title	Trial Balance Dr.	Trial Balance Cr.	Adjustments Dr.	Adjustments Cr.
Cash	12 0 0 0 00			
Office Supplies	2 1 0 0 00			(a) 1 8 0 0 00
Prepaid Insurance	3 6 0 0 00			(b) 2 0 0 0 00
Office Equipment	25 0 0 0 00			
Accum. Depr.—Office Equipment		8 0 0 0 00		(c) 4 0 0 0 00
Accounts Payable		2 7 0 0 00		
Salaries Payable		—		(d) 5 0 0 00
Mary Lamb, Capital		27 7 0 0 00		
Mary Lamb, Drawing	38 0 0 0 00			
Fees Earned		93 0 0 0 00		
Salaries Expense	41 0 0 0 00		(d) 5 0 0 00	
Rent Expense	4 2 0 0 00			
Advertising Expense	3 3 0 0 00			
Telephone Expense	1 5 0 0 00			
Office Supplies Expense	—		(a) 1 8 0 0 00	
Insurance Expense	—		(b) 2 0 0 0 00	
Depr. Expense—Office Equipment	—		(c) 4 0 0 0 00	
Miscellaneous Expense	7 0 0 00			
	131 4 0 0 00	131 4 0 0 00	8 3 0 0 00	8 3 0 0 00
Net Income				

	Adjusted Trial Balance		Income Statement		Balance Sheet	
	Dr.	Cr.	Dr.	Cr.	Dr.	Cr.
	12 0 0 0 00				12 0 0 0 00	
	3 0 0 00				3 0 0 00	
	1 6 0 0 00				1 6 0 0 00	
	25 0 0 0 00				25 0 0 0 00	
		12 0 0 0 00				12 0 0 0 00
		2 7 0 0 00				2 7 0 0 00
		5 0 0 00				5 0 0 00
		27 7 0 0 00				27 7 0 0 00
	38 0 0 0 00				38 0 0 0 00	
		93 0 0 0 00		93 0 0 0 00		
	41 5 0 0 00		41 5 0 0 00			
	4 2 0 0 00		4 2 0 0 00			
	3 3 0 0 00		3 3 0 0 00			
	1 5 0 0 00		1 5 0 0 00			
	1 8 0 0 00		1 8 0 0 00			
	2 0 0 0 00		2 0 0 0 00			
	4 0 0 0 00		4 0 0 0 00			
	7 0 0 00		7 0 0 00			
	135 9 0 0 00	135 9 0 0 00	59 0 0 0 00	93 0 0 0 00	76 9 0 0 00	42 9 0 0 00
			34 0 0 0 00			34 0 0 0 00
			93 0 0 0 00	93 0 0 0 00	76 9 0 0 00	76 9 0 0 00

PROBLEM 5-4A OR 5-4B (continued)

2., 3. General Journal Page 10

	Date	Account Title	P.R.	Debit	Credit	
1						1
2						2
3						3
4						4
5						5
6						6
7						7
8						8
9						9
10						10
11						11
12						12
13						13
14						14
15						15
16						16
17						17
18						18
19						19
20						20
21						21
22						22
23						23
24						24
25						25
26						26
27						27
28						28
29						29
30						30
31						31
32						32

1., 2., 3.

ACCOUNT **Cash**   ACCOUNT NO. **111**

DATE		ITEM	P.R.	DEBIT	CREDIT	BALANCE	
						DEBIT	CREDIT

ACCOUNT **Office Supplies**   ACCOUNT NO. **112**

DATE		ITEM	P.R.	DEBIT	CREDIT	BALANCE	
						DEBIT	CREDIT

ACCOUNT **Prepaid Insurance**   ACCOUNT NO. **115**

DATE		ITEM	P.R.	DEBIT	CREDIT	BALANCE	
						DEBIT	CREDIT

ACCOUNT **Office Equipment**   ACCOUNT NO. **116**

DATE		ITEM	P.R.	DEBIT	CREDIT	BALANCE	
						DEBIT	CREDIT

ACCOUNT **Accumulated Depreciation—Office Equipment**   ACCOUNT NO. **116.1**

DATE		ITEM	P.R.	DEBIT	CREDIT	BALANCE	
						DEBIT	CREDIT

ACCOUNT Accounts Payable   ACCOUNT NO. 211

DATE	ITEM	P.R.	DEBIT	CREDIT	BALANCE	
					DEBIT	CREDIT

ACCOUNT Salaries Payable   ACCOUNT NO. 212

DATE	ITEM	P.R.	DEBIT	CREDIT	BALANCE	
					DEBIT	CREDIT

ACCOUNT _____, Capital   ACCOUNT NO. 311

DATE	ITEM	P.R.	DEBIT	CREDIT	BALANCE	
					DEBIT	CREDIT

ACCOUNT _____, Drawing   ACCOUNT NO. 312

DATE	ITEM	P.R.	DEBIT	CREDIT	BALANCE	
					DEBIT	CREDIT

ACCOUNT Income Summary   ACCOUNT NO. 313

DATE	ITEM	P.R.	DEBIT	CREDIT	BALANCE	
					DEBIT	CREDIT

ACCOUNT **Fees Earned**   ACCOUNT NO. 411

DATE	ITEM	P.R.	DEBIT	CREDIT	BALANCE	
					DEBIT	CREDIT

ACCOUNT **Salaries Expense**   ACCOUNT NO. 511

DATE	ITEM	P.R.	DEBIT	CREDIT	BALANCE	
					DEBIT	CREDIT

ACCOUNT **Rent Expense**   ACCOUNT NO. 512

DATE	ITEM	P.R.	DEBIT	CREDIT	BALANCE	
					DEBIT	CREDIT

ACCOUNT **Advertising Expense**   ACCOUNT NO. 513

DATE	ITEM	P.R.	DEBIT	CREDIT	BALANCE	
					DEBIT	CREDIT

ACCOUNT **Telephone Expense**   ACCOUNT NO. 514

DATE	ITEM	P.R.	DEBIT	CREDIT	BALANCE	
					DEBIT	CREDIT

PROBLEM 5-4A OR 5-4B (continued)

ACCOUNT Office Supplies Expense   ACCOUNT NO. 515

DATE	ITEM	P.R.	DEBIT	CREDIT	BALANCE DEBIT	BALANCE CREDIT

ACCOUNT Insurance Expense   ACCOUNT NO. 516

DATE	ITEM	P.R.	DEBIT	CREDIT	BALANCE DEBIT	BALANCE CREDIT

ACCOUNT Depreciation Expense—Office Equipment   ACCOUNT NO. 517

DATE	ITEM	P.R.	DEBIT	CREDIT	BALANCE DEBIT	BALANCE CREDIT

ACCOUNT Miscellaneous Expense   ACCOUNT NO. 518

DATE	ITEM	P.R.	DEBIT	CREDIT	BALANCE DEBIT	BALANCE CREDIT

4.

ACCOUNT TITLE	DEBIT	CREDIT

This page intentionally left blank.

This page intentionally left blank.

PROBLEM 5-5A OR 5-5B

1.

Account Title	Trial Balance		Adjustments	
	Dr.	Cr.	Dr.	Cr.

	Adjusted Trial Balance		Income Statement		Balance Sheet	
	Dr.	Cr.	Dr.	Cr.	Dr.	Cr.

PROBLEM 5-5A OR 5-5B (continued)

2.

3.

PROBLEM 5-5A OR 5-5B (continued)

4.

5.

General Journal

	Date	Account Title	P.R.	Debit	Credit	
1						1
2						2
3						3
4						4
5						5
6						6
7						7
8						8
9						9
10						10
11						11
12						12
13						13
14						14
15						15
16						16
17						17
18						18
19						19
20						20
21						21
22						22
23						23
24						24
25						25
26						26
27						27
28						28
29						29
30						30
31						31
32						32

6.

General Journal

Page 2

	Date		Account Title	P.R.	Debit	Credit	
1							1
2							2
3							3
4							4
5							5
6							6
7							7
8							8
9							9
10							10
11							11
12							12
13							13
14							14
15							15
16							16
17							17
18							18
19							19
20							20
21							21
22							22
23							23
24							24
25							25
26							26
27							27
28							28
29							29
30							30
31							31
32							32

This page intentionally left blank.

CHALLENGE PROBLEMS

PROBLEM SOLVING

1.

	Date		Account Title	P.R.	Debit	Credit	
1							1
2							2
3							3
4							4
5							5
6							6
7							7
8							8
9							9
10							10

General Journal

Page 1

2.

3.

This page intentionally left blank.

COMMUNICATIONS

_____

_____

_____

_____

_____

_____

_____

_____

_____

_____

_____

_____

_____

_____

_____

_____

_____

_____

_____

_____

ETHICS

_____

_____

_____

_____

_____

_____

_____

_____

_____

_____

_____

_____

_____

_____

_____

_____

_____

_____

This page intentionally left blank.

PART I

1. F
2. T
3. T
4. F
5. F
6. F
7. T
8. T
9. F
10. T
11. T
12. T
13. F
14. T
15. T
16. F
17. T
18. F
19. T
20. F

PART II

1. h
2. c
3. j
4. i
5. g
6. e
7. b
8. f
9. d
10. a

PART III

1. closing entries
2. temporary
3. closing
4. zero
5. Income Summary
6. expense, Income Summary
7. capital
8. owner's capital
9. net income, net loss
10. after
11. debiting
12. crediting
13. work sheet
14. temporary
15. post-closing trial balance
16. post-closing, permanent
17. permanent
18. fiscal year
19. natural business year
20. earned, expenses

PART IV

1. c
2. b
3. a
4. d
5. c
6. a
7. c
8. a
9. c
10. c

PART V

Answers will vary. Please discuss questions with your instructor. You can also discuss issues related to this chapter by logging onto the Paradigm Accounting Web Site at www.emcp.com and clicking on the discussion section.

8.

Fred's Photos
Balance Sheet
July 31, 20X1

12.

Fred's Photos Post-Closing Trial Balance July 31, 20X1		
ACCOUNT TITLE	DEBIT	CREDIT

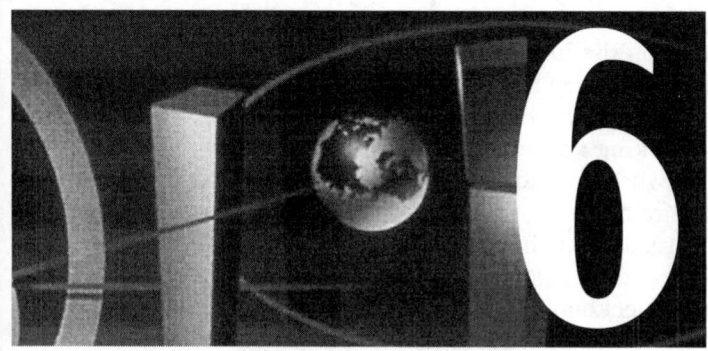

6 Cash and the Combined Journal

CHAPTER SUMMARY

Cash is an asset that is particularly vulnerable to theft, loss, and misuse. Therefore, special controls are necessary to protect and control cash. The protection and control of cash is part of the overall system of internal control. **Internal control** is defined as the procedures used within a company to protect its assets.

Cash is narrowly defined as the amount of currency (paper money) and coin that a business has on hand and on deposit in the bank. To most businesses, however, cash also includes money orders, checks made payable to the business, bank drafts, traveler's checks, and receipts from credit card sales.

All transactions that involve increases and decreases in cash can be recorded in a two-column journal. However, the use of a two-column journal is very time consuming when the volume of transactions is large. Therefore, businesses look for a more efficient way to record business transactions. A **combined journal** is a multicolumn journal used by many small businesses to help save journalizing and posting time. A combined journal—also called a **combination journal**—has several special columns for recording transactions that occur often and two general columns for recording transactions that occur less often. Because it is not necessary to write account titles when recording transactions in special columns, the combined journal saves journalizing time. Special columns are posted by totals, not item by item, and so posting time is also saved. Column totals are checked each month to make sure that the debits and credits are equal. One way to check the totals is the **zero-proof test**, which is done with a calculator.

To aid in the control of cash, most businesses use a bank checking account when making cash payments. However, it is not always practical or possible to write checks for small expenditures. Thus, it is common for businesses to establish an office fund—known as the **petty cash fund**—for making small expenditures. The amount of cash in the petty cash fund varies with the individual business. It can be established for any amount considered necessary. Furthermore, the fund can be increased or decreased at any time.

The petty cash fund is established by debiting the asset Petty Cash and crediting Cash. Often, one person—the **petty cashier**—is responsible for the maintenance of the fund. When a payment is made from the fund, a **petty cash voucher** is prepared; it shows the amount of the payment, the purpose, and the account to be debited. Records of petty cash are kept in an **auxiliary record**, called the **petty cash payments record**.

The petty cash fund is replenished periodically, usually at the end of the month. A check is written for the amount paid out of the fund, and, when this amount is placed in the fund, the fund is brought back up to the balance that it had at the beginning of the month. The entry to record the **replenishment of the petty cash fund** involves a debit to each expense listed in the petty cash payments record and a credit to Cash.

Many businesses will keep a **change fund** for their cash registers. The **Change Fund account** is debited for the amount of the fund. Businesses that have many cash transactions often have a small cash shortage or overage when the amount of cash received is compared with the amount of cash sales. If the source of the shortage or overage cannot be determined, an account entitled **Cash Short and Over** can be used to bring the accounting records into agreement with the actual amount of cash on hand. The Cash Short and Over account is debited for the amount of a shortage, and the Cash Short and Over account is credited for the amount of an overage. Thus, the account will show either a net shortage (debit balance) or a net overage (credit balance). A net shortage is reported on the income statement as miscellaneous expense; a net overage is reported on the income statement as miscellaneous income.

A bank is a financial institution that offers a variety of services to its customers. A primary service offered by banks is the bank checking account. A **bank checking account** is an amount of cash on deposit with a bank that the bank must pay at the order of the depositor. The **depositor** is the person (or business) under whose name the checking account is maintained.

A **deposit slip** should be prepared when a deposit is made in a checking account. A deposit slip summarizes the amount deposited and is the depositor's record of the deposit. A **check** is used to pay money from a checking account. Checks are recorded in a **checkbook** by filling in **check stubs**. Each check has an **ABA number** that identifies the bank and allows efficient processing of the check.

Checks must be endorsed before they can be deposited or cashed. There are three common forms of **endorsement**. A **blank endorsement** is simply a signature on the back of the check. A check with a blank endorsement can be cashed by anyone who has possession of it. A **full endorsement** specifies the party to whom the check is being transferred. A **restrictive endorsement** specifies the purpose for which money from a check is to be used.

There are three parties to a check: (1) the **drawer** is the person (or business) who writes the check, (2) the **drawee** is the bank on which the check is written, and (3) the **payee** is the person (or business) to whom the check is written. When a checking account is opened, a **signature card** must be signed by each person who will be writing checks on the account. The bank uses the signature card as an aid in spotting possible forgeries.

At regular intervals—usually once a month—a bank sends each of its checking account customers a bank statement. A **bank statement** is a copy of the bank's record of the checking account transactions and usually includes **canceled checks**. The bank statement should be compared with the depositor's checkbook. Due to several normal factors, the bank statement balance seldom agrees with the checkbook balance. These factors include **outstanding checks**, **deposits in transit**, **NSF checks**, and **service charges**. When the bank statement balance and the checkbook balance do not agree, the two amounts are reconciled (brought into agreement). The **bank reconciliation** is prepared by the depositor.

PRACTICE TEST

PART I TRUE/FALSE

Please circle the correct answer.

T   F   1. Cash includes currency, coins, checks made payable to the business, money orders, traveler's checks, cashier's checks, bank drafts, and receipts from credit card sales.

T   F   2. Bookkeepers and accountants should be assigned to handle cash because they record the cash transactions.

T   F   3. Cash should be deposited in the bank daily.

T   F   4. All cash payments, except for petty cash, should be made by check.

T   F   5. Checks should be prenumbered so that it is easy to spot a check that is unrecorded.

T   F   6. When a combined journal is used, entries should be recorded in the general journal also.

T   F   7. Use of a combined journal makes it easier and faster to record and post transactions.

T   F   8. It is not necessary for debits to equal credits in a combined journal.

T   F   9. A petty cash fund is used as a convenient way to pay small expenses.

T   F   10. A petty cash payments record is an example of an auxiliary record.

T   F   11. To replenish a petty cash fund, it is necessary to debit Petty Cash and credit Cash for the amount that is needed to bring the fund back up to its original total.

T   F   12. Cash Short and Over is debited whenever there is a cash overage and credited whenever there is a cash shortage.

T   F   13. The balance in Cash Short and Over is reported on the income statement as miscellaneous income or miscellaneous expense.

T   F   14. When a payment is made by check, the check stub should always be filled out first.

T   F   15. A bank statement is the bank's way of informing the depositor of the transactions that have been recorded in the depositor's account during the period.

T   F   16. The bank statement will always have the same ending balance as the balance shown in the depositor's checkbook and Cash account unless there is a mistake.

T   F   17. Outstanding checks are checks that have been written by the business but that have not yet been paid by the bank.

T   F   18. A bank reconciliation is necessary to arrive at the true cash balance.

T   F   19. All adjustments to the checkbook balance need to be recorded in the journal and posted.

T   F   20. In order to deposit a check in the bank, the depositor must use a restrictive endorsement.

PART II MATCHING

Please match each of the following terms with its definition.

a. bank charges
b. bank reconciliation
c. bank statement
d. blank endorsement
e. cash
f. Cash Short and Over
g. combined journal
h. deposit in transit
i. depositor
j. drawee

k. drawer
l. full endorsement
m. internal control
n. NSF check charge
o. outstanding check
p. payee
q. petty cash fund
r. restrictive endorsement
s. signature card
t. zero-proof test

_____ 1. An endorsement that specifies the purpose for which the money from a check is to be used.

_____ 2. A report, usually sent out monthly by the bank, that shows the bank's record of the checking account transactions.

_____ 3. A check that was written and is recorded in the checkbook but does not appear on the bank statement.

_____ 4. Making the bank statement balance agree with the checkbook balance.

_____ 5. A small amount of cash kept in the office for making small payments for items such as postage and office supplies.

_____ 6. The methods used within a company to protect its assets.

_____ 7. An account used to bring the accounting records into agreement with the actual amount of cash on hand when that amount is less or more than it should be.

_____ 8. A record prepared when opening a checking account that lists personal information about the depositor and the signatures of all persons who are authorized to sign checks.

_____ 9. The person or business who writes a check.

_____ 10. The endorsement that uses the phrase "pay to the order of" so that the check can only be cashed by that person or business.

_____ 11. The person or business to whom a check is made payable.

_____ 12. Currency, coins, checks, money orders, bank drafts, etc.

_____ 13. A multicolumned journal used by small businesses to help save journalizing and posting time.

_____ 14. A test performed by adding all debit balances and subtracting all credit balances—debits equal credits when the total is zero.

_____ 15. A deposit made and appearing in the checkbook but not appearing on the bank statement.

_____ 16. A charge made by the bank when a check that was deposited is returned because of insufficient funds.

_____ 17. Charges or fees that are subtracted by the bank directly from the depositor's account and appear on the bank statement; also called service charges.

_____ 18. An endorsement that consists only of a signature on the back of a check and that allows anyone who possesses the check to cash it.

_____ 19. The person or business in whose name a checking account is opened.

_____ 20. The bank on which a check is drawn.

PART III FILL IN THE BLANKS

Please complete each sentence with the correct word or words.

1. On a bank reconciliation, deposits in transit should be _____ to the _____ balance.

2. A(n) _____ is prepared when payment is made from the petty cash fund. It shows the purpose and amount of the payment and the account to be debited.

3. When the petty cash fund is low, it is necessary to _____ it.

4. The _____ columns of a combined journal are used to record transactions that occur often in a business.

5. Posting of the special columns is done by _____.

6. The _____ columns of a combined journal are used to record transactions that occur less often.

7. Posting of the general columns is done _____ by _____.

8. A petty cash payments record is an example of a(n) _____ record.

9. Cash shortages are recorded with a(n) _____ to Cash Short and Over; cash overages are recorded with a(n) _____.

10. A bank reconciliation is done to bring the ending balance shown on the bank statement into agreement with the balance shown in the _____.

PART IV MULTIPLE CHOICE

Please circle the correct answer.

1. Which of the following items are included in cash?
   a. coins and currency
   b. checks
   c. receipts from credit card sales
   d. all of the above

2. Steps to control and protect cash include which of the following?
   a. making bank deposits daily
   b. assigning the handling of cash to the bookkeeper or accountant
   c. keeping enough cash on hand so that all bills can be paid with cash
   d. none of the above

3. The combined journal is used by small businesses
   a. as a second journal in which to record transactions before posting.
   b. to save journalizing and posting time.
   c. instead of a ledger.
   d. because there is no need to post when the combined journal is used.

4. The combined journal has special columns for
   a. every account in the ledger.
   b. accounts that are used infrequently.
   c. accounts such as Cash that are used often.
   d. Cash only.

5. The equality of debits and credits in the combined journal can be found by
   a. preparing a trial balance.
   b. adding the totals of all debit columns and comparing them with the totals of all credit columns.
   c. posting and determining the account balances.
   d. Debits do not equal credits in the combined journal.

6. Posting is done from the combined journal by
   a. posting the totals of the special columns and posting items from the general columns individually.
   b. posting each item individually.
   c. posting only the items in the general columns.
   d. It is not necessary to post from the combined journal.

7. When a petty cash fund is established
   a. the Cash account is debited and the Petty Cash account is credited.
   b. the Cash account is credited and the various expense accounts are debited.
   c. the Petty Cash account is debited and the Cash account is credited.
   d. No entry needs to be made because there is a transfer of cash from one account to another.

8. When the petty cash fund is replenished
   a. the Petty Cash account is debited and the Cash account is credited.
   b. various expense accounts are debited and the Cash account is credited.
   c. the Cash account is debited and various expense accounts are credited.
   d. the Petty Cash account is debited and various expense accounts are credited.

9. On a bank reconciliation, outstanding checks are
   a. deducted from the checkbook balance.
   b. added to the bank balance.
   c. added to the checkbook balance.
   d. deducted from the bank balance.

10. On a bank reconciliation, bank service charges are
    a. deducted from the checkbook balance.
    b. added to the bank balance.
    c. added to the checkbook balance.
    d. deducted from the bank balance.

PART V WRITING/SHORT ANSWER

1. **Reflect** Make a list, in words or simple phrases, of the most important and meaningful points in this chapter.

2. **Question** Think about the most confusing points or the material you do not understand in this chapter. Write down two or three questions that remain unanswered.

3. **Connect** Explain, in one or two sentences, the connection between the main points of this chapter and the major goals of the entire course.

4. **Summarize** Review this chapter's Joining the Pieces visual summary and explain the concept(s) illustrated in a few sentences.

WORKING PAPERS

SKILLS REVIEW

EXERCISE 6-1

Classified as Cash

		Yes	No
(a)	Checks made payable to the business		
(b)	Money orders		
(c)	Postage stamps		
(d)	Savings bonds due to mature in ten years		
(e)	Currency		
(f)	Cashier's check		
(g)	Coin		
(h)	Traveler's check		
(i)	Petty cash		
(j)	Change fund		
(k)	Amount on deposit in a bank checking account		

EXERCISE 6-2

General Journal   Page 1

	Date	Account Title	P.R.	Debit	Credit	
1						1
2						2
3						3
4						4
5						5
6						6
7						7
8						8
9						9
10						10

EXERCISE 6-3

General Journal

Page 1

	Date		Account Title	P.R.	Debit	Credit	
1							1
2							2
3							3
4							4
5							5
6							6
7							7
8							8
9							9
10							10

EXERCISE 6-4

General Journal

Page 1

	Date		Account Title	P.R.	Debit	Credit	
1							1
2							2
3							3
4							4
5							5
6							6
7							7
8							8
9							9
10							10
11							11
12							12
13							13
14							14
15							15
16							16
17							17
18							18

EXERCISE 6-5

General Journal

Page 1

	Date		Account Title	P.R.	Debit	Credit	
1							1
2							2
3							3
4							4
5							5
6							6
7							7
8							8
9							9
10							10

EXERCISE 6-6

General Journal

Page 1

	Date		Account Title	P.R.	Debit	Credit	
1							1
2							2
3							3
4							4
5							5
6							6
7							7
8							8
9							9
10							10
11							11
12							12
13							13
14							14
15							15
16							16
17							17
18							18

EXERCISE 6-7

1. _____
2. _____
3. _____
4. _____
5. _____
6. _____

EXERCISE 6-8

EXERCISE 6-9

EXERCISE 6-10

General Journal

Page 1

	Date		Account Title	P.R.	Debit	Credit	
1							1
2							2
3							3
4							4
5							5
6							6
7							7
8							8
9							9
10							10

This page intentionally left blank.

This page intentionally left blank.

CASE PROBLEMS

PROBLEM 6-1A OR 6-1B

1., 2.   **Combined Journal for Month of _____, 20X2**

Cash		Ck. No.	Day	Description	P.R.	General	
Debit	Credit					Debit	Credit

Page 5

Accounts Payable		Fees Earned	Salaries Expense
Debit	Credit	Credit	Debit

This page intentionally left blank.

This page intentionally left blank.

2., 3.   **Combined Journal for Month of** _____ **, 20**_____

Cash		Ck. No.	Day	Description	P.R.	General	
Debit	Credit					Debit	Credit

Page 2

Accounts Payable		Fees Earned	Salaries Expense
Debit	Credit	Credit	Debit

1., 3.

ACCOUNT Cash   ACCOUNT NO. 111

DATE	ITEM	P.R.	DEBIT	CREDIT	BALANCE	
					DEBIT	CREDIT

ACCOUNT Office Supplies   ACCOUNT NO. 114

DATE	ITEM	P.R.	DEBIT	CREDIT	BALANCE	
					DEBIT	CREDIT

ACCOUNT Advertising Supplies   ACCOUNT NO. 115

DATE	ITEM	P.R.	DEBIT	CREDIT	BALANCE	
					DEBIT	CREDIT

ACCOUNT Office Equipment   ACCOUNT NO. 125

DATE	ITEM	P.R.	DEBIT	CREDIT	BALANCE	
					DEBIT	CREDIT

ACCOUNT Accounts Payable   ACCOUNT NO. 211

DATE	ITEM	P.R.	DEBIT	CREDIT	BALANCE	
					DEBIT	CREDIT

PROBLEM 6-2A OR 6-2B (continued)

ACCOUNT Notes Payable   ACCOUNT NO. 215

DATE	ITEM	P.R.	DEBIT	CREDIT	BALANCE DEBIT	BALANCE CREDIT

ACCOUNT _____, Capital   ACCOUNT NO. 311

DATE	ITEM	P.R.	DEBIT	CREDIT	BALANCE DEBIT	BALANCE CREDIT

ACCOUNT _____, Drawing   ACCOUNT NO. 312

DATE	ITEM	P.R.	DEBIT	CREDIT	BALANCE DEBIT	BALANCE CREDIT

ACCOUNT Fees Earned   ACCOUNT NO. 411

DATE	ITEM	P.R.	DEBIT	CREDIT	BALANCE DEBIT	BALANCE CREDIT

ACCOUNT Rent Expense   ACCOUNT NO. 511

DATE	ITEM	P.R.	DEBIT	CREDIT	BALANCE DEBIT	BALANCE CREDIT

ACCOUNT Salaries Expense

ACCOUNT NO. 512

DATE		ITEM	P.R.	DEBIT	CREDIT	BALANCE	
						DEBIT	CREDIT

ACCOUNT Repairs Expense

ACCOUNT NO. 513

DATE		ITEM	P.R.	DEBIT	CREDIT	BALANCE	
						DEBIT	CREDIT

ACCOUNT Utilities Expense

ACCOUNT NO. 514

DATE		ITEM	P.R.	DEBIT	CREDIT	BALANCE	
						DEBIT	CREDIT

ACCOUNT Miscellaneous Expense

ACCOUNT NO. 518

DATE		ITEM	P.R.	DEBIT	CREDIT	BALANCE	
						DEBIT	CREDIT

4.

ACCOUNT TITLE	DEBIT	CREDIT

This page intentionally left blank.

PROBLEM 6-3A OR 6-3B

1., 4.

General Journal

Page 1

	Date		Account Title	P.R.	Debit	Credit	
1							1
2							2
3							3
4							4
5							5
6							6
7							7
8							8
9							9
10							10
11							11
12							12

2., 3.

Petty Cash Payments for Month of _____, 20X

Page 1

Day	Description	Vou. No.	Total Amount	Office Supp. Exp.	Misc. Exp.	Postage Exp.	Other Accounts	Amount

Distribution of Charges

1.

SUSAN SHEPPARD				
Bank Reconcilliation Statement				
JULY 31, 20X1				
Balance Per Bank statement				7600
ADD: Deposit in Transit				75
				7675
DEDUCT: Outstanding Checks				
# 122		400		
# 126		50		
# 129		125		
# 130		200		775
Adjusted bank statement balance				6900
Balance Per Checkbook				6000
DEDUCT:	collection note			931
Service charge		13		
imprinting check charge		18		
note receivable		931		962
adjusted checkbook balance				5038

2.

General Journal

	Date		Account Title	P.R.	Debit					Credit					
1	20X1 July	31	CASH			9	3	1							1
2			notes Receivable								9	3	1		2
3			note collected by bank												3
4															4
5		30	Bank service				1	3							5
6			cash									1	3		6
7			Bank fees												7
8		30	imprinting check charge				1	8							8
9			cash									1	8		9
10			Bank fees												10

CHALLENGE PROBLEMS

PROBLEM SOLVING

1.

PROBLEM SOLVING (continued)

2. **General Journal** Page 1

	Date		Account Title	P.R.	Debit	Credit	
1							1
2							2
3							3
4							4
5							5
6							6
7							7
8							8
9							9
10							10
11							11
12							12
13							13
14							14

COMMUNICATIONS

ETHICS

This page intentionally left blank.

PRACTICE TEST ANSWERS

PART I

1. T
2. F
3. T
4. T
5. T
6. F
7. T
8. F
9. T
10. T
11. F
12. F
13. T
14. T
15. T
16. F
17. T
18. T
19. T
20. F

PART II

1. r
2. c
3. o
4. b
5. q
6. m
7. f
8. s
9. k
10. l
11. p
12. e
13. g
14. t
15. h
16. n
17. a
18. d
19. i
20. j

PART III

1. added, bank
2. petty cash voucher
3. replenish
4. special
5. total
6. general
7. item, item
8. auxiliary
9. debit, credit
10. checkbook

PART IV

1. d
2. a
3. b
4. c
5. b
6. a
7. c
8. b
9. d
10. a

PART V

Answers will vary. Please discuss questions with your instructor. You can also discuss issues related to this chapter by logging onto the Paradigm Accounting Web Site at www.emcp.com and clicking on the discussion section.

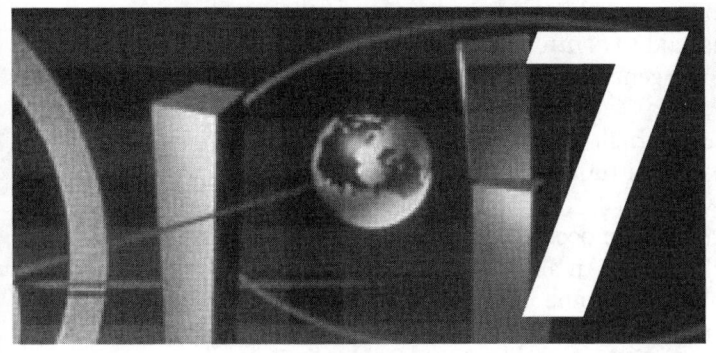

7 Accounting for a Merchandising Business—Purchases and Cash Payments

CHAPTER SUMMARY

A **merchandising business** is a business that buys and resells goods. Goods held for sale to customers are called **merchandise** or **merchandise inventory**. Merchandise is also referred to as **stock in trade**.

Merchandising activity occurs at both the retail level and the wholesale level. At the retail level, merchandisers sell directly to the consuming public. At the wholesale level, merchandise is purchased in bulk from manufacturers or other **wholesalers** and is sold primarily to **retail businesses**.

The purchase of merchandise requires specific procedures and forms for proper control. In a small merchandising business, purchasing is usually done by the store manager or the owner. In a large merchandising business, purchasing begins with the preparation of a **purchase requisition** by a department in the organization. The purchasing department, upon receipt of a properly prepared requisition, prepares a **purchase order**, which is sent to a supplier. When the ordered goods are received, a **receiving report** is prepared to verify that all the goods arrived and were accepted.

An **invoice** is a form prepared by the seller to describe the goods and the terms of the sale. A copy of the invoice is sent to the purchaser. Thus, the same document is both a **sales invoice** and a **purchase invoice**. It is the source document for recording the sale on the books of the seller and the purchase on the books of the buyer.

Sellers often offer buyers discounts on goods purchased. Two common types of discounts are **trade discounts** and **cash discounts**. A trade discount is a reduction from the **list price** of goods, such as offering goods at $600 less a 10% discount. This practice allows sellers to vary the price of their merchandise without having to print new catalogs. Trade discounts are not recorded on the books of the seller or the buyer.

A cash discount is a discount offered to encourage prompt payment by a buyer. The most common form of cash discount is 2/10,n/30 (two ten, net thirty), which means that if a buyer makes payment for a credit purchase within ten days from the date of the invoice, a 2% discount can be taken. The buyer records the amount of the discount in the **Purchases Discounts** account.

The cost of merchandise purchased is debited to a temporary owner's equity account entitled **Purchases**. The Purchases account is used only for recording the cost of merchandise purchased for resale to customers. It is one of several **cost accounts**.

All purchases can be recorded in the general journal. When the volume of purchases is large, however, it is more efficient to use a **purchases journal**. A purchases journal is a **special journal** that is designed to meet the needs of the business using it. In this chapter, we worked with a purchases journal that was designed to record only credit purchases of merchandise. It has one money column, entitled Purchases Dr., Accounts Payable Cr.

The Accounts Payable account is a liability account that shows amounts owed to the creditors of a business. However, the Accounts Payable account does not show information regarding the balances owed to individual creditors. Therefore, it is a common practice to set up accounts for creditors in a separate ledger. A separate ledger containing only one type of account is called a **subsidiary ledger**. A subsidiary ledger containing only creditors' accounts is called an **accounts payable ledger**.

Accounts in the accounts payable ledger are arranged in alphabetical order to make it easier to add new accounts and remove old accounts. Accounts in the **general ledger** are numbered in the standard way.

The balances of creditors' accounts, when fully posted, should equal the balance of the Accounts Payable account. Thus, the Accounts Payable account is said to *control* or summarize the accounts payable ledger. A **controlling account** is an account in the general ledger that summarizes the balances of accounts in a related subsidiary ledger.

There are two types of postings from the purchases journal: (1) posting of individual credits to creditors' accounts on a daily basis and (2) monthly posting of the total of the money column as a debit to Purchases and as a credit to Accounts Payable.

In merchandising businesses, returns and allowances often occur. A return of merchandise results when a buyer sends back part, or all, of a purchase to the seller. An allowance results when the buyer keeps the goods purchased but asks for a price reduction due to some factor, such as damage to the goods while in shipment. Source documents for returns and allowances are the **debit memorandum**, prepared by the buyer, and the **credit memorandum**, prepared by the seller.

The buyer records returns and allowances involving merchandise in a contra purchases account entitled **Purchases Returns and Allowances**. Since the Purchases Returns and Allowances account is contra to the Purchases account, it will have a credit balance that is opposite to the debit balance of the Purchases account.

Cash payments can be recorded in the general journal. However, a more efficient use of journalizing and posting time is to record them in another special journal, the **cash payments journal**. The cash payments journal is used to record all types of cash payments.

Because the cash payments journal is designed to record decreases in the Cash account, a Cash Cr. column must be used. The number of other special columns and their titles are determined by the needs of the business. Posting the cash payments journal follows the same procedures as those for posting the purchases journal: There is daily posting to the accounts payable ledger and monthly posting to the general ledger.

The posting accuracy of a subsidiary ledger is proved by preparing a schedule. A **schedule of accounts payable** is a listing of the balances of the creditors' accounts. The total of this schedule should agree with the balance of the Accounts Payable controlling account in the general ledger.

Purchases carry freight terms. The **Freight In account** is used to record the freight costs on incoming merchandise. **FOB destination** and **FOB shipping point** are common freight terms. FOB destination means that the seller is responsible for all freight costs while the goods are in transit. FOB shipping point means that the buyer is responsible for all freight costs while the goods are in transit.

PRACTICE TEST

PART I TRUE/FALSE

Please circle the correct answer.

T F   1. A merchandising business buys merchandise for resale to its customers.

T F   2. Office desks are merchandise inventory to a dealer in office furniture but are equipment to a business that is using them in the office.

T F   3. A purchase requisition is a form sent to a supplier by the business making the purchase.

T F   4. An invoice is a bill.

T F   5. A trade discount is given by a seller of merchandise to encourage prompt payment of the invoice.

T F   6. Trade discounts are not recorded in the accounting records by either the buyer or the seller.

T F   7. The Purchases account is a temporary owner's equity account.

T F   8. All purchases made by a company for any purpose are debited to the Purchases account.

T F   9. Cost accounts are used only to determine the cost of merchandise sold to customers.

T F   10. The source document used to record a purchase in the accounting records is usually the purchase order.

T F   11. The purchases journal is used to record only purchases of merchandise for cash.

T F   12. A separate ledger containing only one type of account is called a subsidiary ledger.

T F   13. Management usually does not wish to maintain a separate account for purchases returns and allowances.

T F   14. Items from special journals are usually posted to the subsidiary ledger daily and to the general ledger at the end of the month.

T F   15. The schedule of accounts payable is prepared to see if the subsidiary ledger is in balance with the controlling account in the general ledger.

PART II MATCHING

Please match each of the following terms with its definition.

a. cash discounts
b. cash payments journal
c. controlling account
d. cost accounts
e. cost of goods sold
f. FOB destination
g. FOB shipping point
h. Freight In
i. invoice
j. merchandise inventory

k. Purchases account
l. purchases discounts
m. purchases journal
n. purchase order
o. purchase requisition
p. Purchases Returns and Allowances
q. receiving report
r. schedule of accounts payable
s. subsidiary ledgers
t. trade discount

_____ 1. Goods held for sale to customers.

_____ 2. A percentage reduction in the list price of merchandise.

_____ 3. A form prepared by the purchasing department describing the goods ordered to the seller.

_____ 4. A business document that shows the names and addresses of the buyer and the seller, the date and terms of the sale, a description of the goods purchased, and the mode of transportation to ship the goods. It is a bill.

_____ 5. A form indicating what goods were received and in what quantity.

_____ 6. Discounts offered to encourage prompt payment by buyers.

_____ 7. A written request for certain goods.

_____ 8. Accounts that are presented on the income statement and that are used to determine the cost of goods sold.

_____ 9. Ledgers that contain only one type of account.

_____ 10. An account in the general ledger that summarizes accounts in the related subsidiary ledger.

_____ 11. A contra account that is used to record returns of merchandise and allowances received on merchandise.

_____ 12. A special journal used only to record credit purchases of merchandise.

_____ 13. The cost of the merchandise that a business sells to its customers.

_____ 14. The temporary owner's equity account used to record the cost of all merchandise purchased for resale to customers.

_____ 15. The shipping term that means the buyer is responsible for all freight costs while the goods are in transit.

_____ 16. The account used to record the shipping charges on incoming merchandise.

_____ 17. A listing of accounts and balances from the accounts payable ledger.

_____ 18. A special journal that is used to record only cash payments.

_____ 19. A contra account that a buyer uses to record discounts received for prompt payment of invoices.

_____ 20. The shipping term that means the seller is responsible for all freight costs until the goods reach the buyer.

PART III FILL IN THE BLANKS

Please complete each sentence with the correct word or words.

1. _____ are businesses that sell directly to consumers, such as drugstores, grocery stores, and department stores; _____ are businesses that buy in bulk from manufacturers.

2. Managers identify goods needed and request them by preparing a(n) _____.

3. When goods arrive, they are counted and checked against the purchase order and a(n) _____ is prepared.

4. To permit price changes without the necessity of printing new catalogs, many businesses offer _____.

5. When goods are sold below the list price, the buyer and seller always record these transactions in their accounting records at actual _____.

6. _____ are given to encourage prompt payment of invoices.

7. The Purchases account is used to record purchases of _____.

8. If supplies are purchased for use in a firm's office, the account debited would be _____.

9. The balances of all the accounts in the accounts payable ledger should equal the balance of the _____ account in the general ledger.

10. In the purchases journal, individual credits should be posted to the _____ accounts in the _____ ledger on a daily basis; the total of the money column should be posted as a(n) _____ to Purchases and a(n) _____ to Accounts Payable at the end of the month.

11. Purchases Returns and Allowances is a(n) _____ account to Purchases.

12. When a buyer returns merchandise to the seller, the buyer issues a(n) _____.

13. The seller will usually respond to a debit memorandum with a(n) _____.

14. When the seller must pay all shipping costs, the term used is _____.

15. _____ means that the buyer must pay all shipping costs.

PART IV MULTIPLE CHOICE

Please circle the correct answer.

1. Which of the following would be considered merchandise?
   a. the company delivery truck
   b. the desks and fax machines in the office
   c. the items on the shelves in the store that are for sale to customers
   d. the supplies in the supply room

2. Which of the following is a step in the purchasing process?
   a. preparing a purchase order
   b. preparing a receiving report
   c. recording an invoice in the journal
   d. all of the above

3. ABC Company purchases merchandise for $500, terms 2/10,n/30. The date of the invoice is May 1. Payment is made on May 9. What is the amount of the check prepared by the company?
   a. $500
   b. $490
   c. $400
   d. none of the above

4. When a company purchases merchandise on account
   a. Purchases is debited and Accounts Payable is credited.
   b. Merchandise Inventory is debited and Accounts Payable is credited.
   c. Accounts Payable is debited and Purchases is credited.
   d. none of the above.

5. Cost of goods available for sale is determined by taking the amount of merchandise inventory at the beginning of the period and adding the
   a. ending inventory.
   b. cost of goods sold.
   c. net purchases.
   d. balance of Accounts Payable.

6. Cost of goods sold is determined by taking the cost of goods available for sale and deducting the
   a. beginning inventory.
   b. ending inventory.
   c. net purchases.
   d. balance of Accounts Payable.

7. The purchase journal is designed to record
   a. purchases of merchandise for cash.
   b. purchases of merchandise for cash or on account.
   c. purchases of merchandise on account.
   d. purchases of any items for cash or on account.

8. Subsidiary ledgers and special journals are used in order to
   a. make it possible to divide the work between several persons in the accounting department.
   b. simplify the trial balance and balance sheet.
   c. streamline recording and posting of common transactions.
   d. all of the above.

9. Which of the following describes the difference between costs and expenses?
   a. Costs are associated with merchandise and cost of goods sold, while expenses are the costs of operating the company.
   b. Costs are the prices of the items purchased by the company, while expenses are bills that are paid for services.
   c. Costs are just another term for expenses.
   d. none of the above.

10. Two contra accounts to Purchases are
    a. Freight In and Purchases Discounts.
    b. Purchases Discounts and Purchases Returns and Allowances.
    c. Purchases Returns and Allowances and Freight In.
    d. none of the above.

PART V WRITING/SHORT ANSWER

1. **Reflect** Make a list, in words or simple phrases, of the most important and meaningful points in this chapter.

2. **Question** Think about the most confusing points or the material you do not understand in this chapter. Write down two or three questions that remain unanswered.

3. **Connect** Explain, in one or two sentences, the connection between the main points of this chapter and the major goals of the entire course.

4. **Summarize** Review this chapter's Joining the Pieces visual summary and explain the concept(s) illustrated in a few sentences.

This page intentionally left blank.

WORKING PAPERS

SKILLS REVIEW

EXERCISE 7-1

(a) _____

(b) _____

(c) _____

(d) _____

(e) _____

EXERCISE 7-2

(a) _____

(b) _____

(c) _____

(d) _____

(e) _____

EXERCISE 7-3

General Journal

Page 1

	Date		Account Title	P.R.	Debit	Credit	
1							1
2							2
3							3
4							4
5							5
6							6
7							7
8							8
9							9
10							10
11							11
12							12
13							13
14							14
15							15
16							16
17							17
18							18
19							19
20							20
21							21
22							22
23							23
24							24
25							25

EXERCISE 7-4

General Journal

	Date	Account Title	P.R.	Debit	Credit	
1						1
2						2
3						3
4						4
5						5
6						6
7						7
8						8
9						9
10						10
11						11
12						12
13						13
14						14
15						15
16						16
17						17
18						18

Purchases Journal

	Date	Invoice No.	Account Credited	P.R.	Purchases Dr. Accts. Pay. Cr.	
1						1
2						2
3						3
4						4
5						5
6						6
7						7
8						8
9						9
10						10
11						11
12						12

EXERCISE 7-5

	Date		Account Title	P.R.	Debit	Credit	
1							1
2							2
3							3
4							4
5							5
6							6
7							7
8							8
9							9
10							10
11							11
12							12
13							13
14							14
15							15
16							16
17							17
18							18
19							19
20							20
21							21
22							22
23							23
24							24
25							25
26							26
27							27
28							28
29							29
30							30
31							31
32							32

EXERCISE 7-6

	Date	Account Title	P.R.	Debit	Credit	
1						1
2						2
3						3
4						4
5						5
6						6
7						7
8						8
9						9
10						10
11						11
12						12
13						13
14						14
15						15
16						16
17						17
18						18
19						19
20						20
21						21
22						22
23						23
24						24
25						25
26						26
27						27
28						28
29						29
30						30
31						31
32						32

EXERCISE 7-7

Cash Payments Journal

Date	Ck. No.	Account Debited	P.R.	General Dr.	Accounts Payable Dr.	Purchases Discounts Cr.	Cash Cr.

EXERCISE 7-8

General Journal

	Date	Account Title	P.R.	Debit	Credit	
1						1
2						2
3						3
4						4
5						5
6						6
7						7
8						8
9						9
10						10

EXERCISE 7-9

	Date		Account Title	P.R.	Debit	Credit	
1							1
2							2
3							3
4							4
5							5
6							6
7							7
8							8
9							9
10							10
11							11
12							12
13							13
14							14
15							15

CASE PROBLEMS

PROBLEM 7-1A OR 7-1B

General Journal

	Date		Account Title	P.R.	Debit	Credit	
1	20X2 MAY	1	Purchases		9 9 5		1
2			A/P – CLARK CO.			9 9 5	2
3			Purchase merchandise on Acct				3
4							4
5		6	Purchases		2 4 0		5
6			A/P – ELLIS Co			2 4 0	6
7			Purchases offi suplies on Acct				7
8		7	Purchases		7 8 0		8
9			A/P – Puan Co			7 8 0	9
10			Purchase Merch. on Acct				10
11		11	A/R – Puan Co		4 5		11
12			Purchase returns + allowance			4 5	12
13			Returned Merchandise for Credit				13
14		12	A/P – Ellis Co		3 0		14
15			Purchase returned + allowance			3 0	15
16			shortage on purchase				16
17		18	Purchase		8 7 5		17
18			cash			8 7 5	18
19			Purchase merchandise for cash				19
20		22	A/P –		5 0		20
21			Purchases returns + allowances			5 0	21
22		23	Purchases – Astor Co.		1 0 0 0		22
23			Cash			4 0 0	23
24			A/P – Astor CO.			6 0 0	24
25			Purchases Store equip.				25
26		27	Purchase		8 5 0		26
27			A/P – Wilson Co.			8 5 0	27
28			Purchases merchandise on Acct				28
29		29	A/P – Astor Co		2 5		29
30			Purchases returns + allowances			2 5	30
31			recieved allowance on purchase				31
32							32

Handwritten margin notes: SC Pg 254; Visit CASH; CASH or A/R

Purchases Journal

Page 1

C Pg 254

	Date	Invoice No.	Account Credited	P.R.	Purchases Dr. Accts. Pay. Cr.	
1	20X2 MAY 1	1	CLARK CO. ✓		9 9 5	1
2	6	2	Ellis Co.		2 4 0	2
3	7	3	Phan Co. ✓		7 8 0	3
4	25	4	Astor		6 0 0	4
5	27	5	Wilson ✓		8 5 0	5
6						6

not gonna Resell

nothing that we gonna resell →

3., 4.   **General Journal**   Page 1

	Date		Account Title	P.R.	Debit		Credit			
1	20X2 Sept	1	Purchases		2 5 5 0					1
2			A/P - LANG Co				2 5 5 0			2
3			Purch. merch. on Acct							3
4		4	Purchases		6 8 9 0					4
5			A/P - Midwest Publishing				6 8 9 0			5
6			Purch. merch. on Acct							6
7		7	A/P - Clothing wholesalers		1 2 5 6 25					7
8			Purchase Discount				2 5 1 25			8
9			Cash				1 0 0 5			9
10		10	Purchases		9 7 5					10
11			A/P - LANG Co.				9 7 5			11
12			Purchase merch. on acct							12
13		11	Purchases		2 4 5 80					13
14			A/P - Regents Supply Co				2 4 5 80			14
15			Purchases office supplies							15
16		14	Purchases		1 3 5 0 0					16
17			A/P - HAMER Equip. Co				1 3 5 0 0			17
18			Purch. off. equip. on Acct							18
19		15	Purchase		7 0 0					19
20			A/P - Addington				7 0 0			20
21		16	A/P - Regent supply		6 0					21
22			Purchases Return + allowances				6 0			22
23		18	Purchase		4 7 0 0					23
24			A/P - Midwest Publishing				4 7 0 0			24
25		21	Purchases		5 3 0					25
26			A/P - Hamer Equip.				5 3 0			26
27		25	A/P - Midwest Publishing		1 1 0					27
28			Purchases Return + allowances				1 1 0			28
29		28	Purchases		9 5 0					29
30			A/P - Addington Co.				9 5 0			30
31		30	Purchases		6 5					31
32			A/P - Regents Supply Co.				6 5			32

SC

SC

Clue - Merchandise - Resell

Purchases Journal

Page 1

	Date	Invoice No.	Account Credited	P.R.	Purchases Dr. Accts. Pay. Cr.	
1	20x2 Sept	1	LANG CO ✓ ✓		2 5 5 0	1
2		4	Midwest Publishing ✓		6 8 9 0	2
3		7	Clothing Wholesalers ✓		1 2 5 6 25	3
4		10	LANG CO ✓		9 7 5	4
5		11	Regents Supply Co.		2 4 5 80	5
6		14	HAMMER Equipment ✓		13 5 0 0	6
7		15	ADDINGTON CO ✓ ✓		7 0 0	7
8		18	Midwest Publishing ✓		4 7 0 0	8
9		21	HAMER Equipment		5 3 0	9
10		28	ADDINGTON Co. ✓		9 5 0	10
11		30	Regents Supply Co		6 5	11
12						12

32,362.05

1., 4.

General Ledger

ACCOUNT Store Supplies   ACCOUNT NO. 113

DATE		ITEM	P.R.	DEBIT	CREDIT	BALANCE	
						DEBIT	CREDIT
20x2 Sept	1			6 7 5 90		6 7 5 90	

ACCOUNT Office Supplies   ACCOUNT NO. 114

DATE		ITEM	P.R.	DEBIT	CREDIT	BALANCE	
						DEBIT	CREDIT
20x2 Sep	1			3 4 5 75		3 4 5 75	

ACCOUNT **Office Equipment**   ACCOUNT NO. 121

DATE	ITEM	P.R.	DEBIT	CREDIT	BALANCE DEBIT	BALANCE CREDIT
20X2 Sept 1			12 9 5 6		12 9 5 6	

ACCOUNT **Accounts Payable**   ACCOUNT NO. 211

DATE	ITEM	P.R.	DEBIT	CREDIT	BALANCE DEBIT	BALANCE CREDIT
20X2 Sept 1			9 6 0 0		9 6 0 0	

ACCOUNT **Purchases**   ACCOUNT NO. 511

DATE	ITEM	P.R.	DEBIT	CREDIT	BALANCE DEBIT	BALANCE CREDIT
20X2 Sept 1			98 5 6 8 35		98 5 6 8 35	

ACCOUNT **Purchases Returns and Allowances**   ACCOUNT NO. 511.1

DATE	ITEM	P.R.	DEBIT	CREDIT	BALANCE DEBIT	BALANCE CREDIT
20X2 Sept 1			1 4 5 0		1 4 5 0	

2., 3.   **Accounts Payable Ledger**

NAME ADDINGTON CO.

ADDRESS

Date		Item	P.R.	Debit	Credit	Balance
20X2 Sep	1			1400		1400
	15					

NAME CLOTHING WHolesalers

ADDRESS

Date		Item	P.R.	Debit	Credit	Balance
20X2 Sept	1			1250		1250

NAME HAMER EQUIPMENT CO.

ADDRESS

Date		Item	P.R.	Debit	Credit	Balance
20X2 Sept	1	Start w/ balance →		2500		2500

NAME LANG CO.

ADDRESS

Date		Item	P.R.	Debit	Credit	Balance
20X2 Sept	1	Balance		1810		1810
	1					
	10					

PROBLEM 7-2A OR 7-2B (continued)

NAME MidWEST Publishing Co.

ADDRESS

Date		Item	P.R.	Debit	Credit	Balance
20X2 Sept	1	Balance		9 6 0		9 6 0
	4					
	16					
	25					

NAME Regents Supply Co.

ADDRESS

Date		Item	P.R.	Debit	Credit	Balance
20X2 Sept	1			1 6 8 0		1 6 8 0

owe less ——— Debit ↗

5.

CAMPUS BOOK STORE
Schedule of Accounts Payable
September 30, 20X2

ADDINGTON CO.	1 4 0 0		
Clothing Wholesalers	1 2 5 0		
Hamer Equipment Co.	2 5 0 0		
Lang Co	1 8 1 0		
MidWEST Publishing CO.	9 6 0		
Regents Supply	1 6 8 0		

6. The balance of the Accounts Payable controlling account: _____

This page intentionally left blank.

3., 4.   **General Journal**   Page 1

	Date	Account Title	P.R.	Debit	Credit	
1						1
2						2
3						3
4						4
5						5
6						6
7						7
8						8
9						9
10						10
11						11

Purchases Journal   Page 1

Date	Account Credited	Inv No.	Post. Ref.	Accounts Payable Credit	Freight In Debit	Purchases Debit

1., 4.   **General Ledger**

ACCOUNT Office Equipment   ACCOUNT NO. 118

DATE	ITEM	P.R.	DEBIT	CREDIT	BALANCE	
					DEBIT	CREDIT

ACCOUNT Store Equipment   ACCOUNT NO. 119

DATE	ITEM	P.R.	DEBIT	CREDIT	BALANCE	
					DEBIT	CREDIT

ACCOUNT Accounts Payable   ACCOUNT NO. 211

DATE	ITEM	P.R.	DEBIT	CREDIT	BALANCE	
					DEBIT	CREDIT

ACCOUNT Purchases   ACCOUNT NO. 511

DATE	ITEM	P.R.	DEBIT	CREDIT	BALANCE	
					DEBIT	CREDIT

ACCOUNT Freight In   ACCOUNT NO. 512

DATE		ITEM	P.R.	DEBIT	CREDIT	BALANCE	
						DEBIT	CREDIT

2., 3.

Accounts Payable Ledger

NAME

ADDRESS

Date		Item	P.R.	Debit	Credit	Balance

NAME

ADDRESS

Date		Item	P.R.	Debit	Credit	Balance

NAME

ADDRESS

Date		Item	P.R.	Debit	Credit	Balance

NAME

ADDRESS

Date		Item	P.R.	Debit	Credit	Balance

NAME

ADDRESS

Date		Item	P.R.	Debit	Credit	Balance

NAME

ADDRESS

Date		Item	P.R.	Debit	Credit	Balance

* FOR 7-3B ONLY

NAME

ADDRESS

Date		Item	P.R.	Debit	Credit	Balance

5.

The balance of the Accounts Payable controlling account: _____

This page intentionally left blank.

PROBLEM 7-4A OR 7-4B

3., 4.　　　　　　　　　　**General Journal**　　　　　　　　　Page 1

	Date		Account Title	P.R.	Debit	Credit	
1							1
2							2
3							3
4							4
5							5
6							6
7							7
8							8
9							9
10							10
11							11

Purchases Journal　　　　　　　　　Page 1

	Date	Invoice No.	Account Credited	P.R.	Purchases Dr. Accts. Pay. Cr.	
1						1
2						2
3						3
4						4
5						5
6						6

Cash Payments Journal

Date	Ck. No.	Account Debited	P.R.	General Dr.	Accounts Payable Dr.	Purchases Discounts Cr.	Cash Cr.

1., 4.

General Ledger

ACCOUNT Cash   ACCOUNT NO. 111

DATE	ITEM	P.R.	DEBIT	CREDIT	BALANCE DEBIT	BALANCE CREDIT

ACCOUNT Office Supplies   ACCOUNT NO. 112

DATE	ITEM	P.R.	DEBIT	CREDIT	BALANCE DEBIT	BALANCE CREDIT

ACCOUNT Prepaid Insurance   ACCOUNT NO. 113

DATE		ITEM	P.R.	DEBIT	CREDIT	BALANCE	
						DEBIT	CREDIT

ACCOUNT Store Equipment   ACCOUNT NO. 116

DATE		ITEM	P.R.	DEBIT	CREDIT	BALANCE	
						DEBIT	CREDIT

ACCOUNT Accounts Payable   ACCOUNT NO. 211

DATE		ITEM	P.R.	DEBIT	CREDIT	BALANCE	
						DEBIT	CREDIT

ACCOUNT _____, Drawing   ACCOUNT NO. 312

DATE		ITEM	P.R.	DEBIT	CREDIT	BALANCE	
						DEBIT	CREDIT

ACCOUNT Purchases   ACCOUNT NO. 511

DATE	ITEM	P.R.	DEBIT	CREDIT	BALANCE	
					DEBIT	CREDIT

ACCOUNT Purchases Discounts   ACCOUNT NO. 511.2

DATE	ITEM	P.R.	DEBIT	CREDIT	BALANCE	
					DEBIT	CREDIT

ACCOUNT Freight In   ACCOUNT NO. 512

DATE	ITEM	P.R.	DEBIT	CREDIT	BALANCE	
					DEBIT	CREDIT

ACCOUNT Salaries Expense   ACCOUNT NO. 612

DATE	ITEM	P.R.	DEBIT	CREDIT	BALANCE	
					DEBIT	CREDIT

ACCOUNT Rent Expense   ACCOUNT NO. 613

DATE		ITEM	P.R.	DEBIT	CREDIT	BALANCE	
						DEBIT	CREDIT

2., 3.

Accounts Payable Ledger

NAME

ADDRESS

Date		Item	P.R.	Debit	Credit	Balance

NAME

ADDRESS

Date		Item	P.R.	Debit	Credit	Balance

NAME

ADDRESS

Date		Item	P.R.	Debit	Credit	Balance

NAME _____

ADDRESS _____

Date	Item	P.R.	Debit	Credit	Balance

5.

6. The balance of the Accounts Payable controlling account: _____

3., 4.

General Journal

Page 1

	Date		Account Title	P.R.	Debit	Credit	
1							1
2							2
3							3
4							4
5							5
6							6
7							7
8							8
9							9
10							10
11							11
12							12
13							13
14							14
15							15
16							16
17							17
18							18
19							19
20							20

Purchases Journal

Page 1

	Date	Invoice No.	Account Credited	P.R.	Purchases Dr. Accts. Pay. Cr.	
1						1
2						2
3						3
4						4
5						5

Cash Payments Journal

Date	Ck. No.	Account Debited	P.R.	General Dr.	Accounts Payable Dr.	Purchases Discounts Cr.	Cash Cr.

2., 4.

General Ledger

ACCOUNT Cash   ACCOUNT NO. 111

DATE	ITEM	P.R.	DEBIT	CREDIT	BALANCE DEBIT	BALANCE CREDIT

ACCOUNT Office Supplies   ACCOUNT NO. 115

DATE	ITEM	P.R.	DEBIT	CREDIT	BALANCE DEBIT	BALANCE CREDIT

PROBLEM 7-5A OR 7-5B (continued)

ACCOUNT Store Supplies   ACCOUNT NO. 116

DATE	ITEM	P.R.	DEBIT	CREDIT	BALANCE DEBIT	BALANCE CREDIT

ACCOUNT Prepaid Insurance   ACCOUNT NO. 117

DATE	ITEM	P.R.	DEBIT	CREDIT	BALANCE DEBIT	BALANCE CREDIT

ACCOUNT Office Equipment   ACCOUNT NO. 121

DATE	ITEM	P.R.	DEBIT	CREDIT	BALANCE DEBIT	BALANCE CREDIT

ACCOUNT Store Equipment   ACCOUNT NO. 122

DATE	ITEM	P.R.	DEBIT	CREDIT	BALANCE DEBIT	BALANCE CREDIT

PROBLEM 7-5A OR 7-5B (continued)

ACCOUNT Accounts Payable   ACCOUNT NO. 211

DATE	ITEM	P.R.	DEBIT	CREDIT	BALANCE DEBIT	BALANCE CREDIT

ACCOUNT Purchases   ACCOUNT NO. 511

DATE	ITEM	P.R.	DEBIT	CREDIT	BALANCE DEBIT	BALANCE CREDIT

ACCOUNT Purchases Returns and Allowances   ACCOUNT NO. 511.1

DATE	ITEM	P.R.	DEBIT	CREDIT	BALANCE DEBIT	BALANCE CREDIT

ACCOUNT Purchases Discounts   ACCOUNT NO. 511.2

DATE	ITEM	P.R.	DEBIT	CREDIT	BALANCE DEBIT	BALANCE CREDIT

ACCOUNT Freight In   ACCOUNT NO. 512

DATE	ITEM	P.R.	DEBIT	CREDIT	BALANCE DEBIT	BALANCE CREDIT

ACCOUNT Rent Expense   ACCOUNT NO. 613

DATE	ITEM	P.R.	DEBIT	CREDIT	BALANCE DEBIT	BALANCE CREDIT

1., 3.   **Accounts Payable Ledger**

NAME   Best Diamond Co.

ADDRESS

Date	Item	P.R.	Debit	Credit	Balance

NAME   Carter's Supplies

ADDRESS

Date	Item	P.R.	Debit	Credit	Balance

NAME   Modern Equipment Co.

ADDRESS

Date	Item	P.R.	Debit	Credit	Balance

NAME   Nash Jewelers

ADDRESS

Date	Item	P.R.	Debit	Credit	Balance

NAME   Wilson's Gems

ADDRESS

Date	Item	P.R.	Debit	Credit	Balance

PROBLEM 7-5A OR 7-5B (continued)

5.

Diamond Jewelers		
Schedule of Accounts Payable		
July 31, 20X1		

The balance of the Accounts Payable controlling account: _____

This page intentionally left blank.

PROBLEM SOLVING

General Journal   Page 1

	Date		Account Title	P.R.	Debit	Credit	
1							1
2							2
3							3
4							4
5							5
6							6
7							7
8							8
9							9
10							10
11							11
12							12
13							13
14							14
15							15
16							16
17							17
18							18
19							19
20							20
21							21
22							22
23							23
24							24
25							25
26							26
27							27
28							28
29							29
30							30
31							31
32							32

General Journal

	Date		Account Title	P.R.	Debit	Credit	
1							1
2							2
3							3
4							4
5							5
6							6
7							7
8							8
9							9
10							10
11							11
12							12
13							13
14							14
15							15
16							16
17							17
18							18
19							19
20							20
21							21
22							22
23							23
24							24
25							25
26							26
27							27
28							28
29							29
30							30
31							31
32							32

COMMUNICATIONS

_____

_____

_____

_____

_____

_____

_____

_____

_____

_____

_____

_____

_____

_____

_____

_____

_____

_____

_____

_____

_____

ETHICS

_____

_____

_____

_____

_____

_____

_____

_____

_____

_____

_____

_____

_____

_____

_____

_____

_____

_____

_____

_____

This page intentionally left blank.

PRACTICE TEST ANSWERS

PART I

1. T
2. T
3. F
4. T
5. F
6. T
7. T
8. F
9. T
10. F
11. F
12. T
13. F
14. T
15. T

PART II

1. j
2. t
3. n
4. i
5. q
6. a
7. o
8. d
9. s
10. c
11. p
12. m
13. e
14. k
15. g
16. h
17. r
18. b
19. l
20. f

PART III

1. Retailers, wholesalers
2. purchase requisition
3. receiving report
4. trade discounts
5. cost
6. Cash discounts
7. merchandise
8. Office Supplies
9. Accounts Payable
10. creditors', accounts payable, debit, credit
11. contra
12. debit memorandum
13. credit memorandum
14. FOB destination
15. FOB shipping point

PART IV

1. c
2. d
3. b
4. a
5. c
6. b
7. c
8. d
9. a
10. b

PART V

Answers will vary. Please discuss questions with your instructor. You can also discuss issues related to this chapter by logging onto the Paradigm Accounting Web Site at www.emcp.com and clicking on the discussion section.

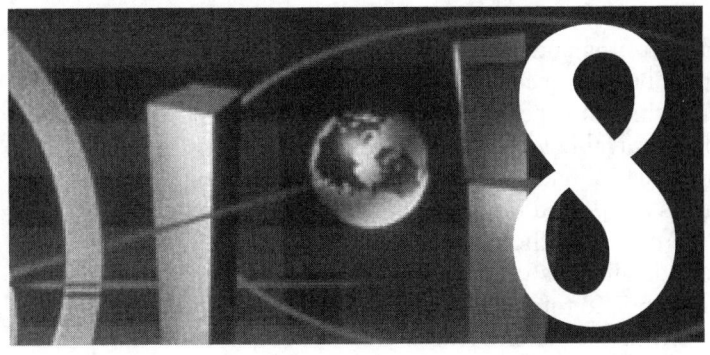

8 Accounting for a Merchandising Business—Sales and Cash Receipts

CHAPTER SUMMARY

Sales of merchandise are made for cash and on credit, with the latter being more common in many businesses. Sales on credit are initiated when a purchase order is received from a customer or when one of a firm's salespersons prepares a sales order. A **sales order** is a form used to describe goods to be shipped to the customer. A **sales invoice** is prepared by the billing department and sent to the buyer. Some sales are made on **revolving charge plans**, allowing the buyer to pay so much a month.

Cash sales are written up on **sales tickets**, which serve as source documents for later journal entries. A variation of the sales ticket is the **cash register tape**.

Sales of merchandise are recorded in a revenue account entitled **Sales**. The Sales account—like all revenue accounts—is a temporary owner's equity account that is closed to the Income Summary account at the end of the period.

Cash sales are recorded by debiting the Cash account and crediting the Sales account. Credit sales are recorded by debiting an asset account entitled **Accounts Receivable** and crediting the Sales account. The Accounts Receivable account shows the amount due from credit customers.

Accounts for customers are often set up in a subsidiary ledger called the **accounts receivable ledger**. The accounts receivable ledger is summarized (controlled) by the Accounts Receivable account in the general ledger. Thus, the accounts receivable ledger shows the amounts owed by individual credit customers, whereas the Accounts Receivable controlling account shows the aggregate amount owed by all credit customers.

When the volume of credit sales is large, many businesses use a **sales journal** to save journalizing and posting time. The sales journal introduced in this chapter has one money column entitled Accounts Receivable Dr. and Sales Cr. One money column is sufficient because all credit sales of merchandise involve a debit to the Accounts Receivable account and a credit to the Sales account.

Each entry in the sales journal requires an individual posting to the account of the credit customer who made the purchase. To keep the accounts receivable ledger up to date, posting is usually done on a daily basis. At the end of the month, the money column of the sales journal is totaled, and the total is posted twice: to the debit side of the Accounts Receivable account and to the credit side of the Sales account.

In Chapter 7, merchandise returns and allowances were referred to as purchases returns and allowances by the buyer. In this chapter, sellers refer to merchandise returns and allowances as **sales returns and allowances**. The amount of sales returns and allowances is recorded on the debit side of a contra revenue account entitled **Sales Returns and Allowances**. Sellers usually issue a **credit memorandum** to customers to indicate that credit has been granted for a return or an allowance.

Every sale has a **credit period** and **credit terms**. When the seller grants a cash discount (such as the 2% discount available under credit terms of 2/10,n/30), it is referred to as a **sales discount** and is recorded as a debit to a contra revenue account entitled **Sales Discounts**. Certain sales have terms of **C.O.D. (cash on delivery)**.

A **cash receipts journal** is a special journal used to record all cash receipts, regardless of the source. Source documents for entries in the cash receipts journal include checks, cash register tapes, and sales tickets.

Since the cash receipts journal is designed to record increases in the Cash account, a Cash Dr. column must be included. The number of other special columns and their titles are determined by the accounts most often affected by the firm's cash receipts. The cash receipts journal also contains a General Cr. column for recording credits to accounts for which no special column is provided.

The cash receipts journal is posted to the accounts receivable ledger daily. Two types of postings are made from the cash receipts journal to the general ledger: (1) individual amounts from the General Cr. column and (2) special column totals. Individual amounts are posted from the General Cr. column on a daily, weekly, or monthly basis. Special column totals are posted at the end of the month.

A **schedule of accounts receivable** is prepared periodically—usually at the end of the month—to check the posting accuracy of the accounts receivable ledger. The total of the schedule must agree with the balance of the Accounts Receivable controlling account in the general ledger.

A **sales tax** is a tax on the retail price of goods. Most state governments (and some local governments) charge a sales tax that ranges from 3% to 8% and higher. Sales taxes are recorded by crediting the Sales Tax Payable account.

Credit card sales have become a popular means for merchants to offer the convenience of credit to their customers. Yet, at the same time, certain types of credit card sales allow merchants to avoid the risks of traditional credit sales such as slow payments from customers and uncollectible accounts. There are three common types of credit cards: (1) those issued by banks (referred to as bank cards), such as VISA and MasterCard; (2) those issued by card systems (referred to as nonbank cards), such as American Express and Diners Club; and (3) those issued by private companies, such as Sears, Exxon, and some airlines. Bank credit card sales are accounted for as cash sales since the receipts can be deposited in the bank and the firm's checking account is credited for the total of the receipts less a bank fee (discount). Nonbank credit card sales are recorded as sales on account since the receipts must be accumulated and sent to the system for payment. The **Accounts Receivable—Credit Cards** account is debited to record these sales. The **Credit Card Expense account** is debited for the fees (discounts) that a firm pays to banks and card systems when submitting receipts for sales made with their credit cards. Credit card sales made with a company's own card—such as a Sears card—are recorded as regular sales on account since the company that issued the card does its own billing and collection.

PRACTICE TEST

PART I TRUE/FALSE

Please circle the correct answer.

T F 1. There should always be a definite understanding between the buyer and the seller concerning the terms of payment for merchandise.

T F 2. FOB shipping point means that the seller pays the freight.

T F 3. Just as with a purchase, the invoice serves as the source document for recording a sale.

T F 4. The revenue account used to record sales of merchandise is called Sales.

T F 5. The sales journal is used to record all sales of merchandise.

T F 6. The Accounts Receivable account in the general ledger is the controlling account for the accounts receivable ledger.

T F 7. It is customary to post to the accounts receivable subsidiary ledger on a daily basis and to the controlling account in the general ledger at the end of the month.

T F 8. Sales Returns and Allowances is a contra account to Sales.

T F 9. A sales discount is offered to customers as a way of changing the price of merchandise without issuing a new catalog.

T F 10. A cash receipts journal is a special journal used to record all receipts of cash.

T F 11. A schedule of accounts receivable is prepared to assure the accuracy of posting to the controlling account in the general ledger.

T F 12. Sales tax usually must be paid to the state tax authority by the end of the month in which it was collected.

T F 13. Bank credit card sales are treated as cash sales.

T F 14. Other credit card sales are treated as cash sales.

T F 15. The accounts receivable subsidiary ledger is used to keep individual records of all customers' accounts.

PART II MATCHING

Please match each of the following terms with its definition.

a. accounts receivable ledger
b. Credit Card Expense
c. cash receipts journal
d. cash register tape
e. credit memorandum
f. credit terms
g. credit period
h. Sales account

i. Sales Discounts
j. sales journal
k. sales order
l. Sales Returns and Allowances
m. sales tax
n. sales ticket
o. schedule of accounts receivable

_____ 1. The terms set by a company for allowing its customers a certain amount of time in which to make payment.

_____ 2. A form prepared by a salesperson on receipt of a purchase order or when making a credit sale.

_____ 3. A subsidiary ledger containing only accounts of credit customers.

_____ 4. A contra revenue account that is used to record returns of merchandise accepted from customers and allowances granted to customers.

_____ 5. A form sent to customers showing the amount of credit granted for a return of merchandise.

_____ 6. A revenue account used only to record sales of merchandise.

_____ 7. The time allowed customers to make payment.

_____ 8. A form prepared by a salesperson when a cash sale is made.

_____ 9. A special journal used only to record credit sales of merchandise.

_____ 10. An account used to record the discounts a firm must pay on credit card sales when submitting receipts for these sales to banks and card systems.

_____ 11. A listing of the balances in the accounts receivable ledger.

_____ 12. A contra revenue account used to record cash discounts granted to credit customers for prompt payment.

_____ 13. A special journal used to record all receipts of cash.

_____ 14. A tax on the retail price of goods sold that is collected and paid to the government by the seller.

_____ 15. A variation of the sales ticket produced by the cash register and used as a source document for recording cash sales.

PART III FILL IN THE BLANKS

Please complete each sentence with the correct word or words.

1. Terms of _____ mean that no credit is allowed by the seller.

2. _____ means cash on delivery.

3. The revenue account used to record the sale of merchandise is called _____.

4. The sales journal is a special journal used only to record _____ sales of _____.

5. Posting from the sales journal is similar to posting from the _____ journal.

6. If a business has many credit customers, individual accounts for these customers are kept in a(n) _____ ledger called the _____ ledger.

7. Accounts in the _____ ledger are arranged _____, just as in the accounts payable ledger.

8. Sales Returns and Allowances is an example of a(n) _____ account.

9. Sales, Sales Returns and Allowances, and Sales Discounts are all _____ accounts that are closed at the end of the period.

10. A cash receipts journal is used to record all _____ of _____.

11. A cash receipts journal must have a column to record _____ to Cash.

12. Posting of the cash receipts journal is done by posting individual accounts receivable amounts to the _____ ledger daily; individual amounts from the general column to the _____ ledger accounts daily, weekly, or monthly; and column totals to the general ledger accounts _____.

13. Agreement between the Accounts Receivable controlling account and the accounts receivable ledger is checked by preparing a(n) _____ of accounts receivable.

14. A tax on the retail sale of goods is called a(n) _____.

15. A bank credit card sale is treated as a(n) _____ sale.

PART IV MULTIPLE CHOICE

Please circle the correct answer.

1. The source document used to record a credit sale is the
   a. purchase order.
   b. sales order.
   c. invoice.
   d. shipping document.

2. The Sales account is a
   a. revenue account.
   b. cost account.
   c. permanent account.
   d. balance sheet account.

3. The sales journal is used to record
   a. sales of merchandise for cash.
   b. sales of merchandise on credit.
   c. sales of anything on credit.
   d. sales of anything for cash.

4. The accounts receivable ledger contains
   a. an account for each creditor.
   b. an account for each credit customer.
   c. an account for each customer whether cash or credit.
   d. none of the above.

5. It is important to post to the accounts receivable ledger daily because
   a. customers may call to ask how much they owe.
   b. the credit manager may want to see how much a customer owes before granting additional credit.
   c. the bookkeeper may need to send out statements.
   d. all of the above.

6. It is usually acceptable to post to the general ledger accounts
   a. monthly.
   b. weekly.
   c. daily.
   d. annually.

7. A record of sales returns and allowances is maintained in a separate account because
   a. management needs information about customer dissatisfaction.
   b. it is improper to record returns and allowances as a direct reduction of sales.
   c. it is traditionally done that way.
   d. none of the above.

8. A sales discount is given to customers
   a. because the seller does not want to print a new catalog to show new prices.
   b. to encourage prompt payment of invoices.
   c. to reward special customers who buy often.
   d. to encourage customers to pay cash for their purchases.

9. A cash receipts journal is a special journal used to record
   a. all cash transactions.
   b. all receipts of cash from sales of merchandise.
   c. all receipts of cash from any source.
   d. only payments received on accounts receivable.

10. Posting from the cash receipts journal is similar to posting from the
    a. sales journal.
    b. purchases journal.
    c. general journal.
    d. cash payments journal.

11. A schedule of accounts receivable is a listing of all
    a. creditor accounts and their balances.
    b. accounts in the general ledger and their balances.
    c. credit customer accounts and their balances.
    d. sales made on account.

12. Sales tax is a tax on
    a. wholesale sales of merchandise.
    b. retail sales of merchandise.
    c. any sales of merchandise.
    d. any sales.

13. Types of credit cards include
    a. bank credit cards.
    b. credit cards issued by card systems.
    c. credit cards issued by private companies such as oil companies and department stores.
    d. all of the above.

14. The type of credit card sale that is handled as a cash transaction is a sale made with a(n)
    a. American Express card.
    b. oil company credit card.
    c. bank credit card.
    d. Diners Club card.

15. One of the benefits of credit card sales is
    a. the merchant does not have to worry about uncollectible accounts.
    b. the merchant does not have to pay any fees.
    c. the merchant always gets the money on the day the sales receipts are deposited.
    d. none of the above.

PART V WRITING/SHORT ANSWER

1. **Reflect** Make a list, in words or simple phrases, of the most important and meaningful points in this chapter.

2. **Question** Think about the most confusing points or the material you do not understand in this chapter. Write down two or three questions that remain unanswered.

3. **Connect** Explain, in one or two sentences, the connection between the main points of this chapter and the major goals of the entire course.

4. **Summarize** Review this chapter's Joining the Pieces visual summary and explain the concept(s) illustrated in a few sentences.

This page intentionally left blank.

WORKING PAPERS

SKILLS REVIEW

EXERCISE 8-1

Sales Journal   Page 1

	Date	Invoice No.	Customer's Name	P.R.	Accts. Rec. Dr. Sales Cr.	
1						1
2						2
3						3
4						4
5						5
6						6
7						7
8						8
9						9
10						10

General Ledger

ACCOUNT **Accounts Receivable**   ACCOUNT NO. 112

DATE	ITEM	P.R.	DEBIT	CREDIT	BALANCE DEBIT	BALANCE CREDIT

ACCOUNT **Sales**   ACCOUNT NO. 411

DATE	ITEM	P.R.	DEBIT	CREDIT	BALANCE DEBIT	BALANCE CREDIT

Accounts Receivable Ledger

NAME   Adams Co.

ADDRESS

Date	Item	P.R.	Debit	Credit	Balance

NAME   Brown Co.

ADDRESS

Date	Item	P.R.	Debit	Credit	Balance

NAME   Heard, Inc.

ADDRESS

Date	Item	P.R.	Debit	Credit	Balance

NAME   Mallory, Inc.

ADDRESS

Date	Item	P.R.	Debit	Credit	Balance

EXERCISE 8-2

General Journal

	Date		Account Title	P.R.	Debit	Credit	
1							1
2							2
3							3
4							4
5							5
6							6
7							7
8							8
9							9
10							10
11							11
12							12
13							13
14							14
15							15
16							16
17							17
18							18
19							19
20							20
21							21
22							22
23							23
24							24
25							25
26							26
27							27
28							28
29							29
30							30
31							31
32							32

EXERCISE 8-3

General Journal

	Date		Account Title	P.R.	Debit	Credit	
1							1
2							2
3							3
4							4
5							5
6							6
7							7
8							8
9							9
10							10
11							11
12							12
13							13
14							14
15							15
16							16
17							17
18							18
19							19
20							20
21							21
22							22
23							23
24							24
25							25
26							26
27							27
28							28
29							29
30							30
31							31
32							32

EXERCISE 8-4

Cash Receipts Journal

Page 1

Date	Account Credited	P.R.	General Cr.	Sales Cr.	Accounts Rec. Cr.	Sales Discounts Dr.	Cash Dr.

EXERCISE 8-5

General Journal

	Date		Account Title	P.R.	Debit	Credit	
1							1
2							2
3							3
4							4
5							5
6							6
7							7
8							8
9							9
10							10
11							11
12							12
13							13
14							14
15							15
16							16
17							17
18							18
19							19
20							20
21							21
22							22
23							23
24							24
25							25
26							26
27							27
28							28
29							29
30							30
31							31
32							32

EXERCISE 8-6

	Date		Account Title	P.R.	Debit	Credit	
1							1
2							2
3							3
4							4
5							5
6							6
7							7
8							8
9							9
10							10
11							11
12							12
13							13
14							14
15							15
16							16
17							17
18							18
19							19
20							20
21							21
22							22
23							23
24							24
25							25
26							26
27							27
28							28
29							29

EXERCISE 8-7

1. _____

_____

2., 3.   **General Journal**   Page 1

	Date	Account Title	P.R.	Debit	Credit	
1						1
2						2
3						3
4						4
5						5
6						6
7						7
8						8
9						9
10						10
11						11
12						12

EXERCISE 8-8

1., 2.   **Sales Journal**   Page 1

Date	Inv. No.	Customer's Name	P.R.	Accounts Receivable Dr.	Sales Cr.	Sales Tax Payable Cr.

EXERCISE 8-9

General Journal Page 1

	Date	Account Title	P.R.	Debit	Credit	
1						1
2						2
3						3
4						4
5						5
6						6
7						7
8						8
9						9
10						10
11						11
12						12
13						13
14						14

EXERCISE 8-10

	P	S	CR	CP	G
(a)					
(b)					
(c)					
(d)					
(e)					
(f)					
(g)					
(h)					
(i)					
(j)					
(k)					
(l)					
(m)					
(n)					
(o)					

This page intentionally left blank.

CASE PROBLEMS

PROBLEM 8-1A OR 8-1B

3., 4.

General Journal

	Date		Account Title	P.R.	Debit	Credit	
1							1
2							2
3							3
4							4
5							5
6							6
7							7
8							8
9							9
10							10
11							11
12							12
13							13
14							14

Sales Journal

Page 1

	Date	Invoice No.	Customer's Name	P.R.	Accts. Rec. Dr. Sales Cr.	
1						1
2						2
3						3
4						4
5						5
6						6
7						7
8						8
9						9
10						10
11						11
12						12

2., 4.   **General Ledger**

ACCOUNT Accounts Receivable   ACCOUNT NO. 112

DATE	ITEM	P.R.	DEBIT	CREDIT	BALANCE	
					DEBIT	CREDIT

ACCOUNT Sales   ACCOUNT NO. 411

DATE	ITEM	P.R.	DEBIT	CREDIT	BALANCE	
					DEBIT	CREDIT

ACCOUNT Sales Returns and Allowances   ACCOUNT NO. 411.1

DATE	ITEM	P.R.	DEBIT	CREDIT	BALANCE	
					DEBIT	CREDIT

1., 3.   **Accounts Receivable Ledger**

NAME

ADDRESS

	Date	Item	P.R.	Debit	Credit	Balance

NAME

ADDRESS

	Date	Item	P.R.	Debit	Credit	Balance

NAME

ADDRESS

	Date	Item	P.R.	Debit	Credit	Balance

NAME

ADDRESS

	Date	Item	P.R.	Debit	Credit	Balance

NAME

ADDRESS

Date		Item	P.R.	Debit	Credit	Balance

5.

6. The balance of the Accounts Receivable controlling account: _____

PROBLEM 8-2A OR 8-2B

3., 4.

Sales Journal

Date	Inv. No.	Customer's Name	P.R.	Accounts Receivable Dr.	Sales Cr.	Sales Tax Payable Cr.

2., 4.

General Ledger

ACCOUNT **Accounts Receivable**   ACCOUNT NO. 112

DATE	ITEM	P.R.	DEBIT	CREDIT	BALANCE DEBIT	BALANCE CREDIT

ACCOUNT **Sales Tax Payable**   ACCOUNT NO. 212

DATE	ITEM	P.R.	DEBIT	CREDIT	BALANCE DEBIT	BALANCE CREDIT

ACCOUNT **Sales**   ACCOUNT NO. 411

DATE	ITEM	P.R.	DEBIT	CREDIT	BALANCE DEBIT	BALANCE CREDIT

1., 3.   **Accounts Receivable Ledger**

NAME

ADDRESS

Date		Item	P.R.	Debit	Credit	Balance

NAME

ADDRESS

Date		Item	P.R.	Debit	Credit	Balance

NAME

ADDRESS

Date		Item	P.R.	Debit	Credit	Balance

NAME

ADDRESS

Date		Item	P.R.	Debit	Credit	Balance

5.

The balance of the Accounts Receivable controlling account: _____

This page intentionally left blank.

1., 2.

Cash Receipts Journal

Date		Account Credited	P.R.	General Cr.	Sales Cr.	Accounts Rec. Cr.	Sales Discounts Dr.	Cash Dr.

This page intentionally left blank.

PROBLEM 8-4A OR 8-4B

3., 4.

General Journal

Page 1

	Date		Account Title	P.R.	Debit	Credit	
1							1
2							2
3							3
4							4
5							5
6							6
7							7
8							8
9							9
10							10
11							11
12							12
13							13
14							14

Sales Journal

Page 1

	Date	Invoice No.	Customer's Name	P.R.	Accts. Rec. Dr. Sales Cr.	
1						1
2						2
3						3
4						4
5						5
6						6
7						7
8						8
9						9
10						10
11						11
12						12
13						13
14						14

Cash Receipts Journal

Date	Account Credited	P.R.	General Cr.	Sales Cr.	Accounts Rec. Cr.	Sales Discounts Dr.	Cash Dr.

2., 3.

General Ledger

ACCOUNT Cash   ACCOUNT NO. 111

DATE	ITEM	P.R.	DEBIT	CREDIT	BALANCE DEBIT	BALANCE CREDIT

ACCOUNT Accounts Receivable   ACCOUNT NO. 112

DATE	ITEM	P.R.	DEBIT	CREDIT	BALANCE DEBIT	BALANCE CREDIT

ACCOUNT Sales   ACCOUNT NO. 411

DATE		ITEM	P.R.	DEBIT	CREDIT	BALANCE	
						DEBIT	CREDIT

ACCOUNT Sales Returns and Allowances   ACCOUNT NO. 411.1

DATE		ITEM	P.R.	DEBIT	CREDIT	BALANCE	
						DEBIT	CREDIT

ACCOUNT Sales Discounts   ACCOUNT NO. 411.2

DATE		ITEM	P.R.	DEBIT	CREDIT	BALANCE	
						DEBIT	CREDIT

1., 3.   **Accounts Receivable Ledger**

NAME

ADDRESS

Date	Item	P.R.	Debit	Credit	Balance

NAME

ADDRESS

Date	Item	P.R.	Debit	Credit	Balance

NAME

ADDRESS

Date	Item	P.R.	Debit	Credit	Balance

NAME

ADDRESS

Date	Item	P.R.	Debit	Credit	Balance

NAME

ADDRESS

Date	Item	P.R.	Debit	Credit	Balance

NAME

ADDRESS

Date	Item	P.R.	Debit	Credit	Balance

5.

The balance of the Accounts Receivable controlling account: _____

PROBLEM 8-5A OR 8-5B

4., 5.

General Journal Page 5

	Date		Account Title	P.R.	Debit	Credit	
1							1
2							2
3							3
4							4
5							5
6							6
7							7
8							8
9							9
10							10
11							11
12							12
13							13
14							14
15							15
16							16
17							17
18							18
19							19
20							20
21							21
22							22

Sales Journal Page 8

	Date		Invoice No.	Customer's Name	P.R.	Accts. Rec. Dr. Sales Cr.	
1							1
2							2
3							3
4							4
5							5
6							6
7							7

Purchases Journal

	Date	Invoice No.	Account Credited	P.R.	Purchases Dr. Accts. Pay. Cr.	
1						1
2						2
3						3
4						4
5						5
6						6
7						7

Cash Receipts Journal

Date	Account Credited	P.R.	General Cr.	Sales Cr.	Accounts Rec. Cr.	Sales Discounts Dr.	Cash Dr.

PROBLEM 8-5A OR 8-5B (continued)

Cash Payments Journal

Page 10

Date	Ck. No.	Account Debited	P.R.	General Dr.	Accounts Payable Dr.	Purchases Discounts Cr.	Cash Cr.

1., 5.

General Ledger

ACCOUNT Cash   ACCOUNT NO. 111

DATE	ITEM	P.R.	DEBIT	CREDIT	BALANCE DEBIT	BALANCE CREDIT

ACCOUNT Accounts Receivable   ACCOUNT NO. 112

DATE	ITEM	P.R.	DEBIT	CREDIT	BALANCE	
					DEBIT	CREDIT

ACCOUNT Store Supplies   ACCOUNT NO. 113

DATE	ITEM	P.R.	DEBIT	CREDIT	BALANCE	
					DEBIT	CREDIT

ACCOUNT Office Supplies   ACCOUNT NO. 114

DATE	ITEM	P.R.	DEBIT	CREDIT	BALANCE	
					DEBIT	CREDIT

ACCOUNT Store Equipment   ACCOUNT NO. 121

DATE	ITEM	P.R.	DEBIT	CREDIT	BALANCE	
					DEBIT	CREDIT

ACCOUNT Office Equipment   ACCOUNT NO. 122

DATE	ITEM	P.R.	DEBIT	CREDIT	BALANCE	
					DEBIT	CREDIT

ACCOUNT Accounts Payable   ACCOUNT NO. 211

DATE	ITEM	P.R.	DEBIT	CREDIT	BALANCE DEBIT	BALANCE CREDIT

ACCOUNT Sales   ACCOUNT NO. 411

DATE	ITEM	P.R.	DEBIT	CREDIT	BALANCE DEBIT	BALANCE CREDIT

ACCOUNT Sales Returns and Allowances   ACCOUNT NO. 411.1

DATE	ITEM	P.R.	DEBIT	CREDIT	BALANCE DEBIT	BALANCE CREDIT

ACCOUNT Sales Discounts   ACCOUNT NO. 411.2

DATE	ITEM	P.R.	DEBIT	CREDIT	BALANCE DEBIT	BALANCE CREDIT

ACCOUNT Purchases

ACCOUNT NO. 511

DATE	ITEM	P.R.	DEBIT	CREDIT	BALANCE	
					DEBIT	CREDIT

ACCOUNT Purchases Returns and Allowances

ACCOUNT NO. 511.1

DATE	ITEM	P.R.	DEBIT	CREDIT	BALANCE	
					DEBIT	CREDIT

ACCOUNT Purchases Discounts

ACCOUNT NO. 511.2

DATE	ITEM	P.R.	DEBIT	CREDIT	BALANCE	
					DEBIT	CREDIT

ACCOUNT Rent Expense

ACCOUNT NO. 611

DATE	ITEM	P.R.	DEBIT	CREDIT	BALANCE	
					DEBIT	CREDIT

ACCOUNT Salaries Expense

ACCOUNT NO. 612

DATE	ITEM	P.R.	DEBIT	CREDIT	BALANCE	
					DEBIT	CREDIT

ACCOUNT Utilities Expense ACCOUNT NO. 613

DATE	ITEM	P.R.	DEBIT	CREDIT	BALANCE DEBIT	BALANCE CREDIT

ACCOUNT Repairs Expense ACCOUNT NO. 614

DATE	ITEM	P.R.	DEBIT	CREDIT	BALANCE DEBIT	BALANCE CREDIT

ACCOUNT Advertising Expense ACCOUNT NO. 615

DATE	ITEM	P.R.	DEBIT	CREDIT	BALANCE DEBIT	BALANCE CREDIT

ACCOUNT Gas and Oil Expense ACCOUNT NO. 616

DATE	ITEM	P.R.	DEBIT	CREDIT	BALANCE DEBIT	BALANCE CREDIT

ACCOUNT Miscellaneous Expense ACCOUNT NO. 618

DATE	ITEM	P.R.	DEBIT	CREDIT	BALANCE DEBIT	BALANCE CREDIT

2., 4.   **Accounts Receivable Ledger**

NAME

ADDRESS

Date	Item	P.R.	Debit	Credit	Balance

NAME

ADDRESS

Date	Item	P.R.	Debit	Credit	Balance

NAME

ADDRESS

Date	Item	P.R.	Debit	Credit	Balance

NAME

ADDRESS

Date	Item	P.R.	Debit	Credit	Balance

NAME

ADDRESS

Date	Item	P.R.	Debit	Credit	Balance

3., 4.   **Accounts Payable Ledger**

NAME _____

ADDRESS _____

Date	Item	P.R.	Debit	Credit	Balance

NAME _____

ADDRESS _____

Date	Item	P.R.	Debit	Credit	Balance

NAME _____

ADDRESS _____

Date	Item	P.R.	Debit	Credit	Balance

NAME

ADDRESS

	Date		Item	P.R.	Debit	Credit	Balance

NAME

ADDRESS

	Date		Item	P.R.	Debit	Credit	Balance

6.

The balance of the Accounts Receivable controlling account: _____

The balance of the Accounts Payable controlling account: _____

This page intentionally left blank.

CHALLENGE PROBLEMS

PROBLEM SOLVING

4., 5.   **General Journal**

	Date	Account Title	P.R.	Debit	Credit	
1						1
2						2
3						3
4						4
5						5
6						6
7						7
8						8
9						9
10						10
11						11
12						12
13						13
14						14
15						15
16						16
17						17
18						18
19						19
20						20
21						21
22						22
23						23
24						24
25						25
26						26
27						27
28						28
29						29
30						30
31						31
32						32

Sales Journal

	Date	Invoice No.	Customer's Name	P.R.	Accts. Rec. Dr. Sales Cr.	
1						1
2						2
3						3
4						4
5						5
6						6
7						7
8						8
9						9
10						10
11						11
12						12

Purchases Journal

	Date	Invoice No.	Account Credited	P.R.	Purchases Dr. Accts. Pay. Cr.	
1						1
2						2
3						3
4						4
5						5
6						6
7						7
8						8

Cash Receipts Journal

Date	Account Credited	P.R.	General Cr.	Sales Cr.	Accounts Rec. Cr.	Sales Discounts Dr.	Cash Dr.

Cash Payments Journal

Date	Ck. No.	Account Debited	P.R.	General Dr.	Accounts Payable Dr.	Purchases Discounts Cr.	Cash Cr.

1., 6.   **General Ledger**

ACCOUNT Cash   ACCOUNT NO. 111

DATE	ITEM	P.R.	DEBIT	CREDIT	BALANCE	
					DEBIT	CREDIT

ACCOUNT Accounts Receivable   ACCOUNT NO. 112

DATE	ITEM	P.R.	DEBIT	CREDIT	BALANCE	
					DEBIT	CREDIT

ACCOUNT Store Supplies   ACCOUNT NO. 113

DATE	ITEM	P.R.	DEBIT	CREDIT	BALANCE	
					DEBIT	CREDIT

ACCOUNT Office Supplies   ACCOUNT NO. 114

DATE	ITEM	P.R.	DEBIT	CREDIT	BALANCE	
					DEBIT	CREDIT

ACCOUNT Prepaid Insurance   ACCOUNT NO. 115

DATE	ITEM	P.R.	DEBIT	CREDIT	BALANCE	
					DEBIT	CREDIT

ACCOUNT Store Equipment   ACCOUNT NO. 119

DATE	ITEM	P.R.	DEBIT	CREDIT	BALANCE	
					DEBIT	CREDIT

ACCOUNT Accumulated Depr.—Store Equipment   ACCOUNT NO. 119.1

DATE	ITEM	P.R.	DEBIT	CREDIT	BALANCE	
					DEBIT	CREDIT

ACCOUNT Office Equipment   ACCOUNT NO. 120

DATE	ITEM	P.R.	DEBIT	CREDIT	BALANCE	
					DEBIT	CREDIT

ACCOUNT Accumulated Depr.—Office Equipment   ACCOUNT NO. 120.1

DATE	ITEM	P.R.	DEBIT	CREDIT	BALANCE	
					DEBIT	CREDIT

PROBLEM SOLVING (continued)

ACCOUNT Accounts Payable   ACCOUNT NO. 211

DATE	ITEM	P.R.	DEBIT	CREDIT	BALANCE DEBIT	BALANCE CREDIT

ACCOUNT H. H. Sapp, Capital   ACCOUNT NO. 312

DATE	ITEM	P.R.	DEBIT	CREDIT	BALANCE DEBIT	BALANCE CREDIT

ACCOUNT H. H. Sapp, Drawing   ACCOUNT NO. 313

DATE	ITEM	P.R.	DEBIT	CREDIT	BALANCE DEBIT	BALANCE CREDIT

ACCOUNT Sales   ACCOUNT NO. 411

DATE	ITEM	P.R.	DEBIT	CREDIT	BALANCE DEBIT	BALANCE CREDIT

ACCOUNT Sales Returns and Allowances   ACCOUNT NO. 411.1

DATE	ITEM	P.R.	DEBIT	CREDIT	BALANCE DEBIT	BALANCE CREDIT

ACCOUNT **Sales Discounts**   ACCOUNT NO. 411.2

DATE		ITEM	P.R.	DEBIT	CREDIT	BALANCE	
						DEBIT	CREDIT

ACCOUNT **Purchases**   ACCOUNT NO. 511

DATE		ITEM	P.R.	DEBIT	CREDIT	BALANCE	
						DEBIT	CREDIT

ACCOUNT **Purchases Returns and Allowances**   ACCOUNT NO. 511.1

DATE		ITEM	P.R.	DEBIT	CREDIT	BALANCE	
						DEBIT	CREDIT

ACCOUNT **Purchases Discounts**   ACCOUNT NO. 511.2

DATE		ITEM	P.R.	DEBIT	CREDIT	BALANCE	
						DEBIT	CREDIT

ACCOUNT **Freight In**   ACCOUNT NO. 512

DATE		ITEM	P.R.	DEBIT	CREDIT	BALANCE	
						DEBIT	CREDIT

ACCOUNT **Salaries Expense**   ACCOUNT NO. 611

DATE	ITEM	P.R.	DEBIT	CREDIT	BALANCE DEBIT	BALANCE CREDIT

ACCOUNT **Rent Expense**   ACCOUNT NO. 612

DATE	ITEM	P.R.	DEBIT	CREDIT	BALANCE DEBIT	BALANCE CREDIT

ACCOUNT **Utilities Expense**   ACCOUNT NO. 613

DATE	ITEM	P.R.	DEBIT	CREDIT	BALANCE DEBIT	BALANCE CREDIT

ACCOUNT **Advertising Expense**   ACCOUNT NO. 614

DATE	ITEM	P.R.	DEBIT	CREDIT	BALANCE DEBIT	BALANCE CREDIT

ACCOUNT **Telephone Expense**   ACCOUNT NO. 615

DATE	ITEM	P.R.	DEBIT	CREDIT	BALANCE DEBIT	BALANCE CREDIT

ACCOUNT **Repairs Expense**   ACCOUNT NO. 616

DATE	ITEM	P.R.	DEBIT	CREDIT	BALANCE DEBIT	BALANCE CREDIT

ACCOUNT Miscellaneous Expense   ACCOUNT NO. 622

DATE	ITEM	P.R.	DEBIT	CREDIT	BALANCE DEBIT	BALANCE CREDIT

2., 4.

Accounts Receivable Ledger

NAME   Aims Corp.

ADDRESS

Date	Item	P.R.	Debit	Credit	Balance

NAME   Hanks Co.

ADDRESS

Date	Item	P.R.	Debit	Credit	Balance

NAME   Illinois Central Products Co.

ADDRESS

Date	Item	P.R.	Debit	Credit	Balance

NAME   Leland Co.

ADDRESS

Date		Item	P.R.	Debit	Credit	Balance

NAME   McFarland Co.

ADDRESS

Date		Item	P.R.	Debit	Credit	Balance

NAME   Tom Larkin

ADDRESS

Date		Item	P.R.	Debit	Credit	Balance

NAME   Xavier Corp.

ADDRESS

Date		Item	P.R.	Debit	Credit	Balance

3., 4.   **Accounts Payable Ledger**

NAME   Adams Inc.

ADDRESS

Date		Item	P.R.	Debit	Credit	Balance

NAME   Allan Co.

ADDRESS

Date		Item	P.R.	Debit	Credit	Balance

NAME   Dunlop Co.

ADDRESS

Date		Item	P.R.	Debit	Credit	Balance

NAME   Dwyar Products Co.

ADDRESS

Date		Item	P.R.	Debit	Credit	Balance

PROBLEM SOLVING (continued)

NAME   Elgin Co.

ADDRESS

	Date	Item	P.R.	Debit	Credit	Balance

NAME   Faulk Co.

ADDRESS

	Date	Item	P.R.	Debit	Credit	Balance

NAME   McFadden Co.

ADDRESS

	Date	Item	P.R.	Debit	Credit	Balance

NAME   Thompson Suppliers

ADDRESS

	Date	Item	P.R.	Debit	Credit	Balance

NAME   Wall Supply Inc.

ADDRESS

	Date	Item	P.R.	Debit	Credit	Balance

7.

ACCOUNT TITLE	DEBIT	CREDIT

8.

9.

10.

The balance of the Accounts Receivable controlling account: _____.

The balance of the Accounts Payable controlling account: _____.

This page intentionally left blank.

COMMUNICATIONS

_____

_____

_____

_____

_____

_____

_____

_____

_____

_____

_____

_____

_____

_____

_____

_____

_____

_____

_____

_____

_____

ETHICS

_____

_____

_____

_____

_____

_____

_____

_____

_____

_____

_____

_____

_____

_____

_____

_____

_____

_____

_____

_____

This page intentionally left blank.

PRACTICE TEST ANSWERS

PART I

1. T
2. F
3. T
4. T
5. F
6. T
7. T
8. T
9. F
10. T
11. F
12. F
13. T
14. F
15. T

PART II

1. f
2. k
3. a
4. l
5. e
6. h
7. g
8. n
9. j
10. b
11. o
12. i
13. c
14. m
15. d

PART III

1. net cash
2. COD

3. Sales
4. credit, merchandise
5. purchases
6. subsidiary, accounts receivable
7. accounts receivable, alphabetically
8. contra
9. temporary
10. receipts, cash
11. debits
12. accounts receivable, general, monthly
13. schedule
14. sales tax
15. cash

PART IV

1. c
2. a
3. b
4. b
5. d
6. a
7. a
8. b
9. c
10. d
11. c
12. b
13. d
14. c
15. a

PART V

Answers will vary. Please discuss questions with your instructor. You can also discuss issues related to this chapter by logging onto the Paradigm Accounting Web Site at www.emcp.com and clicking on the discussion section.

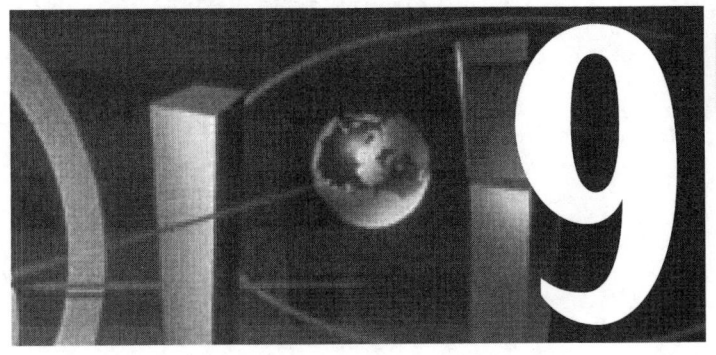

Work Sheet and Adjustments for a Merchandising Business

CHAPTER SUMMARY

The end-of-period activities for a merchandising business are similar to those of a service business. Both types of businesses determine needed adjustments at the end of the period. Adjusting entries are based on the *matching principle* of accounting, which states that the revenue for a period should be offset by the expenses necessary to generate that revenue.

We recorded several adjustments in this chapter. One of the new adjustments we looked at is for merchandise inventory. The cost of merchandise purchased during the accounting period is recorded in the Purchases account. However, the Purchases account only shows the amount purchased—not the value of the goods on hand at the end of an accounting period. Therefore, it is necessary to take an **inventory**, a physical count of the goods on hand, periodically and adjust the **Merchandise Inventory account** to reflect the latest inventory value.

The adjustment for merchandise inventory is relatively simple. The Merchandise Inventory account is reduced by the old inventory (**beginning inventory**) figure and increased by the **ending inventory** figure. This is accomplished by debiting the Income Summary account and crediting the Merchandise Inventory account for the value of the old inventory. Then the new inventory figure is recorded by debiting the Merchandise Inventory account and crediting the Income Summary account.

Other adjustments typically needed by a merchandising business are those to record the cost of prepaid items consumed, depreciation of long-term assets, and **accrued salaries** (salaries that are unpaid and unrecorded at the end of an accounting period). Another name for accrued salaries is **accrued wages**.

This page intentionally left blank.

PRACTICE TEST

PART I TRUE/FALSE

Please circle the correct answer.

T   F   1. The matching principle states that every transaction should be recorded at cost.

T   F   2. The chart of accounts shows the page numbers where each account is to be found in the general ledger.

T   F   3. The first step in the end-of-period activities is to take a trial balance of the general ledger.

T   F   4. Some adjusting entries for a merchandising firm are the same as those for a service business.

T   F   5. The first step in adjusting the Merchandise Inventory account is to credit Income Summary and debit Merchandise Inventory for the beginning balance in the inventory account.

T   F   6. The beginning balance in Merchandise Inventory represents the amount of inventory that was on hand at the beginning of the accounting period.

T   F   7. The second step in adjusting the Merchandise Inventory account is to debit Merchandise Inventory and credit Income Summary for the ending inventory figure.

T   F   8. In recording depreciation, each depreciation expense account is credited and each accumulated depreciation account is debited.

T   F   9. An accumulated depreciation account is a contra asset account.

T   F   10. A depreciation expense account is a temporary account that will be closed to Income Summary.

T   F   11. Each accumulated depreciation account will be closed to Income Summary at the end of the period.

T   F   12. A work sheet is an informal working paper.

T   F   13. An adjusted trial balance is used to check the accuracy of the combined trial balance and adjustments before extending the amounts to the financial statement columns of the work sheet.

T   F   14. If an account has a debit balance and a debit adjustment is made to it, the new balance is determined by subtracting the adjustment from the old balance.

T   F   15. If an account has a balance and no adjustment is made to it, it may be left off the adjusted trial balance.

PART II MATCHING

Please match each of the following terms with its definition.

a. adjusted trial balance
b. adjusting entries
c. chart of accounts
d. Income Summary

e. matching principle
f. Merchandise Inventory
g. ten-column work sheet
h. trial balance

_____ 1. An informal working paper that is used by accountants to summarize end-of-period data; it includes columns for entering adjustments and preparing an adjusted trial balance.

_____ 2. A listing of all accounts in the general ledger and the debit or credit balance of each.

_____ 3. The account that provides a record of the cost of goods on hand at a given time.

_____ 4. Entries made at the end of an accounting period to update certain accounts.

_____ 5. The principle of accounting that states that the revenue for an accounting period should be offset by the expenses necessary to generate that revenue.

_____ 6. The trial balance taken to show updated account balances after adjustments.

_____ 7. A clearing account used to summarize revenues and expenses.

_____ 8. The directory of accounts in the general ledger.

PART III FILL IN THE BLANKS

Please complete each sentence with the correct word or words.

1. End-of-period activities for a merchandising business are similar to those for a(n) _____ business.

2. The _____ states that the revenue earned during an accounting period should be offset by the _____ that were necessary to generate that revenue.

3. The first step in the end-of-period activities is to take a(n) _____ of the general ledger.

4. The second step is to determine needed _____.

5. The adjustment to _____ requires that a count be made to determine how much merchandise is unsold at the end of the period.

6. Merchandise Inventory is a(n) _____ account.

7. The first step in adjusting the Merchandise Inventory account requires a debit to _____ and a credit to _____ for the beginning balance in the Merchandise Inventory account.

8. The second step in adjusting the Merchandise Inventory account is to _____ Merchandise Inventory and _____ Income Summary for the amount of the inventory value at the end of the period.

9. The two-step procedure for adjusting Merchandise Inventory is preferred by accountants because both the _____ and _____ balances of inventory appear on the _____.

10. Many of the adjustments needed in a merchandising business are the same as those needed in a(n) _____ business.

11. An accumulated depreciation account does not relate to a single period; it is a(n) _____ account used to _____ depreciation over the useful life of the asset to which it relates.

12. Recording accrued salaries for the period is required by the _____ principle.

13. The _____ trial balance contains the updated balances that result from combining the original trial balance amounts and the adjustments.

14. If an account has a debit balance and the adjustment is a credit, the _____ between the two amounts is entered in the adjusted trial balance.

15. If an account has a credit balance and the adjustment is a credit, the two numbers are _____ and entered in the _____ column of the adjusted trial balance.

16. All _____ and _____ accounts and the owner's _____ and _____ accounts are extended to the Balance Sheet columns of the work sheet.

PART IV MULTIPLE CHOICE

Please circle the correct answer.

1. All merchandise purchased during the accounting period is debited to the
   a. Purchases account.
   b. Accounts Receivable account.
   c. Merchandise Inventory account.
   d. Accounts Payable account.

2. The adjustment to Merchandise Inventory requires that
   a. a count of inventory be taken to determine the ending inventory amount.
   b. the beginning balance of inventory be debited to Income Summary and credited to Merchandise Inventory.
   c. the ending balance of inventory be debited to Merchandise Inventory and credited to Income Summary.
   d. all of the above.

3. Super Stores had a balance of $1,500 in Store Supplies before adjustment. A count of the supplies on hand revealed that $400 of supplies were still unused. What is the adjusting entry needed at the end of the period?
   a. Debit Store Supplies Expense and credit Store Supplies for $1,100.
   b. Debit Store Supplies and credit Store Supplies Expense for $1,100.
   c. Debit Store Supplies and credit Store Supplies Expense for $400.
   d. Debit Store Supplies Expense and credit Store Supplies for $400.

4. An adjustment to record accrued salaries is required by the
   a. cost principle.
   b. matching principle.
   c. business entity principle.
   d. none of the above.

5. Purchases Discounts and Accumulated Depreciation are both examples of
   a. accounts with debit balances.
   b. expense accounts.
   c. asset accounts.
   d. contra accounts.

6. Sales, Purchases Returns and Allowances, and Purchases Discounts are found in which column of the work sheet?
   a. Income Statement, Dr.
   b. Income Statement, Cr.
   c. Balance Sheet, Dr.
   d. Balance Sheet, Cr.

7. The owner's drawing account is found in which column of the work sheet?
   a. Income Statement, Dr.
   b. Income Statement, Cr.
   c. Balance Sheet, Dr.
   d. Balance Sheet, Cr.

PART V WRITING/SHORT ANSWER

1. **Reflect** Make a list, in words or simple phrases, of the most important and meaningful points in this chapter.

2. **Question** Think about the most confusing points or the material you do not understand in this chapter. Write down two or three questions that remain unanswered.

3. **Connect** Explain, in one or two sentences, the connection between the main points of this chapter and the major goals of the entire course.

4. **Summarize** Review this chapter's Joining the Pieces visual summary and explain the concept(s) illustrated in a few sentences.

WORKING PAPERS

SKILLS REVIEW

EXERCISE 9-1

Policy Number	Monthly Expiration	Expense for 20XX
(1)		
(2)		
(3)		

EXERCISE 9-2

(a) _____

(b) _____

(c) _____

EXERCISE 9-3

(a)

(b)

(c)

(d)

EXERCISE 9-4

(a)

(b)

(c)

(d)

(e)

(f)

EXERCISE 9-5

1. _____   5. _____   9. _____
2. _____   6. _____   10. _____
3. _____   7. _____   11. _____
4. _____   8. _____   12. _____

EXERCISE 9-6

Account Title	Trial Balance				Adjustments			
	Dr.		Cr.		Dr.		Cr.	

	Adjusted Trial Balance		Income Statement		Balance Sheet	
	Dr.	Cr.	Dr.	Cr.	Dr.	Cr.

This page intentionally left blank.

CASE PROBLEMS

PROBLEM 9-1A OR 9-1B

(a) _____

_____

_____

_____

(b) _____

_____

_____

_____

(c) _____

(d) _____

This page intentionally left blank.

PROBLEM 9-2A OR 9-2B

(a)

(b)

(c)

(d)

(e)

(f)

This page intentionally left blank.

This page intentionally left blank.

Account Title	Trial Balance		Adjustments	
	Dr.	Cr.	Dr.	Cr.

Adjusted Trial Balance		Income Statement		Balance Sheet	
Dr.	Cr.	Dr.	Cr.	Dr.	Cr.

This page intentionally left blank.

This page intentionally left blank.

Account Title	Trial Balance				Adjustments			
	Dr.		Cr.		Dr.		Cr.	

PROBLEM 9-4A OR 9-4B (continued)

	Adjusted Trial Balance		Income Statement		Balance Sheet	
	Dr.	Cr.	Dr.	Cr.	Dr.	Cr.

This page intentionally left blank.

This page intentionally left blank.

CHALLENGE PROBLEMS

PROBLEM SOLVING

1., 2.

Account Title	Trial Balance		Adjustments	
	Dr.	Cr.	Dr.	Cr.

	Adjusted Trial Balance		Income Statement		Balance Sheet	
	Dr.	Cr.	Dr.	Cr.	Dr.	Cr.

This page intentionally left blank.

COMMUNICATIONS

_____
_____
_____
_____
_____
_____
_____
_____
_____
_____
_____
_____
_____
_____
_____
_____
_____
_____
_____
_____

ETHICS

_____
_____
_____
_____
_____
_____
_____
_____
_____
_____
_____
_____
_____
_____
_____
_____
_____
_____
_____
_____

This page intentionally left blank.

PRACTICE TEST ANSWERS

PART I

1. F
2. F
3. T
4. T
5. F
6. T
7. T
8. F
9. T
10. T
11. F
12. T
13. T
14. F
15. F

PART II

1. g
2. h
3. f
4. b
5. e
6. a
7. d
8. c

PART III

1. service
2. matching principle, expenses
3. trial balance

4. adjustments
5. Merchandise Inventory
6. asset
7. Income Summary, Merchandise Inventory
8. debit, credit
9. beginning, ending, income statement
10. service
11. contra, accumulate
12. matching
13. adjusted
14. difference
15. added, Credit
16. asset, liability, capital, drawing

PART IV

1. a
2. d
3. a
4. b
5. d
6. b
7. c

PART V

Answers will vary. Please discuss questions with your instructor. You can also discuss issues related to this chapter by logging onto the Paradigm Accounting Web Site at www.emcp.com and clicking on the discussion section.

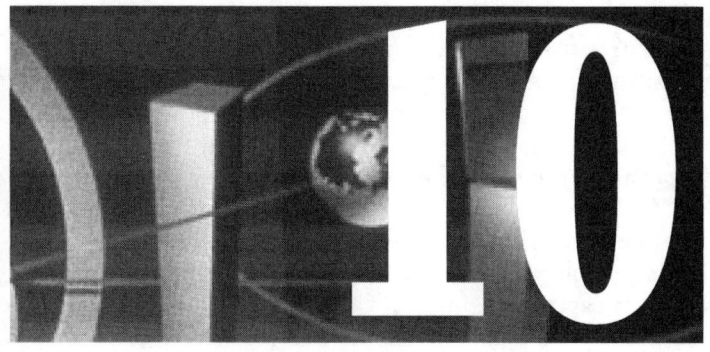

10 Financial Statements and Closing Entries for a Merchandising Business

CHAPTER SUMMARY

Financial statements are prepared soon after the work sheet has been completed. All the information needed to prepare formal financial statements can be taken directly from the work sheet.

A *classified financial statement* is one divided into major sections. A **classified income statement** for a merchandising business usually has sections for revenue, cost of goods sold, operating expenses, income from operations, and other income and expenses. Revenue for a merchandising business is expressed as **net sales**. Net sales is calculated by deducting sales returns and allowances and sales discounts from sales. **Cost of goods sold** is the cost of merchandise sold to customers during the accounting period. For some merchandising businesses, the volume of sales may be too large to calculate the cost of goods as they are being sold. In such cases, cost of goods sold is usually determined at the end of an accounting period by using the following formula. The amount of net purchases in the formula is calculated by deducting purchases returns and allowances and purchases discounts from purchases and adding the freight cost for incoming merchandise.

$$
\begin{array}{l}
 \text{Beginning merchandise inventory} \\
+\ \text{Net purchases of merchandise} \\
\hline
=\ \text{Goods available for sale} \\
-\ \text{Ending merchandise inventory} \\
\hline
=\ \text{Cost of goods sold}
\end{array}
$$

Net sales less cost of goods sold yields **gross profit**. The total operating expenses are deducted from the gross profit to find the **income from operations**.

Two types of operating expenses are **general expenses** and **selling expenses**. **Operating expenses** are those incurred in the normal operations of the business. **Nonoperating expenses** are those that are not directly associated with the actual operations of the business. Interest paid on loans is an example of a nonoperating expense. Nonoperating expenses are usually referred to as **other expenses**. Similarly, **nonoperating income**, such as the interest received on loans, is usually called **other income**. Other income is added to the income from operations and other expenses are deducted from it to determine the **net income**.

A **classified balance sheet** has sections for assets, liabilities, and owner's equity; and subsections for **current assets** and **plant assets** and **current liabilities** and **long-term liabilities**. Current assets include cash and any other asset that will be realized in cash, used up, sold, or expired within one year. Current assets are listed on the balance sheet in the order of their **liquidity**—how quickly they can be turned into cash. A plant asset is one that will be used in the business for more than one year. Plant assets are listed in the order of their **stability**—how long they will last.

A current liability is a debt that is due for payment within one year. A long-term liability is a debt that is not due for payment within one year.

A financial statement is a decision-making tool. It provides information necessary for decisions and judgments about a business. For maximum benefit, it is common to make certain analyses from the financial statements. In this chapter, we introduced financial statement analysis by presenting two very common analyses from the balance sheet: working capital and the current ratio. **Working capital** is the excess of a firm's current assets over its current liabilities. A strong working capital position indicates that a business is able to carry on current operations. The **current ratio** is obtained by dividing current assets by current liabilities. It gives an indication of the ability of a business to pay its short-term debts as they fall due.

After financial statements are prepared, the next step in the accounting cycle is to journalize adjusting and closing entries. Adjusting entries already appear on the work sheet. They simply need to be copied into the journal.

The closing process involves making entries to close the temporary accounts. Revenue, expense, and cost accounts are closed to Income Summary, which, in turn, is closed to the owner's capital account. The owner's drawing account is closed directly to the owner's capital account.

After the adjusting and closing entries are journalized and posted, a post-closing trial balance is taken to ensure that the general ledger is still in balance. Only permanent accounts (assets, contra assets, liabilities, and owner's capital) appear on the post-closing trial balance—the temporary accounts have been closed.

In Chapters 4 and 9 we learned the proper accounting treatment for expenses that have been incurred, but are unpaid, when the accounting period ends. We learned that an expense account (such as Salaries Expense) is debited and a liability account (such as Salaries Payable) is credited. In this chapter, we looked at the entry necessary to record the payment of an accrued expense in the next accounting period. We learned that to make this entry properly, we had to split the entry between the liability recorded at the end of the last accounting period and the amount of expense incurred in the new accounting period. However, some accountants do not like to refer to the records of the previous period and split the entry. A technique called **reversing entries** allows us to make a routine accounting entry to record the payment of an accrued expense, even though two accounting periods are involved. Reversing entries are made as of the first day of the next accounting period and are the exact opposite of the adjusting entries for accrued expenses.

Many businesses prepare **interim statements** for periods of less than 12 months, such as monthly or quarterly statements. However, adjusting and closing entries are not made until the end of the fiscal year.

PRACTICE TEST

PART I TRUE/FALSE

Please circle the correct answer.

T   F   1. An income statement summarizes changes in the owner's capital for the period.

T   F   2. A classified income statement for a merchandising business has a section showing cost of goods sold.

T   F   3. Net sales for the period minus cost of goods sold equals net income.

T   F   4. Gross profit is the profit before subtracting the expenses of doing business.

T   F   5. Cost of goods sold is determined by adding net purchases to beginning inventory and subtracting ending inventory.

T   F   6. Net sales is calculated by taking the amount of sales and adding the amount of sales returns and allowances and the amount of sales discounts.

T   F   7. Operating expenses are expenses incurred in the normal operations of the business.

T   F   8. Interest expense is an example of an item that would be included in the section for other expenses on a classified income statement.

T   F   9. The statement of owner's equity is the link between the income statement and the balance sheet.

T   F   10. The principal objective of the balance sheet is to provide information about the results of the company's operations for the period.

T   F   11. Current assets include cash and those assets that will be realized in cash, sold, used up, or expired within one year.

T   F   12. Current liabilities are those that must be paid within one year.

T   F   13. Working capital is the same as cash.

T   F   14. Adjusting and closing entries do not need to be journalized or posted when using a work sheet.

T   F   15. Reversing entries are made on the last day of an accounting period.

PART II MATCHING

Please match each of the following terms with its definition.

a. classified balance sheet
b. classified income statement
c. cost of goods sold
d. current assets
e. current liabilities
f. current ratio
g. gross profit
h. liquidity

i. long-term liabilities
j. income from operations
k. net sales
l. operating expenses
m. other expenses
n. plant assets
o. reversing entries
p. working capital

_____ 1. Expenses incurred in the normal operations of the business.

_____ 2. The cost of merchandise sold to customers during the accounting period.

_____ 3. The profit before subtracting the expenses of doing business.

_____ 4. The amount obtained by subtracting the amount of sales returns and allowances and the amount of sales discounts from the amount of sales.

_____ 5. Cash and any other asset that will be realized in cash, used up, sold, or expired within one year.

_____ 6. The excess of a firm's current assets over its current liabilities.

_____ 7. Refers to how quickly an asset can be turned into cash.

_____ 8. An income statement divided into sections for revenue, cost of goods sold, operating expenses, income from operations, and other income and expenses.

_____ 9. Debts that are due for payment within one year.

_____ 10. A balance sheet divided into subsections for current and plant assets and current and long-term liabilities.

_____ 11. Gross profit minus operating expenses.

_____ 12. Debts that are not due for payment within one year.

_____ 13. Expenses that are not directly associated with the actual running of the business.

_____ 14. Entries made as of the first day of a new accounting period to offset certain adjusting entries.

_____ 15. The ratio obtained by dividing current assets by current liabilities.

_____ 16. Assets that are expected to be used in the business for more than one year.

PART III FILL IN THE BLANKS

Please complete each sentence with the correct word or words.

1. A classified income statement is divided into sections as follows: _____, cost of goods sold, _____, income from operations, and other income and expenses.

2. Gross profit is determined by taking net sales for the period and subtracting _____.

3. Gross profit minus _____ equals income from operations.

4. Net sales is calculated by subtracting the amount of _____ and the amount of _____ from the amount of sales.

5. Adding _____ to beginning merchandise inventory gives the goods available for sale.

6. Cost of goods sold is determined by computing the _____ and subtracting ending merchandise inventory.

7. Interest expense is an example of _____.

8. Cash is an example of a(n) _____ asset.

9. Accounts payable is an example of a(n) _____.

10. _____ is computed by subtracting current liabilities from current assets.

11. The current ratio is calculated by dividing current assets by _____.

12. The adjusting entries on the work sheet must be _____ and _____.

13. The Income Summary account will have _____ adjusting and closing entries posted to it before it is closed.

14. The _____ is taken to assure that the general ledger is in balance to begin the new period.

15. Adjustments for accrued expenses are often _____ at the start of a new accounting period.

PART IV MULTIPLE CHOICE

Please circle the correct answer.

1. Which of the following represents the divisions found in a classified income statement?
   a. revenue, assets, liabilities, owner's equity
   b. revenue, cost of goods sold, operating expenses, income from operations, other income and expenses
   c. revenue and expenses
   d. assets, liabilities, and owner's equity

2. Net sales for the period is computed by
   a. subtracting the amount of sales returns and allowances and the amount of sales discounts from the amount of sales.
   b. adding the amount of purchases returns and allowances and the amount of purchases discounts to the amount of sales.
   c. adding the amount of sales returns and allowances and the amount of sales discounts to the amount of sales.
   d. footing the Sales account.

3. Cost of goods sold is
   a. the cost of operating a merchandising business.
   b. the cost of merchandise sold by the business.
   c. the cost of purchases made during the period.
   d. the cost of purchases plus the beginning inventory of the period.

4. The three figures needed to determine cost of goods sold are
   a. purchases, purchases returns and allowances, and purchases discounts.
   b. purchases, freight in, and purchases returns and allowances.
   c. beginning inventory, purchases, and freight in.
   d. beginning inventory, net purchases, and ending inventory.

5. Gross profit is
   a. revenues minus expenses.
   b. revenues minus cost of goods sold and operating expenses.
   c. revenues minus all costs and expenses.
   d. revenues minus cost of goods sold.

6. Some examples of operating expenses are
   a. salaries, utilities, and rent.
   b. insurance, interest, and supplies used.
   c. salaries, utilities, and the owner's withdrawals.
   d. utilities, supplies used, and accounts payable.

7. An example of other expenses is
   a. rent expense.
   b. depreciation expense.
   c. interest expense.
   d. salaries expense.

8. Current assets include such assets as
   a. cash, accounts receivable, and prepaid insurance.
   b. cash, equipment, and land.
   c. cash, buildings, and owner's capital.
   d. cash, merchandise inventory, and office furniture.

9. Plant assets include such assets as
   a. cash, accounts receivable, and prepaid insurance.
   b. buildings, equipment, and accounts receivable.
   c. land, buildings, and cash.
   d. land, buildings, and equipment.

10. Current assets are generally listed on the balance sheet according to their
    a. stability.
    b. cost.
    c. liquidity.
    d. durability.

11. Some examples of current liabilities include
    a. accounts payable and mortgages payable.
    b. accounts payable and salaries payable.
    c. salaries payable and long-term notes payable.
    d. only accounts payable.

12. Working capital analysis attempts to answer which of the following questions?
    a. Does the business have enough capital to operate?
    b. Does the business have enough capital to continue growing?
    c. Does the business have enough capital to pay its current debts on time?
    d. all of the above

13. Working capital is
    a. current assets divided by current liabilities.
    b. current liabilities divided by current assets.
    c. current assets minus current liabilities.
    d. current liabilities minus current assets.

14. The current ratio is
    a. current assets divided by current liabilities.
    b. current liabilities divided by current assets.
    c. current assets minus current liabilities.
    d. current liabilities minus current assets.

15. Before it is closed, the Income Summary account will have four entries posted to it. They are
    a. beginning inventory and revenues on the debit side and ending inventory and expenses on the credit side.
    b. ending inventory and revenues on the debit side and beginning inventory and expenses on the credit side.
    c. beginning inventory and expenses on the debit side and ending inventory and revenues on the credit side.
    d. none of the above.

PART V WRITING/SHORT ANSWER

1. **Reflect** Make a list, in words or simple phrases, of the most important and meaningful points in this chapter.

2. **Question** Think about the most confusing points or the material you do not understand in this chapter. Write down two or three questions that remain unanswered.

3. **Connect** Explain, in one or two sentences, the connection between the main points of this chapter and the major goals of the entire course.

4. **Summarize** Review this chapter's Joining the Pieces visual summary and explain the concept(s) illustrated in a few sentences.

This page intentionally left blank.

WORKING PAPERS

SKILLS REVIEW

EXERCISE 10-1

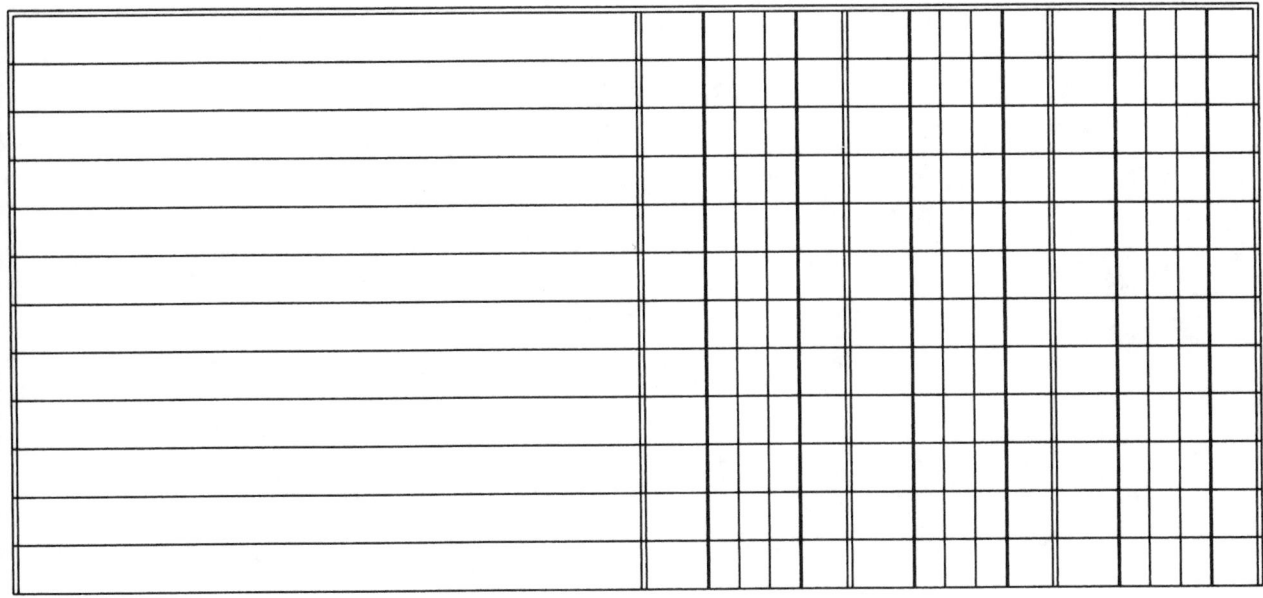

EXERCISE 10-2

(a)

(b)

(c)

(d)

EXERCISE 10-3

(a)

(b)

(c)

EXERCISE 10-4

1.

2.

3.

4.

General Journal

	Date	Account Title	P.R.	Debit	Credit	
1						1
2						2
3						3
4						4
5						5
6						6
7						7
8						8
9						9
10						10
11						11
12						12
13						13
14						14
15						15
16						16
17						17
18						18
19						19
20						20
21						21
22						22
23						23
24						24
25						25
26						26
27						27
28						28
29						29
30						30
31						31
32						32

EXERCISE 10-5

EXERCISE 10-6

1. _____   6. _____
2. _____   7. _____
3. _____   8. _____
4. _____   9. _____
5. _____   10. _____

EXERCISE 10-7

(a) _____

(b) _____

EXERCISE 10-8

Income Summary

B. LOGAN CLOTHING STORE
INCOME Statement
FOR YEAR ENDED DEC 31, 20XX

Revenue from Sales:					
Sales				395 140	
Less: sale return & allowance		15 505			
Sale discount		7 400		22 905	
Net sales					372 235
COST of Goods Sold:					
Merch. Inventory Jan 1				42 400	
Purchase		219 550			
Less: Purchases Ret. & Allow.	13 465				
Purchases discount	6 300	19 765			
		199 785			
Add: FREIGHT IN		5 200			
NET Purchases				204 985	
Goods Available for sale				247 388	
Less: merch. INVENTORY					
DEC 31, 20XX				37 600	5
Cost of Goods Sold					209 788
Gross profit					162 447
					450
Operating Expenses:					
Selling Expenses:					
Sale salaries Exp.		23 000			
advertising Exp.		16 100			
Store supplies exp.		5 300			
Dep. exp. off. equip		13 000			
Dep. exp. Store equip		16 000		84 050	
Total selling exp.				63 400	
General Expense:					
Rent expense		25 200			
office salar expense		28 300			
Insurance Expen		7 000			
Utilities		5 800			

Total General
Total Operating expense 66 300 → 129,700

Income from operation → 32,747

NET income 28,000

This page intentionally left blank.

1.

2.

(a)

(b) _____

PROBLEM 10-3A OR 10-3B

1.

2.

3.

This page intentionally left blank.

PROBLEM 10-4A OR 10-4B

General Journal

	Date		Account Title	P.R.	Debit	Credit	
1			CLOSING ENTRIES				1
2	20XX DEC	31	Sales		194375		2
3			Purchases Ret & allowans		9310		3
4			Purchase discount		2140		4
5			Income summary			205825	5
6					188695		6
7		31	Income summary		172970		7
8			Sales Ret & Allowances			14505	8
9			Purchases			110540	9
10			Sale salaries Exp.			12000	10
11			Depr. Exp. office equip.			1600	11
12			Store supplies expense			9425	12
13			Rent Expense			4800	13
14			Office supplies			18000	14
15			Insurance expense			600	15
16			Depr. Exp. store Equip			2100	16
17							17
18		31	Income summary		37490		18
19			Peggy Wilson capital			37490	19
20							20
21							21
22		31	Peggy Wilson, Capital		7000		22
23			Peggy Wilson, Drawing			7000	23
24							24
25							25
26							26
27							27
28							28
29							29
30							30
31							31
32							32

This page intentionally left blank.

General Journal

Page _____

	Date		Account Title	P.R.	Debit	Credit	
1							1
2							2
3							3
4							4
5							5
6							6
7							7
8							8
9							9
10							10
11							11
12							12
13							13
14							14
15							15
16							16
17							17
18							18
19							19
20							20
21							21
22							22
23							23
24							24
25							25
26							26
27							27
28							28
29							29
30							30
31							31
32							32

This page intentionally left blank.

General Journal

Page 1

	Date		Account Title	P.R.	Debit	Credit	
1							1
2							2
3							3
4							4
5							5
6							6
7							7
8							8
9							9
10							10
11							11
12							12
13							13
14							14
15							15
16							16
17							17
18							18
19							19
20							20
21							21
22							22
23							23
24							24
25							25
26							26
27							27
28							28
29							29
30							30
31							31
32							32

This page intentionally left blank.

CHALLENGE PROBLEMS

PROBLEM SOLVING

1., 6., 7.

General Ledger

ACCOUNT Cash
ACCOUNT NO. 111

DATE		ITEM	P.R.	DEBIT	CREDIT	BALANCE	
						DEBIT	CREDIT

ACCOUNT Accounts Receivable
ACCOUNT NO. 112

DATE		ITEM	P.R.	DEBIT	CREDIT	BALANCE	
						DEBIT	CREDIT

ACCOUNT Merchandise Inventory
ACCOUNT NO. 113

DATE		ITEM	P.R.	DEBIT	CREDIT	BALANCE	
						DEBIT	CREDIT

ACCOUNT Office Supplies
ACCOUNT NO. 114

DATE		ITEM	P.R.	DEBIT	CREDIT	BALANCE	
						DEBIT	CREDIT

PROBLEM SOLVING (continued)

ACCOUNT Store Supplies   ACCOUNT NO. 115

DATE		ITEM	P.R.	DEBIT	CREDIT	BALANCE	
						DEBIT	CREDIT

ACCOUNT Prepaid Insurance   ACCOUNT NO. 117

DATE		ITEM	P.R.	DEBIT	CREDIT	BALANCE	
						DEBIT	CREDIT

ACCOUNT Office Equipment   ACCOUNT NO. 118

DATE		ITEM	P.R.	DEBIT	CREDIT	BALANCE	
						DEBIT	CREDIT

ACCOUNT Accumulated Depreciation—Office Equipment   ACCOUNT NO. 118.1

DATE		ITEM	P.R.	DEBIT	CREDIT	BALANCE	
						DEBIT	CREDIT

ACCOUNT Store Equipment   ACCOUNT NO. 119

DATE		ITEM	P.R.	DEBIT	CREDIT	BALANCE	
						DEBIT	CREDIT

ACCOUNT Accumulated Depreciation—Store Equipment   ACCOUNT NO. 119.1

DATE	ITEM	P.R.	DEBIT	CREDIT	BALANCE	
					DEBIT	CREDIT

ACCOUNT Delivery Equipment   ACCOUNT NO. 120

DATE	ITEM	P.R.	DEBIT	CREDIT	BALANCE	
					DEBIT	CREDIT

ACCOUNT Accumulated Depreciation—Delivery Equipment   ACCOUNT NO. 120.1

DATE	ITEM	P.R.	DEBIT	CREDIT	BALANCE	
					DEBIT	CREDIT

ACCOUNT Accounts Payable   ACCOUNT NO. 211

DATE	ITEM	P.R.	DEBIT	CREDIT	BALANCE	
					DEBIT	CREDIT

ACCOUNT Salaries Payable   ACCOUNT NO. 212

DATE	ITEM	P.R.	DEBIT	CREDIT	BALANCE	
					DEBIT	CREDIT

ACCOUNT Notes Payable   ACCOUNT NO. 221

DATE	ITEM	P.R.	DEBIT	CREDIT	BALANCE	
					DEBIT	CREDIT

PROBLEM SOLVING (continued)

ACCOUNT Doreen Woods, Capital   ACCOUNT NO. 311

DATE	ITEM	P.R.	DEBIT	CREDIT	BALANCE DEBIT	BALANCE CREDIT

ACCOUNT Doreen Woods, Drawing   ACCOUNT NO. 312

DATE	ITEM	P.R.	DEBIT	CREDIT	BALANCE DEBIT	BALANCE CREDIT

ACCOUNT Income Summary   ACCOUNT NO. 315

DATE	ITEM	P.R.	DEBIT	CREDIT	BALANCE DEBIT	BALANCE CREDIT

ACCOUNT Sales   ACCOUNT NO. 411

DATE	ITEM	P.R.	DEBIT	CREDIT	BALANCE DEBIT	BALANCE CREDIT

ACCOUNT Sales Returns and Allowances   ACCOUNT NO. 411.1

DATE	ITEM	P.R.	DEBIT	CREDIT	BALANCE DEBIT	BALANCE CREDIT

ACCOUNT **Sales Discounts**   ACCOUNT NO. 411.2

DATE	ITEM	P.R.	DEBIT	CREDIT	BALANCE DEBIT	BALANCE CREDIT

ACCOUNT **Purchases**   ACCOUNT NO. 511

DATE	ITEM	P.R.	DEBIT	CREDIT	BALANCE DEBIT	BALANCE CREDIT

ACCOUNT **Purchases Returns and Allowances**   ACCOUNT NO. 511.1

DATE	ITEM	P.R.	DEBIT	CREDIT	BALANCE DEBIT	BALANCE CREDIT

ACCOUNT **Purchases Discounts**   ACCOUNT NO. 511.2

DATE	ITEM	P.R.	DEBIT	CREDIT	BALANCE DEBIT	BALANCE CREDIT

ACCOUNT **Freight In**   ACCOUNT NO. 512

DATE	ITEM	P.R.	DEBIT	CREDIT	BALANCE DEBIT	BALANCE CREDIT

PROBLEM SOLVING (continued)

ACCOUNT Sales Salaries Expense   ACCOUNT NO. 611

DATE	ITEM	P.R.	DEBIT	CREDIT	BALANCE DEBIT	BALANCE CREDIT

ACCOUNT Store Supplies Expense   ACCOUNT NO. 612

DATE	ITEM	P.R.	DEBIT	CREDIT	BALANCE DEBIT	BALANCE CREDIT

ACCOUNT Advertising Expense   ACCOUNT NO. 613

DATE	ITEM	P.R.	DEBIT	CREDIT	BALANCE DEBIT	BALANCE CREDIT

ACCOUNT Depreciation Expense—Store Equipment   ACCOUNT NO. 614

DATE	ITEM	P.R.	DEBIT	CREDIT	BALANCE DEBIT	BALANCE CREDIT

ACCOUNT Depreciation Expense—Delivery Equipment   ACCOUNT NO. 615

DATE	ITEM	P.R.	DEBIT	CREDIT	BALANCE DEBIT	BALANCE CREDIT

PROBLEM SOLVING (continued)

ACCOUNT Rent Expense   ACCOUNT NO. 616

DATE	ITEM	P.R.	DEBIT	CREDIT	BALANCE DEBIT	BALANCE CREDIT

ACCOUNT Office Salaries Expense   ACCOUNT NO. 617

DATE	ITEM	P.R.	DEBIT	CREDIT	BALANCE DEBIT	BALANCE CREDIT

ACCOUNT Office Supplies Expense   ACCOUNT NO. 618

DATE	ITEM	P.R.	DEBIT	CREDIT	BALANCE DEBIT	BALANCE CREDIT

ACCOUNT Utilities Expense   ACCOUNT NO. 619

DATE	ITEM	P.R.	DEBIT	CREDIT	BALANCE DEBIT	BALANCE CREDIT

ACCOUNT Depreciation Expense—Office Equipment   ACCOUNT NO. 620

DATE	ITEM	P.R.	DEBIT	CREDIT	BALANCE DEBIT	BALANCE CREDIT

PROBLEM SOLVING (continued)

ACCOUNT Insurance Expense   ACCOUNT NO. 621

DATE	ITEM	P.R.	DEBIT	CREDIT	BALANCE	
					DEBIT	CREDIT

ACCOUNT Miscellaneous Expense   ACCOUNT NO. 622

DATE	ITEM	P.R.	DEBIT	CREDIT	BALANCE	
					DEBIT	CREDIT

ACCOUNT Interest Expense   ACCOUNT NO. 623

DATE	ITEM	P.R.	DEBIT	CREDIT	BALANCE	
					DEBIT	CREDIT

2.

Save Mart Department Store
Income Statement
For Year Ended December 31, 20X2

3.

Save Mart Department Store Statement of Owner's Equity For Year Ended December 31, 20X2									

4.

Save Mart Department Store								
Balance Sheet								
December 31, 20X2								

5. _____

_____

6. **General Journal**   Page 1

	Date	Account Title	P.R.	Debit	Credit	
1						1
2						2
3						3
4						4
5						5
6						6
7						7
8						8
9						9
10						10
11						11
12						12
13						13
14						14
15						15
16						16
17						17
18						18
19						19
20						20
21						21
22						22
23						23
24						24
25						25
26						26
27						27
28						28
29						29

7.   **General Journal**

	Date		Account Title	P.R.	Debit	Credit	
1							1
2							2
3							3
4							4
5							5
6							6
7							7
8							8
9							9
10							10
11							11
12							12
13							13
14							14
15							15
16							16
17							17
18							18
19							19
20							20
21							21
22							22
23							23
24							24
25							25
26							26
27							27
28							28
29							29
30							30
31							31
32							32

8.

Save Mart Department Store Post-Closing Trial Balance December 31, 20X2		
ACCOUNT TITLE	DEBIT	CREDIT

9.

General Journal   Page 3

	Date	Account Title	P.R.	Debit	Credit	
1						1
2						2
3						3
4						4
5						5
6						6
7						7
8						8

10. Comments on the financial condition of the company:

_____

_____

_____

_____

_____

_____

_____

_____

_____

_____

_____

_____

_____

_____

_____

_____

_____

_____

_____

This page intentionally left blank.

COMMUNICATIONS

ETHICS

This page intentionally left blank.

PRACTICE TEST ANSWERS

PART I

1. F
2. T
3. F
4. T
5. T
6. F
7. T
8. T
9. T
10. F
11. T
12. T
13. F
14. F
15. F

PART II

1. l
2. c
3. g
4. k
5. d
6. p
7. h
8. b
9. e
10. a
11. j
12. i
13. m
14. o
15. f
16. n

PART III

1. revenue, operating expenses
2. cost of goods sold
3. operating expenses
4. sales returns and allowances, sales discounts
5. net purchases
6. goods available for sale
7. other expenses
8. current
9. current liability
10. Working capital
11. current liabilities
12. journalized, posted
13. four
14. post-closing trial balance
15. reversed

PART IV

1. b
2. a
3. b
4. d
5. d
6. a
7. c
8. a
9. d
10. c
11. b
12. d
13. c
14. a
15. c

PART V

Answers will vary. Please discuss questions with your instructor. You can also discuss issues related to this chapter by logging onto the Paradigm Accounting Web Site at www.emcp.com and clicking on the discussion section.

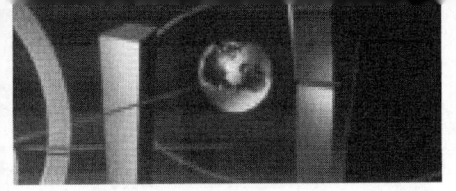

Comprehensive Review Problem 2

WORKING PAPERS

1., 6., 10., 11., 18., 22., 23.

General Ledger

ACCOUNT Cash   ACCOUNT NO. 111

DATE	ITEM	P.R.	DEBIT	CREDIT	BALANCE DEBIT	BALANCE CREDIT

ACCOUNT Accounts Receivable   ACCOUNT NO. 112

DATE	ITEM	P.R.	DEBIT	CREDIT	BALANCE DEBIT	BALANCE CREDIT

ACCOUNT **Office Supplies**   ACCOUNT NO. 113

DATE	ITEM	P.R.	DEBIT	CREDIT	BALANCE	
					DEBIT	CREDIT

ACCOUNT **Store Supplies**   ACCOUNT NO. 114

DATE	ITEM	P.R.	DEBIT	CREDIT	BALANCE	
					DEBIT	CREDIT

ACCOUNT **Merchandise Inventory**   ACCOUNT NO. 115

DATE	ITEM	P.R.	DEBIT	CREDIT	BALANCE	
					DEBIT	CREDIT

ACCOUNT Prepaid Insurance   ACCOUNT NO. 116

DATE		ITEM	P.R.	DEBIT	CREDIT	BALANCE DEBIT	BALANCE CREDIT

ACCOUNT Office Equipment   ACCOUNT NO. 121

DATE		ITEM	P.R.	DEBIT	CREDIT	BALANCE DEBIT	BALANCE CREDIT

ACCOUNT Accumulated Depreciation—Office Equipment   ACCOUNT NO. 121.1

DATE		ITEM	P.R.	DEBIT	CREDIT	BALANCE DEBIT	BALANCE CREDIT

ACCOUNT Store Equipment   ACCOUNT NO. 122

DATE		ITEM	P.R.	DEBIT	CREDIT	BALANCE DEBIT	BALANCE CREDIT

ACCOUNT Accumulated Depreciation—Store Equipment   ACCOUNT NO. 122.1

DATE		ITEM	P.R.	DEBIT	CREDIT	BALANCE DEBIT	BALANCE CREDIT

ACCOUNT Delivery Equipment   ACCOUNT NO. 123

DATE	ITEM	P.R.	DEBIT	CREDIT	BALANCE	
					DEBIT	CREDIT

ACCOUNT Accumulated Depreciation—Delivery Equipment   ACCOUNT NO. 123.1

DATE	ITEM	P.R.	DEBIT	CREDIT	BALANCE	
					DEBIT	CREDIT

ACCOUNT Accounts Payable   ACCOUNT NO. 211

DATE	ITEM	P.R.	DEBIT	CREDIT	BALANCE	
					DEBIT	CREDIT

ACCOUNT Cindy Mills, Capital   ACCOUNT NO. 311

DATE	ITEM	P.R.	DEBIT	CREDIT	BALANCE DEBIT	BALANCE CREDIT

ACCOUNT Cindy Mills, Drawing   ACCOUNT NO. 312

DATE	ITEM	P.R.	DEBIT	CREDIT	BALANCE DEBIT	BALANCE CREDIT

ACCOUNT Income Summary   ACCOUNT NO. 313

DATE	ITEM	P.R.	DEBIT	CREDIT	BALANCE DEBIT	BALANCE CREDIT

ACCOUNT Sales   ACCOUNT NO. 411

DATE	ITEM	P.R.	DEBIT	CREDIT	BALANCE	
					DEBIT	CREDIT

ACCOUNT Sales Returns and Allowances   ACCOUNT NO. 412

DATE	ITEM	P.R.	DEBIT	CREDIT	BALANCE	
					DEBIT	CREDIT

ACCOUNT Sales Discounts   ACCOUNT NO. 413

DATE	ITEM	P.R.	DEBIT	CREDIT	BALANCE	
					DEBIT	CREDIT

ACCOUNT Purchases   ACCOUNT NO. 511

DATE	ITEM	P.R.	DEBIT	CREDIT	BALANCE	
					DEBIT	CREDIT

ACCOUNT Purchases Returns and Allowances   ACCOUNT NO. 512

DATE	ITEM	P.R.	DEBIT	CREDIT	BALANCE DEBIT	BALANCE CREDIT

ACCOUNT Purchases Discounts   ACCOUNT NO. 513

DATE	ITEM	P.R.	DEBIT	CREDIT	BALANCE DEBIT	BALANCE CREDIT

ACCOUNT Freight In   ACCOUNT NO. 514

DATE	ITEM	P.R.	DEBIT	CREDIT	BALANCE DEBIT	BALANCE CREDIT

ACCOUNT Salaries Expense   ACCOUNT NO. 611

DATE	ITEM	P.R.	DEBIT	CREDIT	BALANCE DEBIT	BALANCE CREDIT

ACCOUNT Rent Expense   ACCOUNT NO. 612

DATE	ITEM	P.R.	DEBIT	CREDIT	BALANCE DEBIT	BALANCE CREDIT

ACCOUNT Utilities Expense   ACCOUNT NO. 613

DATE	ITEM	P.R.	DEBIT	CREDIT	BALANCE DEBIT	BALANCE CREDIT

ACCOUNT Office Supplies Expense   ACCOUNT NO. 614

DATE	ITEM	P.R.	DEBIT	CREDIT	BALANCE DEBIT	BALANCE CREDIT

ACCOUNT Store Supplies Expense   ACCOUNT NO. 615

DATE	ITEM	P.R.	DEBIT	CREDIT	BALANCE DEBIT	BALANCE CREDIT

ACCOUNT Insurance Expense   ACCOUNT NO. 616

DATE	ITEM	P.R.	DEBIT	CREDIT	BALANCE DEBIT	BALANCE CREDIT

ACCOUNT Depreciation Expense—Office Equipment   ACCOUNT NO. 617

DATE	ITEM	P.R.	DEBIT	CREDIT	BALANCE DEBIT	BALANCE CREDIT

ACCOUNT Depreciation Expense—Store Equipment   ACCOUNT NO. 618

DATE	ITEM	P.R.	DEBIT	CREDIT	BALANCE DEBIT	BALANCE CREDIT

ACCOUNT Depreciation Expense—Delivery Equipment   ACCOUNT NO. 619

DATE	ITEM	P.R.	DEBIT	CREDIT	BALANCE DEBIT	BALANCE CREDIT

NAME   H. Galvin

ADDRESS

Date	Item	P.R.	Debit	Credit	Balance

NAME   Lee Maddox

ADDRESS

Date	Item	P.R.	Debit	Credit	Balance

NAME   Neagle Co.

ADDRESS

Date	Item	P.R.	Debit	Credit	Balance

NAME Smitz, Inc.

ADDRESS

Date	Item	P.R.	Debit	Credit	Balance

3., 6., 18.   **Accounts Payable Ledger**

NAME W. Bedford Co.

ADDRESS

Date	Item	P.R.	Debit	Credit	Balance

NAME Jones Co.

ADDRESS

Date	Item	P.R.	Debit	Credit	Balance

NAME   Lemke Brothers

ADDRESS

Date		Item	P.R.	Debit	Credit	Balance

NAME   Wohlers, Inc.

ADDRESS

Date		Item	P.R.	Debit	Credit	Balance

	Date		Account Title	P.R.	Debit	Credit	
1							1
2							2
3							3
4							4
5							5
6							6
7							7
8							8
9							9
10							10
11							11
12							12
13							13
14							14
15							15
16							16
17							17
18							18
19							19
20							20
21							21
22							22
23							23
24							24
25							25
26							26
27							27
28							28
29							29
30							30
31							31
32							32

	Date		Account Title	P.R.	Debit	Credit	
1							1
2							2
3							3
4							4
5							5
6							6
7							7
8							8
9							9
10							10
11							11
12							12
13							13
14							14
15							15
16							16
17							17
18							18
19							19
20							20
21							21
22							22
23							23
24							24
25							25
26							26
27							27
28							28
29							29
30							30
31							31
32							32
33							33
34							34

	Date	Account Title	P.R.	Debit	Credit	
1						1
2						2
3						3
4						4
5						5
6						6
7						7
8						8
9						9
10						10
11						11
12						12
13						13
14						14
15						15
16						16
17						17
18						18
19						19
20						20
21						21
22						22
23						23
24						24
25						25
26						26
27						27
28						28
29						29
30						30
31						31
32						32

	Date		Account Title	P.R.	Debit	Credit	
1							1
2							2
3							3
4							4
5							5
6							6
7							7
8							8
9							9
10							10
11							11
12							12
13							13
14							14
15							15
16							16
17							17
18							18
19							19
20							20
21							21
22							22
23							23
24							24
25							25
26							26
27							27
28							28
29							29
30							30
31							31
32							32

	Date	Account Title	P.R.	Debit	Credit	
1						1
2						2
3						3
4						4
5						5
6						6
7						7
8						8
9						9
10						10
11						11
12						12
13						13
14						14
15						15
16						16
17						17
18						18
19						19
20						20
21						21
22						22
23						23
24						24
25						25
26						26
27						27
28						28
29						29
30						30
31						31
32						32

	Date	Invoice No.	Customer's Name	P.R.	Accts. Rec. Dr. Sales Cr.					
1										1
2										2
3										3
4										4
5										5
6										6
7										7
8										8
9										9
10										10
11										11
12										12
13										13
14										14
15										15

Purchases Journal

	Date	Invoice No.	Account Credited	P.R.	Purchases Dr. Accts. Pay. Cr.					
1										1
2										2
3										3
4										4
5										5
6										6
7										7
8										8
9										9
10										10
11										11
12										12
13										13

Date	Account Credited	P.R.	General Cr.	Sales Cr.	Accounts Rec. Cr.	Sales Discounts Dr.	Cash Dr.

Cash Payments Journal

Date	Ck. No.	Account Debited	P.R.	General Dr.	Accounts Payable Dr.	Purchases Discounts Cr.	Cash Cr.

This page intentionally left blank.

7., 9.

	Mills Sporting Goods Store				
	Work Sheet				
	For Month Ended January 31, 20X1				
Account Title	Trial Balance		Adjustments	
	Dr.	Cr.	Dr.	Cr.

	Adjusted Trial Balance		Income Statement		Balance Sheet	
	Dr.	Cr.	Dr.	Cr.	Dr.	Cr.

8.

Mills Sporting Goods Store										
Schedule of Accounts Receivable										
January 31, 20X1										

Mills Sporting Goods Store
Schedule of Accounts Payable
January 31, 20X1

12.

Mills Sporting Goods Store		
Post-Closing Trial Balance		
January 31, 20X1		
ACCOUNT TITLE	DEBIT	CREDIT

13.

Mills Sporting Goods Store									
Income Statement									
For Month Ended January 31, 20X1									

14.

Mills Sporting Goods Store											
Statement of Owner's Equity											
For Month Ended January 31, 20X1											

15.

Mills Sporting Goods Store
Balance Sheet
January 31, 20X1

19., 21.

Account Title	Trial Balance		Adjustments	
	Dr.	Cr.	Dr.	Cr.

Study Guide and Working Papers • Comprehensive Review Problem 2

	Adjusted Trial Balance		Income Statement		Balance Sheet	
	Dr.	Cr.	Dr.	Cr.	Dr.	Cr.

20.

Mills Sporting Goods Store Schedule of Accounts Receivable February 28, 20X1											

Mills Sporting Goods Store

Schedule of Accounts Payable

February 28, 20X1

24.

Mills Sporting Goods Store Post-Closing Trial Balance February 28, 20X1		
ACCOUNT TITLE	DEBIT	CREDIT

25.

Mills Sporting Goods Store
Income Statement
For Month Ended February 28, 20X1

26.

Mills Sporting Goods Store										
Statement of Owner's Equity										
For Month Ended February 28, 20X1										

27.

Mills Sporting Goods Store																			
Balance Sheet																			
February 28, 20X1																			

Accounting for Payroll–Employee Earnings and Deductions

CHAPTER SUMMARY

Many people are **independent contractors**, individuals who perform a task for hire and have no permanent relationship with the hiring party. More people are **employees**, who work for others and are under the continuing control of those others. Almost all businesses have employees and, therefore, must make regular payments to them. These payments are referred to as payroll expense, wages expense, or salaries expense. Payroll expense is often a significant portion of the operating expenses of a business. Therefore, good control must be exercised over the payroll system.

The term **wage** is usually used to describe an amount paid by the hour. The term **salary** is usually used to describe an amount paid by the week, month, or year. In practice, the terms wage and salary are used interchangeably. Some employees are paid by a **piece-rate plan**, one in which they receive so much per unit produced.

Wage earners are typically covered by the **Fair Labor Standards Act**, commonly referred to as the **Wages and Hours Law**. Under this act, covered workers are entitled to a **minimum wage** and **overtime pay** for hours worked in excess of 40 in any workweek. Overtime means that an employee must be paid at least **time-and-a-half** (1.5 times the regular rate) for overtime hours. Some companies have gone beyond this minimum and pay double time (2 times the regular rate) for weekend and holiday work. Additionally, some companies pay overtime for any hours in excess of 8 in a day, even though total hours may not reach 40 for a week.

Gross earnings is the total amount that an employee earns before any amount is deducted by the employer. Gross earnings may be calculated on a weekly, biweekly, semimonthly, or monthly basis, depending on how often employees are paid. Gross earnings of a **salaried employee** are usually stated on an annual basis and then divided by the number of pay periods in the year to find the amount of gross earnings for each period. Gross earnings of an **hourly worker** are calculated by multiplying the number of hours worked by the hourly rate, including 1.5 or 2 times the hourly rate for overtime hours worked.

A payroll deduction is an amount that the employer **withholds** from the gross earnings of the employee. Payroll deductions are of two types: (1) required deductions and (2) optional deductions. The two required deductions are income taxes and **FICA (Federal Insurance Contributions Act) taxes**. Income taxes are collected by the federal government and may also be collected by state and local governments.

When an employee is hired, he or she fills out **Form W-4 (Employee's Withholding Allowance Certificate)**. On this form, the employee indicates how many **withholding allowances** (or **exemptions**) are claimed. The amount of income tax withheld is then determined based on the employee's gross earnings, marital status, and number of withholding allowances, using an approach called the **wage-bracket method**. Amounts to be withheld can be found in computer programs or in the **Employer's Tax Guide—Circular E**.

FICA taxes, more commonly known as social security taxes, are used to finance (1) the federal old-age, survivors, and disability program (**OASDI**) and (2) the hospital insurance plan (**HIP**), or Medicare. The FICA tax rate is actually in two parts, one for OASDI and one for HIP. All wages are subject to the HIP rate, but there is a limit to the OASDI wages taxed, called the **OASDI taxable wage base**.

Optional deductions include union dues, insurance premiums, loan repayments, and deductions for various types of savings and retirement plans. The employer incurs a liability for each of these deductions and must remit them to the appropriate agency in a timely manner and according to contract terms.

Net earnings (**net pay**) are the result of subtracting all deductions from gross earnings. Another name for net earnings is **take-home pay**.

Employers use two basic means to record payroll information: the payroll register and the employee's earnings record. The **payroll register** is a form that summarizes gross earnings, deductions, and net pay for all employees for a pay period. The payroll register can be prepared manually or be a part of a computerized system. There are many commercial software programs available today to handle payroll inexpensively and effectively. After all data are entered in the payroll register, a check of its totals, or **crossfooting**, occurs.

The payroll register is an auxiliary record. To account for the payroll, it is necessary to make a journal entry to record the total gross earnings, totals of the various deductions, and total net earnings for the pay period. The payroll register serves as the source document for the journal entry to record the payroll: debit one or more **Salaries Expense accounts** for gross earnings; credit liability accounts for the deductions, such as the **FICA Tax Payable—OASDI account**, the **FICA Tax Payable—HIP account**, and the **Federal Income Tax Payable account**; credit the **Salaries Payable account** for net earnings.

An **employee's earnings record** has two parts: a heading that includes information about the employee; and a body that includes the employee's gross earnings, deductions, and net earnings for each pay period of the year.

PART I TRUE/FALSE

Please circle the correct answer.

T F 1. An employee is under the direct control of an employer on a continuing basis.

T F 2. Payroll accounting applies to everyone who does any work for a firm, whether he or she is an employee or an independent contractor.

T F 3. Salaried employees work for a fixed amount for a definite period of time, such as a week or a month.

T F 4. All salaried employees are covered by the overtime provisions of the Fair Labor Standards Act.

T F 5. The Fair Labor Standards Act requires overtime pay for covered employees at one and one-half times the regular hourly rate for any hours worked beyond the normal 40 hours per week.

T F 6. Overtime pay beyond 8 hours a day is a matter of company policy, not federal law, if an employee works 40 or fewer hours during a week.

T F 7. A piece-rate plan pays workers a certain rate per unit produced.

T F 8. Gross earnings are the amount that is left after deductions.

T F 9. The federal government requires withholdings for federal income taxes and social security taxes.

T F 10. Deductions other than income taxes and FICA taxes are optional, not required.

T F 11. The same rate applies to both the OASDI and HIP parts of the FICA tax.

T F 12. Net earnings is gross earnings minus all deductions.

T F 13. Employers are required to keep a record called the payroll register for each employee during a calendar year.

T F 14. The Salaries Expense account is debited for the amount of net earnings.

T F 15. The payroll register and the employee's earnings record serve different purposes in a payroll system.

PART II MATCHING

Please match each of the following terms with its definition.

a. crossfooting
b. employee
c. employee's earnings record
d. Employer's Tax Guide (Circular E)
e. Fair Labor Standards Act
f. FICA
g. Form W-4
h. gross earnings
i. independent contractor
j. minimum wage

k. net earnings
l. OASDI taxable wage base
m. overtime pay
n. payroll register
o. piece-rate plan
p. salary
q. wage
r. wage-bracket method
s. withhold
t. withholding allowance or exemption

_____ 1. A person under the direct control of an employer on a continuing basis.

_____ 2. A person who agrees to perform and complete a specific job or task, and is left to choose the ways and methods of achieving that job or task.

_____ 3. A fixed amount paid to employees for a certain period of time, such as a week or a month.

_____ 4. A fixed hourly rate paid to employees.

_____ 5. An act passed by Congress that established standards for minimum wages, overtime pay, child labor, and required payroll record keeping.

_____ 6. An amount set by Congress that is the least that can be paid per hour to employees who are covered under the Fair Labor Standards Act.

_____ 7. A minimum of one and one-half times the regular rate of pay for more than 40 hours of work per week.

_____ 8. A method of payment in which workers are paid for each unit produced, rather than so much per hour worked.

_____ 9. An employee's earnings before any amounts are deducted by the employer.

_____ 10. To deduct amounts from an employee's earnings before they are paid.

_____ 11. The law that requires employees and employers to pay taxes to fund the social security system.

_____ 12. The maximum amount of an employee's earnings during a calendar year that is subject to OASDI taxes.

_____ 13. An amount of earnings that is not subject to taxation.

_____ 14. A form filled out by every employee, showing marital status and number of withholding allowances claimed.

_____ 15. An IRS publication containing federal income tax tables.

_____ 16. A method that uses government tax tables to determine the amount of income tax to withhold from each employee's gross earnings.

_____ 17. Gross earnings minus various deductions.

_____ 18. A summary of the gross earnings, deductions, and net pay for all employees for a specific payroll period.

_____ 19. The addition of columns of figures in different ways to check the accuracy of the totals.

_____ 20. A form that contains basic employee information and a summary of payroll data for that employee for a calendar year.

PART III FILL IN THE BLANKS

Please complete each sentence with the correct word or words.

1. A(n) _____ is a person who agrees to perform and complete a specific job or task and is left to choose the ways and methods of doing so.

2. The Fair Labor Standards Act applies only to firms engaged in _____.

3. The amounts taken from an employee's wages or salary before he or she is paid are called _____.

4. FICA taxes are paid by both the _____ and the _____.

5. The federal government's main source of revenue is the _____.

6. A withholding allowance is also called a(n) _____.

7. Most employers use the _____ method to determine the amount of income tax to be withheld from employees' earnings.

8. Most states also require an employer to withhold _____ from the earnings of employees.

9. Net earnings is _____ minus _____.

10. In recording employee earnings and deductions, separate _____ should be maintained for the earnings and for each _____.

11. The _____ amount of payroll is debited to the Salaries Expense account.

12. Social security taxes deducted from the employees' pay are credited to the _____ and the _____ accounts.

13. The amount of _____ is credited to the Salaries Payable account.

PART IV MULTIPLE CHOICE

Please circle the correct answer.

1. An example of an independent contractor is
    a. a certified public accountant who does auditing and tax work for clients.
    b. a teacher.
    c. a receptionist.
    d. a factory production worker.

2. The number of paychecks received per year by a person who is paid semimonthly is
    a. 12.
    b. 24.
    c. 26.
    d. 52.

3. The federal income tax withheld from an employee's pay depends on three factors. These are
    a. gross earnings, marital status, and occupation.
    b. net pay, exemptions, and marital status.
    c. gross earnings, marital status, and exemptions.
    d. none of the above.

4. In order for an employer to withhold amounts other than required deductions from an employee's pay
   a. the union must give permission.
   b. the employee must give permission.
   c. the supervisor must give permission.
   d. the employer may not deduct anything other than taxes.

5. An individual earnings record must be maintained for each employee. This record shows
   a. the name, address, and social security number of the employee.
   b. the employee's gross earnings and deductions for each payroll period.
   c. the employee's year-to-date gross earnings and deductions.
   d. all of the above.

6. The Salaries Expense account is debited to record
   a. the total amount of net pay.
   b. the total amount of deductions.
   c. the total amount of gross earnings.
   d. none of the above.

7. The journal entry to record a payroll would include a debit to
   a. FICA Tax Payable—OASDI.
   b. Federal Income Tax Payable.
   c. Union Dues Payable.
   d. none of the above.

PART V WRITING/SHORT ANSWER

1. **Reflect** Make a list, in words or simple phrases, of the most important and meaningful points in this chapter.

2. **Question** Think about the most confusing points or the material you do not understand in this chapter. Write down two or three questions that remain unanswered.

3. **Connect** Explain, in one or two sentences, the connection between the main points of this chapter and the major goals of the entire course.

4. **Summarize** Review this chapter's Joining the Pieces visual summary and explain the concept(s) illustrated in a few sentences.

WORKING PAPERS

SKILLS REVIEW

EXERCISE 11-1

Bob Darby _____

_____

_____

Sam Jones _____

_____

_____

Joy Smith _____

_____

Ben White _____

_____

EXERCISE 11-2

Total Hours = _____

Regular Earnings = _____

Overtime Earnings = _____

Gross Earnings = _____

EXERCISE 11-3

	FICA	
Employee	**OASDI**	**HIP**
D. Mack	_____	_____
J. Caray	_____	_____
M. Slats	_____	_____
K. Sharp	_____	_____

EXERCISE 11-4

Employee	**Amount of Withholding**
(a)	_____
(b)	_____
(c)	_____
(d)	_____
(e)	_____

EXERCISE 11-5

Gross Earnings:

    Regular Earnings   _____

    Overtime Earnings   _____

       Gross Earnings   _____

Less Deductions:

   FICA—OASDI   _____

   FICA—HIP   _____

   Federal Income Tax _____

   Medical Insurance   _____

      Total Deductions   _____

Net Earnings   _____

EXERCISE 11-6

General Journal

Page 1

	Date		Account Title	P.R.	Debit	Credit	
1							1
2							2
3							3
4							4
5							5
6							6
7							7
8							8
9							9
10							10
11							11
12							12
13							13
14							14
15							15
16							16
17							17
18							18

PROBLEM 11-1A OR 11-1B

Employee	Regular Pay	Overtime Pay	Gross Earnings	FICA OASDI (6.2)	FICA HIP (1.45)	Fed. Inc. Tax	Net Pay	
H. Akn	320	48.00	368	22.82	5.34	21.00	318.84	
J. Bell	468.	—	468	29.02	6.79	54.00	378.19	
K. Dodd	350.	78.75	428.75	26.58	6.22	45.00	350.95	
B. Frank	375.25	—	375.25	23.27	5.44	7.00	339.54	
A. Gibbs	206.00	7.73	213.73	13.25	3.10	26.00	178.38	
T. Mawn	320.00	—	320.00	19.84	4.65	26.00	271.51	269.52
H. Ross	400.00	60.00	460.00	28.52	6.67	42.00	382.81	380.81

This page intentionally left blank.

PROBLEM 11-2A

1.

(Left side)

FOX FACTS PAYROLL REGISTER

Name	Status	Cumulative Earnings	Tot. Hrs.	Earnings Regular	Earnings Overtime	Earnings Total	Taxable Earnings Unemploy-ment	Taxable Earnings FICA OASDI	Taxable Earnings HIP
Allen, Robert	M-2	37 2 0 0 00	40	3 8 0 00		3 8 0 00			
Bowen, Clarence	M-1	52 0 0 0 00	40	4 2 5 00		4 2 5 00			
Carlson, Wally	M-2	21 3 0 0 00	45	2 4 0 00	4 5 00	2 8 5 00			
Goodman, Mary	S-1	31 6 0 0 00	42	3 2 0 00	2 4 00	3 4 4 00			
Heuy, Jim	S-0	3 8 0 0 00	25	1 2 5 00		1 2 5 00			
Jones, Stan	M-3	27 6 0 0 00	40	3 6 0 00		3 6 0 00			
Totals									

FOR WEEK ENDED DECEMBER 12, 20X3

(Right side)

DEDUCTIONS FICA OASDI	DEDUCTIONS FICA HIP	Federal Income Tax	State Income Tax	Medical Insurance	Savings Bonds	Union Dues	Total	PAYMENTS Net Amount	PAYMENTS Ck. #	EXPENSE ACCT. DEBITED Sales Salaries Expense	EXPENSE ACCT. DEBITED Office Salaries Expense
									201		3 8 0 00
									202		4 2 5 00
									203		2 8 5 00
									204	3 4 4 00	
									205		1 2 5 00
									206	3 6 0 00	

PROBLEM 11-2B

1.

(Left side)

NATHAN'S BONES PAYROLL REGISTER

Name	Status	Cumulative Earnings	Tot. Hrs.	EARNINGS			TAXABLE EARNINGS		
				Regular	Overtime	Total	Unemployment	FICA OASDI	FICA HIP
Alexander, Mary	S-1	18 3 5 0 00	40	2 8 0 00		2 8 0 00			
Burnett, Barbara	M-1	25 4 0 0 00	44	2 6 0 00	3 9 00	2 9 9 00			
Dye, Jan	M-2	36 4 2 0 00	40	3 9 0 00		3 9 0 00			
Gill, Lora	M-3	29 6 0 0 00	38	3 2 3 00		3 2 3 00			
Taylor, Glenn	S-0	27 5 1 0 00	43	3 5 0 00	3 9 38	3 8 9 38			
Zasada, Albert	M-2	17 3 0 0 00	40	2 7 0 00		2 7 0 00			
Totals									

FOR WEEK ENDED OCTOBER 15, 20X3

(Right side)

FICA OASDI	FICA HIP	Federal Income Tax	State Income Tax	DEDUCTIONS Medical Insurance	Savings Bonds	Union Dues	Total	PAYMENTS Ck. #	Net Amount	EXPENSE ACCT. DEBITED Sales Salaries Expense	Office Salaries Expense
								201		2 8 0 00	
								202		2 9 9 00	
								203		3 9 0 00	
								204			3 2 3 00
								205		3 8 9 38	
								206			2 7 0 00

PROBLEM 11-2A OR 11-2B (continued)

2., 3.

General Journal

Page 1

	Date	Account Title	P.R.	Debit	Credit	
1						1
2						2
3						3
4						4
5						5
6						6
7						7
8						8
9						9
10						10
11						11
12						12
13						13
14						14
15						15
16						16
17						17
18						18
19						19
20						20
21						21
22						22
23						23
24						24
25						25
26						26
27						27
28						28
29						29
30						30
31						31
32						32

This page intentionally left blank.

1.

(Left side)

Name	Status	Cumulative Earnings	Tot. Hrs.	EARNINGS			TAXABLE EARNINGS		
				Regular	Overtime	Total	Unemploy-ment	FICA OASDI	FICA HIP

(Right side)

DEDUCTIONS								PAYMENTS		EXPENSE ACCT. DEBITED	
FICA OASDI	FICA HIP	Federal Income Tax	State Income Tax	Medical Insurance	Savings Bonds	Union Dues	Total	Ck. #	Net Amount	Sales Salaries Expense	Office Salaries Expense

2.   **General Journal**   Page 1

	Date		Account Title	P.R.	Debit	Credit	
1							1
2							2
3							3
4							4
5							5
6							6
7							7
8							8
9							9
10							10
11							11
12							12
13							13
14							14
15							15
16							16
17							17
18							18
19							19
20							20
21							21
22							22
23							23
24							24
25							25
26							26
27							27
28							28
29							29
30							30
31							31
32							32

PROBLEM 11-4A OR 11-4B

1., 2.   **General Journal**   Page 1

	Date	Account Title	P.R.	Debit	Credit	
1	20X3 NOV 21					1
2		Sales Salaries Expense		845		2
3		Office Salaries Expense		1 1 90		3
4		FICA TAX Payable — OASDI			1 26 17	4
5		FICA TAX Payable — HI			29 51	5
6		Federal Income TAX Payable			2 06	6
7		State income TAX Payable			77 33	7
8		Medical insurance Payable			60	8
9		Salaries Payable			1 5 35 99	9
10						10
11						11
12						12
13	20X3 NOV 21	Salaries Payable		1 5 35 99		13
14		Cash			1 5 35 99	14
15		Payroll - NOV21				15
16						16
17						17
18						18
19						19
20						20
21						21
22						22
23						23
24						24
25						25
26						26
27						27
28						28
29						29
30						30
31						31
32						32

This page intentionally left blank.

CHALLENGE PROBLEMS

PROBLEM SOLVING

1. Weekly Salary   _____
   Commission on Total Sales   _____
   Bonus on Yearly Salary   _____
       Gross Earnings for Year   _____

2. Federal Income Tax on Salary   _____
   Federal Income Tax on Commission and Bonus   _____
       Total Federal Income Tax for Year   _____

3. FICA Tax
       OASDI   _____
       HIP   _____
       Total FICA Taxes for Year   _____

This page intentionally left blank.

COMMUNICATIONS

_____

_____

_____

_____

_____

_____

_____

_____

_____

_____

_____

_____

_____

_____

_____

_____

_____

_____

ETHICS

_____

_____

_____

_____

_____

_____

_____

_____

_____

_____

_____

_____

_____

_____

_____

_____

_____

_____

_____

This page intentionally left blank.

PRACTICE TEST ANSWERS

PART I

1. T
2. F
3. T
4. F
5. T
6. T
7. T
8. F
9. T
10. T
11. F
12. T
13. F
14. F
15. T

PART II

1. b
2. i
3. p
4. q
5. e
6. j
7. m
8. o
9. h
10. s
11. f
12. l
13. t
14. g
15. d
16. r
17. k
18. n
19. a
20. c

PART III

1. independent contractor
2. interstate commerce
3. payroll deductions
4. employee, employer
5. income tax
6. exemption
7. wage-bracket
8. state income taxes
9. gross earnings, deductions
10. accounts, deduction
11. gross
12. FICA Tax Payable—OASDI, FICA Tax Payable—HIP
13. net earnings

PART IV

1. a
2. b
3. c
4. b
5. d
6. c
7. d

PART V

Answers will vary. Please discuss questions with your instructor. You can also discuss issues related to this chapter by logging onto the Paradigm Accounting Web Site at www.emcp.com and clicking on the discussion section.

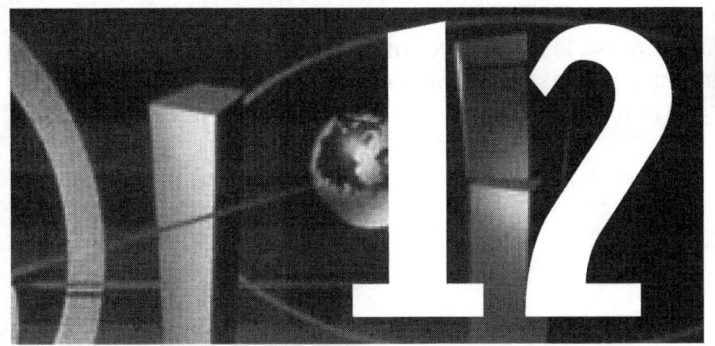

Accounting for Payroll—Employer Taxes and Reports

CHAPTER SUMMARY

Payroll taxes are not only a deduction from the gross earnings of employees. The employer has expenses for payroll taxes, as well as a responsibility to submit a variety of reports about these taxes. Just as individuals have social security numbers, all employers of at least one employee in this country must have an **employer identification number** (**EIN**). This number is listed on all payroll reports filed by the employer.

Employers are obligated to pay FICA tax, federal unemployment tax, and state unemployment tax. All three payroll taxes of the employer are debited to an operating expense account entitled **Payroll Tax Expense**. Each is credited to the appropriate liability account. The FICA Tax Payable—OASDI and FICA Tax Payable—HIP accounts are the same accounts used to record the amounts withheld from the employees' earnings. In fact, the employer must match the amounts that were deducted from employees' earnings for FICA tax. The **FUTA Tax Payable** and **SUTA Tax Payable accounts** are used to record liabilities for the two types of unemployment tax. When any tax or other deduction is paid to the government or appropriate party, the liability account is debited and the Cash account is credited.

The **Federal Unemployment Tax Act** (**FUTA**) requires the payment of taxes to the federal government to provide benefits for workers during periods of unemployment. This tax cannot be withheld from the pay of employees, as it is an expense of the employer. The current rate of the FUTA tax is 6.2% of the first $7,000 of wages paid to each employee during a calendar year. An employer can take a credit of 5.4% for timely contributions to state unemployment funds. This leaves an effective rate for federal unemployment tax of 0.8%.

The **State Unemployment Tax Act** (**SUTA**) requires payments to the state government to provide benefits to workers during periods of unemployment. The rate varies from employer to employer since a **merit-rating system** is used to reward employers with more stable employment.

All three taxes must be reported and paid on a regular basis. FICA and federal income taxes are reported on **Form 941—Employer's Quarterly Federal Tax Return** every three months. If the total of both taxes for the quarter is $500 or less, payment is sent in with Form 941. If the total exceeds $500, the taxes must be deposited in a Federal Reserve or other authorized bank on a monthly or semiweekly basis. The time period that applies depends on the **lookback period**, which is the twelve-month period ending on June 30 of the prior year. If total taxes for the lookback period were $50,000 or less, the employer becomes a monthly depositor this year. If total taxes for the lookback period were over $50,000, semiweekly deposits are made this year. Another time period applies to an employer that owes $100,000 or more per day—that amount must be deposited on the next day. When the taxes are deposited, **Federal Tax Deposit, Form 8109** is completed to accompany the deposit.

Federal unemployment taxes are remitted quarterly, so long as the amount to be deposited is $100 or more. Once a year, **Form 940—Employer's Annual Federal Unemployment Tax Return** is filed to summarize FUTA deposits for the year. State unemployment tax forms and payment guidelines vary from state to state.

Employers must also prepare an annual report to employees, **Form W-2 (Wage and Tax Statement)**, which must be in the hands of employees by January 31. This form summarizes that employee's earnings and deductions for the past year. The employer files **Form W-3 (Transmittal of Wage and Tax Statements)** annually to accompany the federal government's copies of all W-2 forms.

Most state governments require employers to carry **workers' compensation insurance** to provide protection for employees who suffer a job-related illness or injury. The employer usually pays the entire cost of this insurance. The Workers' Compensation Insurance Expense account is debited to record the estimated cost of the insurance. At the end of the year, the amount in the expense account is adjusted to the actual cost through an adjusting entry.

PRACTICE TEST

PART I TRUE/FALSE

Please circle the correct answer.

T   F   1. An EIN is assigned to both employers and employees.

T   F   2. The Payroll Tax Expense account is an operating expense account for a business.

T   F   3. The FICA tax paid by the employer is a different amount from the deduction made from the earnings of the employees.

T   F   4. The amount of federal income tax withheld from an employee's gross earnings must be matched by an equal contribution by the employer.

T   F   5. The rate for FUTA tax depends on the merit rating of the employer.

T   F   6. Employers are required to deposit income taxes withheld and FICA taxes at a bank when the amount is $500 or more for a quarter.

T   F   7. The lookback period for 2003 ends on June 30, 2002.

T   F   8. Employers report income taxes withheld and FICA taxes to the government quarterly on Form 941.

T   F   9. Both federal and state unemployment taxes are withheld from employees' salaries.

T   F   10. Form 940 is filed quarterly to report federal unemployment taxes.

T   F   11. Form W-2 summarizes the earnings and required deductions of an employee for the previous year.

T   F   12. The Workers' Compensation Expense account is adjusted annually for the exact amount of this expense.

PART II MATCHING

Please match each of the following terms with its definition.

a. employer identification number

b. Federal Unemployment Tax Act

c. Form 940

d. Form 941

e. Form 8109

f. Form W-2

g. Form W-3

h. FUTA Tax Payable

i. lookback period

j. merit-rating system

k. Payroll Tax Expense

l. State Unemployment Tax Act

m. SUTA Tax Payable

n. workers' compensation insurance

_____ 1. An identifying number each business with one or more employees must have.

_____ 2. The operating expense account that is debited for the payroll taxes of the employer.

_____ 3. The liability account that is credited to record the amount owed to the federal government for unemployment taxes.

_____ 4. The liability account that is credited to record the amount owed to the state government for unemployment taxes.

_____ 5. A law that requires employers to pay taxes to the federal government to assist unemployed workers.

_____ 6. A law that requires employers to pay taxes to the state governments to assist unemployed workers.

_____ 7. A system of assigning unemployment tax rates based on an employer's record of providing stable employment.

_____ 8. The Employer's Quarterly Federal Tax Return that summarizes the federal income taxes withheld and the employer's and employees' shares of the FICA tax due for the quarter.

_____ 9. The reference time to determine if the employer must make monthly, semiweekly, or next day deposits of taxes.

_____ 10. The form that accompanies any deposit of federal taxes by the employer.

_____ 11. The Employer's Annual Federal Unemployment Tax Return that must be filed by January 31 of each year.

_____ 12. A form given by the employer to the employee and to the IRS by January 31 of each year. It contains a summary of the employee's earnings for the past year and the amount of taxes withheld for that employee.

_____ 13. A form that accompanies the W-2 forms sent to the federal government.

_____ 14. Insurance that must be carried by an employer to provide benefits to employees for job-related illnesses or injuries.

PART III FILL IN THE BLANKS

Please complete each sentence with the correct word or words.

1. The employer must deduct FICA taxes from employees' earnings and pay a(n) _____ amount.

2. There are two FICA tax rates: _____ for OASDI and _____ for HIP.

3. State unemployment tax rates can vary for each employer under a _____ system.

4. Federal and state _____ taxes are paid only by employers.

5. To record the employer's payroll taxes, debit the _____ account and credit each tax liability account.

6. The next day deposit rule for federal income taxes withheld and FICA taxes applies when a firm accumulates a tax liability of _____ or more for that day.

7. Form 941 is used to report _____ taxes withheld and _____ taxes and is filed _____.

8. The employer must furnish each employee with a(n) _____ by January 31 of each year.

9. Form W-3 is sent to the _____ along with copies of the employees' W-2 forms.

10. If a credit is due for overestimated workers' compensation insurance, debit the Workers' Compensation Insurance _____ account.

PART IV MULTIPLE CHOICE

Please circle the correct answer.

1. The employer must pay three payroll taxes. They are
   a. FICA, FUTA, and SUTA.
   b. FICA, state income tax withholding, and federal income tax withholding.
   c. FICA, federal income tax withholding, and workers' compensation insurance.
   d. none of the above.

2. If an employer owes less than $500 for federal income taxes withheld and FICA taxes, the deposit must be made
   a. at the end of the quarter.
   b. at the end of the month.
   c. within 15 days after the end of the month.
   d. at the end of the year.

3. The lookback period for 2004 is
   a. January 1, 2003 to December 31, 2003.
   b. July 1, 2002 to June 30, 2003.
   c. July 1, 2003 to June 30, 2004.
   d. none of the above.

4. Form 941 must be filed by employers
   a. weekly.
   b. quarterly.
   c. annually.
   d. monthly.

5. Form 940 is an annual tax return used to report
   a. federal income taxes withheld.
   b. FICA taxes.
   c. federal unemployment taxes.
   d. state unemployment taxes.

6. A deposit of federal unemployment taxes must be made whenever
   a. the amount exceeds $100 for the quarter.
   b. the amount exceeds $500 at the end of the month.
   c. the amount exceeds $3,000 for the day.
   d. Form 940 is due.

7. By January 31 of each year, every employee must receive
   a. Form 8109.
   b. Form W-2.
   c. Form W-3.
   d. Form 941.

8. If the estimated premium for workers' compensation insurance is $750 and the actual expense is $755, the adjusting entry will include
   a. a debit to Workers' Compensation Insurance Payable for $5.
   b. a debit to Workers' Compensation Insurance Receivable for $5.
   c. a credit to Workers' Compensation Insurance Expense for $5.
   d. none of the above.

PART V WRITING/SHORT ANSWER

1. **Reflect** Make a list, in words or simple phrases, of the most important and meaningful points in this chapter.

2. **Question** Think about the most confusing points or the material you do not understand in this chapter. Write down two or three questions that remain unanswered.

3. **Connect** Explain, in one or two sentences, the connection between the main points of this chapter and the major goals of the entire course.

4. **Summarize** Review this chapter's Joining the Pieces visual summary and explain the concept(s) illustrated in a few sentences.

SKILLS REVIEW

EXERCISE 12-1

Employee	FICA Taxable Earnings		FUTA Taxable Earnings	SUTA Taxable Earnings
	OASDI	HIP		
Burns, Jim	_____	_____	_____	_____
Carrol, Helen	_____	_____	_____	_____
Harold, Barbara	_____	_____	_____	_____
Total Taxable Earnings	_____	_____	_____	_____
Rate	_____	_____	_____	_____
Total Tax Owed	_____	_____	_____	_____

EXERCISE 12-2

General Journal   Page 1

	Date	Account Title	P.R.	Debit	Credit	
1						1
2						2
3						3
4						4
5						5
6						6
7						7
8						8
9						9
10						10

EXERCISE 12-3

	FICA Taxable Earnings		FUTA Taxable Earnings	SUTA Taxable Earnings	
	OASDI	HIP			
	_____	_____	_____	_____	
Rate	_____	_____	_____	_____	
Total Tax Owed	_____	_____	_____	_____	_____

General Journal

Page 1

	Date	Account Title	P.R.	Debit	Credit	
1						1
2						2
3						3
4						4
5						5
6						6
7						7
8						8

EXERCISE 12-4

	FICA Taxable Earnings		FUTA Taxable Earnings	SUTA Taxable Earnings	
	OASDI	HIP			
	_____	_____	_____	_____	
Rate	_____	_____	_____	_____	
Total Tax Owed	_____	_____	_____	_____	_____

General Journal

Page 1

	Date	Account Title	P.R.	Debit	Credit	
1						1
2						2
3						3
4						4
5						5
6						6
7						7
8						8

EXERCISE 12-5

General Journal

Page 1

	Date		Account Title	P.R.		Debit		Credit		
1										1
2										2
3										3
4										4
5										5
6										6
7										7
8										8

EXERCISE 12-6

(a)

(b)

(c)

EXERCISE 12-7

General Journal

	Date		Account Title	P.R.	Debit	Credit	
1							1
2							2
3							3
4							4
5							5
6							6
7							7
8							8
9							9
10							10
11							11
12							12
13							13
14							14
15							15
16							16
17							17

PROBLEM 12-1A OR 12-1B

1. Pg 455

Employee	FICA Taxable Earnings		FUTA Taxable Earnings	SUTA Taxable Earnings
	OASDI	HIP		
B. CASSIDY	465.50	465.50	465.50	465.50
C. ERER	555.70	555.70	555.70	555.70
L. LEUNG	300.30	300.30	300.30	300.30
H. McMAHON	425.80	425.80	425.80	425.80
R. RAMIREZ	641.90	641.90	641.90	641.90
N. THOMAS	790.70	790.70	790.70	790.70
Total Taxable Earnings	3,179.95	3,179.95	3,179.95	3,179.95
Rate	6.2%	1.45%	0.8%	4.1%
Total Tax Owed	197.16	46.11	25.44	130.38

399.09

2.

General Journal

Page 1

	Date	Account Title	P.R.	Debit	Credit	
1	20X3 MARCH 10	Payroll Tax Expense		399 09		1
2		FICA Tax Payable - OASDI			197 16	2
3		FICA Tax Payable - HI			46 11	3
4		FUTA Tax Payable			25 44	4
5		SUTA Tax Payable			130 38	5
6		Recorded Employer's Payroll Taxes				6
7						7
8						8
9						9
10						10

This page intentionally left blank.

PROBLEM 12-2A OR 12-2B

1.

Month	FICA Taxable Earnings		FUTA Taxable Earnings	SUTA Taxable Earnings	
	OASDI	HIP			
_____	_____	_____	_____	_____	
Rate	_____	_____	_____	_____	
Total Tax Owed	_____	_____	_____	_____	_____
_____	_____	_____	_____	_____	
Rate	_____	_____	_____	_____	
Total Tax Owed	_____	_____	_____	_____	_____
_____	_____	_____	_____	_____	
Rate	_____	_____	_____	_____	
Total Tax Owed	_____	_____	_____	_____	_____

2., 3., 4.   **General Journal**   Page 1

	Date	Account Title	P.R.	Debit	Credit	
1						1
2						2
3						3
4						4
5						5
6						6
7						7
8						8
9						9
10						10
11						11
12						12
13						13
14						14
15						15
16						16
17						17
18						18
19						19
20						20
21						21
22						22
23						23
24						24
25						25
26						26
27						27
28						28
29						29
30						30
31						31
32						32

PROBLEM 12-3A OR 12-3B

2.

General Journal

	Date		Account Title	P.R.	Debit	Credit	
1							1
2							2
3							3
4							4
5							5
6							6
7							7
8							8
9							9
10							10
11							11
12							12
13							13
14							14
15							15
16							16
17							17
18							18
19							19
20							20
21							21
22							22
23							23
24							24
25							25
26							26
27							27
28							28
29							29
30							30
31							31
32							32

General Journal

	Date	Account Title	P.R.	Debit	Credit	
1						1
2						2
3						3
4						4
5						5
6						6
7						7
8						8
9						9
10						10
11						11
12						12
13						13
14						14
15						15
16						16
17						17
18						18
19						19
20						20
21						21
22						22
23						23
24						24
25						25
26						26
27						27
28						28
29						29
30						30
31						31
32						32

PROBLEM 12-3A OR 12-3B (continued)

1., 2.

ACCOUNT FICA Tax Payable—OASDI   ACCOUNT NO. 215

DATE	ITEM	P.R.	DEBIT	CREDIT	BALANCE DEBIT	BALANCE CREDIT

ACCOUNT FICA Tax Payable—HIP   ACCOUNT NO. 216

DATE	ITEM	P.R.	DEBIT	CREDIT	BALANCE DEBIT	BALANCE CREDIT

ACCOUNT Federal Income Tax Payable   ACCOUNT NO. 217

DATE	ITEM	P.R.	DEBIT	CREDIT	BALANCE DEBIT	BALANCE CREDIT

ACCOUNT State Income Tax Payable   ACCOUNT NO. 218

DATE	ITEM	P.R.	DEBIT	CREDIT	BALANCE DEBIT	BALANCE CREDIT

PROBLEM 12-3A OR 12-3B (continued)

ACCOUNT FUTA Tax Payable ACCOUNT NO. 219

DATE	ITEM	P.R.	DEBIT	CREDIT	BALANCE DEBIT	BALANCE CREDIT

ACCOUNT SUTA Tax Payable ACCOUNT NO. 220

DATE	ITEM	P.R.	DEBIT	CREDIT	BALANCE DEBIT	BALANCE CREDIT

ACCOUNT Union Dues Payable ACCOUNT NO. 221

DATE	ITEM	P.R.	DEBIT	CREDIT	BALANCE DEBIT	BALANCE CREDIT

ACCOUNT Payroll Tax Expense ACCOUNT NO. 551

DATE	ITEM	P.R.	DEBIT	CREDIT	BALANCE DEBIT	BALANCE CREDIT

PROBLEM 12-4A OR 12-4B

(a)

(c)

(d)

General Journal

		Date	Account Title	P.R.	Debit	Credit	
(b)	1						1
	2						2
	3						3
	4						4
	5						5
	6						6
(c)	7						7
	8						8
	9						9
	10						10
	11						11
(d)	12						12
	13						13
	14						14
	15						15
	16						16

This page intentionally left blank.

CHALLENGE PROBLEMS

PROBLEM SOLVING

Month	FICA Taxable Earnings		FUTA Taxable Earnings	SUTA Taxable Earnings
	OASDI	HIP		
January	_____	_____	_____	_____
Rate	_____	_____	_____	_____
Total Tax Owed	_____	_____	_____	_____
February	_____	_____	_____	_____
Rate	_____	_____	_____	_____
Total Tax Owed	_____	_____	_____	_____
March	_____	_____	_____	_____
Rate	_____	_____	_____	_____
Total Tax Owed	_____	_____	_____	_____
April	_____	_____	_____	_____
Rate	_____	_____	_____	_____
Total Tax Owed	_____	_____	_____	_____
May	_____	_____	_____	_____
Rate	_____	_____	_____	_____
Total Tax Owed	_____	_____	_____	_____
June	_____	_____	_____	_____
Rate	_____	_____	_____	_____
Total Tax Owed	_____	_____	_____	_____

Month	FICA Taxable Earnings		FUTA Taxable Earnings	SUTA Taxable Earnings
	OASDI	HIP		
July	_____	_____	_____	_____
Rate	_____	_____	_____	_____
Total Tax Owed	_____	_____	_____	_____
August	_____	_____	_____	_____
Rate	_____	_____	_____	_____
Total Tax Owed	_____	_____	_____	_____
September	_____	_____	_____	_____
Rate	_____	_____	_____	_____
Total Tax Owed	_____	_____	_____	_____
October	_____	_____	_____	_____
Rate	_____	_____	_____	_____
Total Tax Owed	_____	_____	_____	_____
November	_____	_____	_____	_____
Rate	_____	_____	_____	_____
Total Tax Owed	_____	_____	_____	_____
December	_____	_____	_____	_____
Rate	_____	_____	_____	_____
Total Tax Owed	_____	_____	_____	_____

PROBLEM SOLVING (continued)

General Journal

Page 1

	Date		Account Title	P.R.	Debit	Credit	
1							1
2							2
3							3
4							4
5							5
6							6
7							7
8							8
9							9
10							10
11							11
12							12
13							13
14							14
15							15
16							16
17							17
18							18
19							19
20							20
21							21
22							22
23							23
24							24
25							25
26							26
27							27
28							28
29							29
30							30
31							31
32							32

This page intentionally left blank.

COMMUNICATIONS

_____

_____

_____

_____

_____

_____

_____

_____

_____

_____

_____

_____

_____

_____

_____

_____

_____

_____

ETHICS

_____

_____

_____

_____

_____

_____

_____

_____

_____

_____

_____

_____

_____

_____

_____

_____

_____

_____

_____

_____

This page intentionally left blank.

PRACTICE TEST ANSWERS

PART I

1. F
2. T
3. F
4. F
5. F
6. T
7. T
8. T
9. F
10. F
11. T
12. T

PART II

1. a
2. k
3. h
4. m
5. b
6. l
7. j
8. d
9. i
10. e
11. c
12. f
13. g
14. n

PART III

1. matching
2. 6.2%, 1.45%
3. merit-rating
4. unemployment
5. Payroll Tax Expense
6. $100,000
7. federal income, FICA, quarterly
8. W-2 form
9. federal government
10. Receivable

PART IV

1. a
2. a
3. b
4. b
5. c
6. a
7. b
8. d

PART V

Answers will vary. Please discuss questions with your instructor. You can also discuss issues related to this chapter by logging onto the Paradigm Accounting Web Site at www.emcp.com and clicking on the discussion section.

WORKING PAPERS

(Left side)

CARLSON COMPANY PAYROLL REGISTER

Name	Status	Cumulative Earnings	Tot. Hrs.	EARNINGS Regular	EARNINGS Overtime	EARNINGS Total	TAXABLE EARNINGS Unemployment	TAXABLE EARNINGS FICA OASDI	TAXABLE EARNINGS FICA HIP

(Right side)

FOR WEEK ENDED _____

DEDUCTIONS FICA OASDI	DEDUCTIONS FICA HIP	Federal Income Tax	State Income Tax	Medical Insurance	Savings Bonds	Union Dues	Total	PAYMENTS Ck. #	PAYMENTS Net Amount	EXPENSE ACCT. DEBITED Sales Salaries Expense	EXPENSE ACCT. DEBITED Office Salaries Expense

(Left side)

CARLSON COMPANY PAYROLL REGISTER

Name	Status	Cumulative Earnings	Tot. Hrs.	EARNINGS			TAXABLE EARNINGS	FICA	
				Regular	Overtime	Total	Unemployment	OASDI	HI

FOR WEEK ENDED _____

DEDUCTIONS							PAYMENTS		EXPENSE ACCT. DEBITED	
FICA		Federal Income Tax	State Income Tax	Medical Insurance	Savings Bonds	Union Dues	Total	Ck. #	Net Amount	Sales Salaries Expense	Office Salaries Expense
OASDI	HI										

(Right side)

	Date		Account Title	P.R.	Debit	Credit	
1							1
2							2
3							3
4							4
5							5
6							6
7							7
8							8
9							9
10							10
11							11
12							12
13							13
14							14
15							15
16							16
17							17
18							18
19							19
20							20
21							21
22							22
23							23
24							24
25							25
26							26
27							27
28							28
29							29
30							30
31							31
32							32

	Date		Account Title	P.R.	Debit	Credit	
1							1
2							2
3							3
4							4
5							5
6							6
7							7
8							8
9							9
10							10
11							11
12							12
13							13
14							14
15							15
16							16
17							17
18							18
19							19
20							20
21							21
22							22
23							23
24							24
25							25
26							26
27							27
28							28
29							29
30							30
31							31
32							32

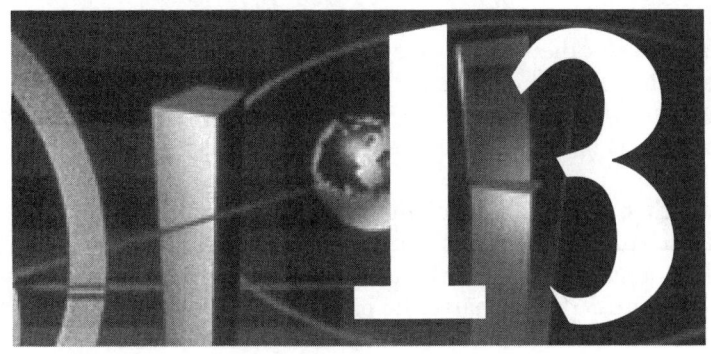

13 Accounting for Notes and Interest

CHAPTER SUMMARY

Most transactions in our country involve the use of credit. **Credit** can be defined as providing cash, goods, or services in the present, with payment expected in the future. Some credit transactions are on an open account basis. That is, they are not evidenced by a formal, written promise to pay but, instead, by an oral promise or a signature on an invoice or receipt. There are some situations in which open credit is not sufficient. For example, when someone is borrowing money or purchasing long-term assets on credit, the lender usually asks for a formal, written promise. A **promissory note** is a written promise to pay a sum of money at a definite time in the future. Promissory notes are frequently referred to simply as **notes**. The sum of money written on the note is its **principal**, or **face value**. The writer of the note is the **maker**. The party to whom it is payable is the **payee**. A note can be transferred by **endorsement** of the payee, making it **negotiable**.

The **due date** of a note is found by counting ahead the number of days expressed in the time of the note. If the time of a note is expressed as a specified number of months, the due date is found by counting ahead the number of months stated. For example, a two-month note dated October 1 will be due on December 1.

Interest on a note can be calculated in various ways. The basic way follows the formula:

$$\text{Interest} = \text{Principal} \times \text{Rate} \times \text{Time or I = PRT}$$

The factors in the formula can be written as fractions to simplify the calculation. For example, the interest on a $600, 90-day, 12% note can be determined as follows:

$$\frac{600}{1} \times \frac{12}{100} \times \frac{90}{360} = \$18$$

The fraction for the **rate** is expressed with a denominator of 100 because percent means per hundred. The **time** is expressed as a fractional part of a 360-day year, which is referred to as the **banker's year** or the **commercial year**.

There are various situations in which notes may be issued. For example, a note may be issued to obtain an extension of time to pay an account payable (called **issuing a note on account**), or to purchase merchandise or other assets, or to borrow cash. When a note is repaid, there is usually an interest charge. The interest charge is debited to the Interest Expense account, which is classified as a **nonoperating expense**. That is, it is an expense of credit, not of operating the business. Interest expense is listed on the income statement under the category "Other Expenses." Some notes are **noninterest-bearing**.

When money is borrowed, some banks deduct the interest in advance. This procedure is referred to as **discounting a note payable**. The amount actually received by the borrower is referred to as the **proceeds**. At maturity, the borrower repays the principal since the interest has already been deducted.

A note receivable is an asset to a business. Just as there are various reasons for issuing notes payable, there are various reasons for accepting notes receivable. It can be said that entries for notes receivable and interest income are the mirror images of entries for notes payable and interest expense. That is, for the person or firm who issues a note payable, there is a person or firm who receives a note receivable. Interest expense paid by a person or firm is interest income to the person or firm who receives payment.

Common situations in which notes are accepted are: (1) when charge customers need additional time to make payments on account, (2) when merchandise—or other assets—are sold to customers who do not have an established line of credit, and (3) when cash is loaned to customers, employees, or others.

Interest income is classified as **nonoperating revenue**—that is, income received from sources other than the normal operations of the business. Interest income is listed on the income statement under the category "Other Income."

On occasion, a note is not paid at maturity. A note that is not paid when due is said to be **dishonored**. The proper accounting treatment of a dishonored note is to transfer the **maturity value** of the note into the Accounts Receivable account. At collection, the amount is then removed from the Accounts Receivable account. The holder of a dishonored note can still charge the payee interest for the time it is unpaid, but in this case the interest is charged on the maturity value rather than on the original principal.

One of the advantages of a note receivable is that if money is needed before the maturity date of the note, the note can be discounted (transferred) to a bank or finance company. In discounting a note, the bank (or finance company) deducts a charge—the **bank discount**—from the maturity value of the note. The difference—the proceeds—is the actual amount received by the person or firm who is discounting the note. The person or firm discounting a note must endorse the note, which transfers ownership of the note to the bank (or finance company) and renders the endorser liable to make full payment at maturity if the maker defaults, including a possible **protest fee**. Thus, the endorser incurs a **contingent liability** on notes discounted for the length of the **discount period** (or **term of discount**). A contingent liability is a potential liability that may become a definite liability if certain events or conditions take place.

To disclose the contingent liability, a business should show discounted notes receivable in a footnote to the balance sheet. This follows the **adequate disclosure principle**, which states that financial statements or their accompanying notes and schedules should disclose all relevant data that relate to the financial position of a business.

PRACTICE TEST

PART I TRUE/FALSE

Please circle the correct answer.

T F   1. Credit can be defined as providing cash, goods, or services in the present, with payment expected in the future.

T F   2. A formal, written promise to pay is an account receivable.

T F   3. A promissory note is a negotiable instrument.

T F   4. A note payable is always a long-term liability.

T F   5. Interest rates are normally expressed on an annual basis.

T F   6. A common reason for a note to be issued is to obtain an extension of time to pay an account payable.

T F   7. If a note is given for an extension of time to pay an account payable, the transaction is referred to as issuing a note on account.

T F   8. The maturity value of a note is the same as the principal.

T F   9. Discounting a note payable means that the lender of the money gives the borrower a discount on the note.

T F 10. Interest on notes receivable is computed by the same formula as interest on notes payable.

T F 11. One advantage of a note receivable is that it is negotiable; it can be exchanged for cash or other assets.

T F 12. The usual practice is to keep subsidiary ledgers for notes receivable and notes payable just as for accounts receivable and accounts payable.

T F 13. Interest expense is an example of an operating expense.

T F 14. Discounting a note receivable creates a contingent liability for the endorser.

T F 15. A dishonored note receivable should be left on the books as a note receivable while collection proceedings are underway.

PART II MATCHING

Please match each of the following terms with its definition.

a. adequate disclosure principle
b. bank discount
c. banker's year
d. contingent liability
e. credit
f. discount period
g. discounting a note payable
h. dishonoring a note
i. interest
j. issuing a note on account

k. maker
l. maturity value
m. negotiable instrument
n. open account
o. payee
p. principal
q. proceeds
r. promissory note
s. protest fee

_____ 1. The person or firm who will be paid when a note reaches its maturity date.

_____ 2. The person or firm who issues a note.

_____ 3. A 360-day year that is used by many companies and financial institutions for convenience in calculating interest on notes.

_____ 4. The amount of principal plus the amount of interest of a note.

_____ 5. Providing cash, goods, or services in the present, with payment expected in the future.

_____ 6. A written promise to pay a sum of money at a definite time in the future.

_____ 7. Giving a note to a creditor for an extension of time to pay an invoice.

_____ 8. The amount borrowed or the amount of credit extended.

_____ 9. Borrowing from a bank when the bank deducts the amount of interest from the principal of the loan at the time of borrowing.

_____ 10. The charge for credit.

_____ 11. An instrument, such as a note or a check, that is capable of being endorsed and exchanged for cash or other assets.

_____ 12. The amount of the principal of a note minus the amount of interest owed.

_____ 13. Interest deducted in advance by a bank.

_____ 14. The accounting principle that states that the financial statements should disclose all relevant data that relate to the financial position of a business.

_____ 15. Fee charged by a bank when a note is dishonored.

_____ 16. Failing to pay a note at maturity.

_____ 17. A form of credit that is based on an oral promise to pay or a signature on an invoice or receipt.

_____ 18. The length of time that a bank holds a note that was discounted; the time from the date the note was discounted until the due date.

_____ 19. A potential liability that may become a definite liability.

PART III FILL IN THE BLANKS

Please complete each sentence with the correct word or words.

1. Credit may be granted on a(n) _____ basis with payment usually due within 30 days.

2. A(n) _____ is a formal, written promise to pay; the words "pay to the order of" make it a(n) _____.

3. The due date of a note is determined by counting from the day _____ the note is issued.

4. If the life of a note is stated in months, the due date is determined by counting ahead that number of _____.

5. The formula for computing interest is: _____ equals _____ times _____ times _____.

6. A note payable is a(n) _____.

7. Interest expense is a(n) _____ expense.

8. The maturity value of a note is the _____ plus the _____.

9. For a discounted note payable, the principal of the note is also its _____ value.

10. Interest income is _____ revenue.

11. An advantage of a note receivable is that it is a(n) _____, written promise to pay.

12. Renewing a note at maturity is sometimes referred to as _____ a note.

13. A discounted note receivable creates a(n) _____ liability for the endorser of the note.

14. The _____ principle requires businesses to reveal contingent liabilities on their financial statements.

PART IV MULTIPLE CHOICE

Please circle the correct answer.

1. A promissory note includes which of the following pieces of information?
   a. date, time, name of payee
   b. principal
   c. due date, name of maker
   d. all of the above

2. A 60-day note dated March 15 is due
   a. May 13.
   b. May 14.
   c. May 15.
   d. May 16.

3. Interest on a 60-day, 12% note for $1,200 is
   a. $24.
   b. $240.
   c. $120.
   d. $12.

4. Interest on a 2-year, 10% note for $5,000 is
   a. $50.
   b. $500.
   c. $100.
   d. $1,000.

5. A common reason to issue a note payable is
   a. to obtain an extension of time to pay an account payable.
   b. to purchase merchandise or other property.
   c. to borrow money.
   d. all of the above.

6. When a note is accepted in settlement of an account receivable,
   a. Notes Receivable is debited and Accounts Receivable is credited.
   b. Accounts Receivable is debited and Notes Receivable is credited.
   c. Notes Receivable is debited, Accounts Receivable is credited, and Interest Income is credited.
   d. Notes Receivable is debited, Interest Expense is debited, and Accounts Receivable is credited.

7. When a note is given in settlement of an account payable,
   a. Notes Payable is debited and Accounts Payable is credited.
   b. Accounts Payable is debited and Notes Payable is credited.
   c. Accounts Payable is debited, Interest Expense is debited, and Notes Payable is credited.
   d. Notes Payable is debited, Interest Expense is debited, and Accounts Payable is credited.

8. When a note payable is discounted at the bank,
   a. the interest is added to the principal of the note and paid at maturity.
   b. the interest is deducted from the principal of the note and the borrower gets only the proceeds.
   c. the borrower pays only the proceeds when the note comes due because the interest has been paid already.
   d. none of the above.

9. Interest income is usually shown on the income statement as
   a. revenue from sales.
   b. operating expense.
   c. other income.
   d. other expense.

10. When an interest-bearing note receivable is dishonored, it should be recorded as
    a. a debit to Notes Receivable, a credit to Accounts Receivable, and a credit to Interest Income.
    b. a debit to Accounts Receivable, a credit to Notes Receivable, and a credit to Interest Income.
    c. a debit to Accounts Receivable and a credit to Notes Receivable.
    d. no entry should be made.

PART V WRITING/SHORT ANSWER

1. **Reflect** Make a list, in words or simple phrases, of the most important and meaningful points in this chapter.

2. **Question** Think about the most confusing points or the material you do not understand in this chapter. Write down two or three questions that remain unanswered.

3. **Connect** Explain, in one or two sentences, the connection between the main points of this chapter and the major goals of the entire course.

4. **Summarize** Review this chapter's Joining the Pieces visual summary and explain the concept(s) illustrated in a few sentences.

WORKING PAPERS

SKILLS REVIEW

EXERCISE 13-1

(a) _____

(b) _____

(c) _____

(d) _____

(e) _____

(f) _____

EXERCISE 13-2

(a) _____

(b) _____

(c) _____

(d) _____

(e) _____

(f) _____

General Journal

	Date		Account Title	P.R.	Debit	Credit	
1							1
2							2
3							3
4							4
5							5
6							6
7							7
8							8
9							9
10							10
11							11
12							12
13							13
14							14
15							15
16							16
17							17
18							18
19							19
20							20
21							21
22							22
23							23
24							24
25							25
26							26
27							27
28							28
29							29
30							30
31							31
32							32

EXERCISE 13-4

	Date	Account Title	P.R.	Debit	Credit	
1						1
2						2
3						3
4						4
5						5
6						6
7						7
8						8
9						9
10						10
11						11
12						12
13						13
14						14
15						15
16						16
17						17
18						18
19						19
20						20
21						21
22						22
23						23
24						24
25						25
26						26
27						27
28						28
29						29
30						30
31						31
32						32

EXERCISE 13-5

	Maturity Value	Discount	Proceeds
(a)	_____	_____	_____
(b)	_____	_____	_____
(c)	_____	_____	_____
(d)	_____	_____	_____

EXERCISE 13-6

General Journal

Page 1

	Date	Account Title	P.R.	Debit	Credit	
1						1
2						2
3						3
4						4
5						5
6						6
7						7
8						8
9						9
10						10
11						11
12						12

EXERCISE 13-7

	Date	Account Title	P.R.	Debit	Credit	
1						1
2						2
3						3
4						4
5						5
6						6
7						7
8						8
9						9
10						10
11						11
12						12
13						13
14						14
15						15
16						16
17						17
18						18
19						19
20						20
21						21
22						22
23						23
24						24
25						25
26						26
27						27
28						28
29						29
30						30
31						31
32						32

This page intentionally left blank.

PROBLEM 13-1A OR 13-1B

General Journal

Page 1

	Date	Account Title	P.R.	Debit	Credit	
1						1
2						2
3						3
4						4
5						5
6						6
7						7
8						8
9						9
10						10
11						11
12						12
13						13
14						14
15						15
16						16
17						17
18						18
19						19
20						20
21						21
22						22
23						23
24						24
25						25
26						26
27						27
28						28
29						29
30						30
31						31
32						32

General Journal

	Date	Account Title	P.R.	Debit	Credit	
1						1
2						2
3						3
4						4
5						5
6						6
7						7
8						8
9						9
10						10
11						11
12						12
13						13
14						14
15						15
16						16
17						17
18						18
19						19
20						20
21						21
22						22
23						23
24						24
25						25
26						26
27						27
28						28
29						29
30						30
31						31
32						32

General Journal

	Date		Account Title	P.R.	Debit	Credit	
1							1
2							2
3							3
4							4
5							5
6							6
7							7
8							8
9							9
10							10
11							11
12							12
13							13
14							14
15							15
16							16
17							17
18							18
19							19
20							20
21							21
22							22
23							23
24							24
25							25
26							26
27							27
28							28
29							29
30							30
31							31
32							32

This page intentionally left blank.

PROBLEM 13-3A OR 13-3B

General Journal

Page 1

	Date	Account Title	P.R.	Debit	Credit	
1						1
2						2
3						3
4						4
5						5
6						6
7						7
8						8
9						9
10						10
11						11
12						12
13						13
14						14
15						15
16						16
17						17
18						18
19						19
20						20
21						21
22						22
23						23
24						24
25						25
26						26
27						27
28						28
29						29
30						30
31						31
32						32

This page intentionally left blank.

General Journal

	Date	Account Title	P.R.	Debit	Credit	
1						1
2						2
3						3
4						4
5						5
6						6
7						7
8						8
9						9
10						10
11						11
12						12
13						13
14						14
15						15
16						16
17						17
18						18
19						19
20						20
21						21
22						22
23						23
24						24
25						25
26						26
27						27
28						28
29						29
30						30
31						31
32						32

General Journal

	Date	Account Title	P.R.	Debit	Credit	
1						1
2						2
3						3
4						4
5						5
6						6
7						7
8						8
9						9
10						10
11						11
12						12
13						13
14						14
15						15
16						16
17						17
18						18
19						19
20						20
21						21
22						22
23						23
24						24
25						25
26						26
27						27
28						28
29						29
30						30
31						31
32						32

PROBLEM 13-5A OR 13-5B

1.

General Journal

	Date	Account Title	P.R.	Debit	Credit	
1						1
2						2
3						3
4						4
5						5
6						6
7						7
8						8
9						9
10						10
11						11
12						12
13						13
14						14
15						15
16						16
17						17
18						18
19						19
20						20
21						21
22						22
23						23
24						24
25						25
26						26
27						27
28						28
29						29
30						30
31						31
32						32

General Journal

	Date	Account Title	P.R.	Debit	Credit	
1						1
2						2
3						3
4						4
5						5
6						6
7						7
8						8
9						9
10						10
11						11
12						12
13						13
14						14
15						15
16						16
17						17
18						18
19						19
20						20
21						21
22						22
23						23
24						24
25						25
26						26
27						27
28						28
29						29
30						30
31						31
32						32

2.   **General Ledger**

ACCOUNT Accounts Receivable   ACCOUNT NO. 112

DATE	ITEM	P.R.	DEBIT	CREDIT	BALANCE DEBIT	BALANCE CREDIT

ACCOUNT Notes Receivable   ACCOUNT NO. 113

DATE	ITEM	P.R.	DEBIT	CREDIT	BALANCE DEBIT	BALANCE CREDIT

Accounts Receivable Ledger

NAME   S. Brown

ADDRESS

	Date	Item	P.R.	Debit	Credit	Balance

NAME   A. Pierce

ADDRESS

	Date	Item	P.R.	Debit	Credit	Balance

NAME   J. Smith

ADDRESS

	Date	Item	P.R.	Debit	Credit	Balance

PROBLEM 13-5A OR 13-5B (continued)

3.

This page intentionally left blank.

PROBLEM SOLVING

1. Seller's books (Dalton Co.)

General Journal

Page 1

	Date		Account Title	P.R.	Debit	Credit	
1							1
2							2
3							3
4							4
5							5
6							6
7							7
8							8
9							9
10							10
11							11
12							12
13							13
14							14
15							15
16							16
17							17
18							18
19							19
20							20
21							21
22							22
23							23
24							24
25							25
26							26
27							27
28							28
29							29
30							30
31							31
32							32

Buyer's books (Billings Co.)   **General Journal**   Page 1

	Date	Account Title	P.R.	Debit	Credit	
1						1
2						2
3						3
4						4
5						5
6						6
7						7
8						8
9						9
10						10
11						11
12						12
13						13
14						14
15						15
16						16
17						17
18						18
19						19
20						20
21						21
22						22
23						23
24						24
25						25
26						26
27						27
28						28
29						29
30						30
31						31
32						32

PROBLEM SOLVING (continued)

2.

(a) _____

(b) _____

(c) _____

This page intentionally left blank.

COMMUNICATIONS

_____

_____

_____

_____

_____

_____

_____

_____

_____

_____

_____

_____

_____

_____

_____

_____

_____

ETHICS

_____

_____

_____

_____

_____

_____

_____

_____

_____

_____

_____

_____

_____

_____

_____

_____

_____

_____

This page intentionally left blank.

PRACTICE TEST ANSWERS

PART I

1. T
2. F
3. T
4. F
5. T
6. T
7. T
8. F
9. F
10. T
11. T
12. F
13. F
14. T
15. F

PART II

1. o
2. k
3. c
4. l
5. e
6. r
7. j
8. p
9. g
10. i
11. m
12. q
13. b
14. a
15. s
16. h
17. n
18. f
19. d

PART III

1. open account
2. promissory note, negotiable instrument
3. after
4. months
5. interest, principal, rate, time
6. liability
7. nonoperating
8. principal, interest
9. maturity
10. nonoperating
11. formal
12. rolling over
13. contingent
14. adequate disclosure

PART IV

1. d
2. b
3. a
4. d
5. d
6. a
7. b
8. b
9. c
10. b

PART V

Answers will vary. Please discuss questions with your instructor. You can also discuss issues related to this chapter by logging onto the Paradigm Accounting Web Site at www.emcp.com and clicking on the discussion section.

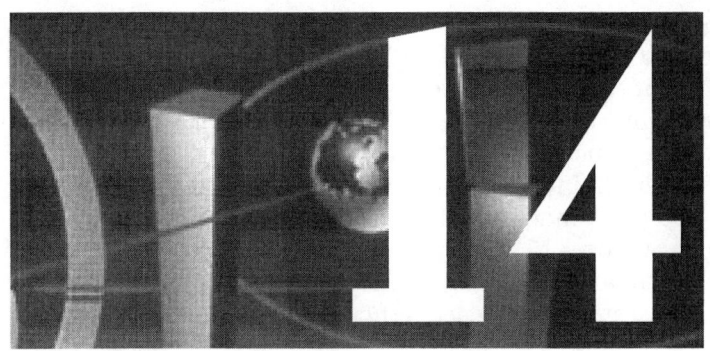

Accounting for Bad Debts

CHAPTER SUMMARY

No matter how closely customers are screened for credit, there will be a few accounts that cannot be collected. An account that cannot be collected is referred to as a **bad debt** or an **uncollectible account**. There are two methods commonly used to account for bad debts: the **direct write-off method** and the **allowance method**. Under the direct write-off method, no entry is made to anticipate the amount of bad debts. All receivables are assumed to be good until one proves to be uncollectible. When an account is believed to be uncollectible, an entry is made to transfer the balance of the account directly into an expense account. The expense account used to record bad debts is called Bad Debts Expense.

On occasion, accounts that were previously written off will be collected. Under the direct write-off method, an entry is made to reverse the write-off. This entry involves a debit to the Accounts Receivable account and the customer's subsidiary ledger account and a credit to the Bad Debts Expense account. The effect of this entry is to **reinstate** the customer's account. An entry is then made to debit the Cash account and credit the Accounts Receivable account and the customer's account. If recovery occurs after the accounting period has ended, an adjustment cannot be made to the Bad Debts Expense account. Instead, an account entitled Recovery of Bad Debts is credited.

The direct write-off method is more suited to the needs of smaller businesses that do not get a major portion of their revenue from credit sales. For businesses with a large amount of credit sales, the direct write-off method could result in an improper matching of revenue and expenses. For example, if a credit sale made in one period proves to be uncollectible in a later period, it is written off in that period. Thus, the direct write-off method could result in a credit sale being recorded in one period and a bad debt associated with that sale being recorded in another period.

To overcome the matching problem associated with the direct write-off method, many businesses use the allowance method. In the allowance method, an advance estimate is made of the amount of bad debts expected for the period. This estimate is made at the end of an accounting period and is recorded as part of the adjusting process.

The adjusting entry to record an estimate of bad debts involves a debit to the Bad Debts Expense account and a credit to a contra asset account entitled Allowance for Doubtful Accounts. The debit part of this entry results in losses from bad debts being recorded in the same period in which related credit sales were recorded. Thus, the allowance method meets the requirements of the **matching principle**.

It is not possible to credit the Accounts Receivable account *directly* when making an adjustment for bad debts because the Accounts Receivable account is a controlling account and a credit would require a posting to an individual customer's account in the accounts receivable ledger. Since it is not possible to know in advance those who will fail to pay their accounts, the credit part of the adjustment is made to the contra-asset account. The balance of the Accounts Receivable account is presented on the balance sheet minus the balance of the Allowance for Doubtful Accounts account. The difference between the Accounts Receivable account and the Allowance for Doubtful Accounts account is called the **net receivables** or the **net realizable value** of the accounts receivable.

When an account actually proves to be uncollectible under the allowance method, an entry is made to debit the allowance account and credit the Accounts Receivable account and the customer's subsidiary ledger account. Since the bad debt had been "allowed for" and the expense recorded at the end of the period in which the credit sale to the customer was recorded, it is not necessary to debit the Bad Debts Expense account again.

There are two methods commonly used to arrive at an estimate of bad debts: the percent of sales method and the aging the receivables method. The **percent of sales method** (called the **income statement approach**) calls for estimating a percent of credit sales that will not be collected. The percent used is usually based on past experience and personal judgment of the individuals involved. The percent of sales method is easy to apply and achieves the matching principle.

Aging the receivables (called the **balance sheet approach**) involves classifying each customer's balance by age and estimating a percent of each age group that cannot be collected. The age category of accounts in the **aging schedule** ranges from "not yet due" to "over 12 months past due." The older an account, the less likely it can be collected. Thus, accounts more than a year old may have a collection rate of no better than 20% to 25%. The estimates for all age groups are added to find the total amount estimated to be uncollectible for the period.

When the amount of the estimate for bad debts is determined by the income statement approach, any previous balance in the Allowance for Doubtful Accounts account is ignored. On the other hand, the balance sheet approach emphasizes the net realizable value of the accounts receivable. Therefore, when making a current adjustment, any balance in the allowance account must be considered.

When a previously written-off account is recovered under the allowance method, the customer's account is reinstated by debiting the Accounts Receivable account and the customer's account and crediting the Allowance for Doubtful Accounts account. Since these accounts are balance sheet accounts, and, thus, are not closed, the same entry is made no matter when recovery takes place. The receipt of cash is recorded by debiting the Cash account and crediting the Accounts Receivable and customer's accounts.

PRACTICE TEST

PART I TRUE/FALSE

Please circle the correct answer.

T   F   1. One way of knowing that an account is uncollectible is the receipt of a notice of the customer's bankruptcy.

T   F   2. A bad debt is an expense.

T   F   3. Under the direct write-off method, an estimate of future bad debts is made based on past experience.

T   F   4. To write off a bad debt using the direct write-off method, Accounts Receivable is debited and Bad Debts Expense is credited.

T   F   5. One shortcoming of the direct write-off method is that improper matching occurs when a credit sale takes place in one accounting period and the account is written off in another period.

T   F   6. The allowance method of accounting for bad debts requires that an estimate of bad debts be made at the end of the accounting period.

T   F   7. The allowance method results in an estimate of bad debts being recorded in the same period as the credit sales that caused the potential loss.

T   F   8. Use of the allowance method shows accounts receivable on the balance sheet at their net realizable value.

T   F   9. The aging of accounts receivable approach to estimating bad debts is called the balance sheet approach.

T   F   10. In recording the adjusting entry for bad debts using the income statement approach, it is necessary to know the previous balance in Allowance for Doubtful Accounts.

T   F   11. Allowance for Doubtful Accounts is a contra account to Accounts Receivable.

T   F   12. Allowance for Doubtful Accounts is needed because use of the allowance method requires the recording of bad debts expense before it is known exactly which accounts are uncollectible.

T   F   13. Recording the adjusting entry for bad debts expense under the allowance method requires a debit to Bad Debts Expense and a credit to Accounts Receivable.

T   F   14. Bad debts expense is reported as a selling expense on the income statement.

T   F   15. Allowance for Doubtful Accounts is a temporary account.

T   F   16. Aging the accounts receivable is done by analyzing the customers' accounts to determine how long each has been outstanding.

T   F   17. How the recovery of a bad debt is recorded under the direct write-off method depends on whether the account was written off in the same period or a different period.

T   F   18. When the recovery of a bad debt is recorded using the allowance method, Accounts Receivable is debited and Bad Debts Expense is credited.

T   F   19. Bad Debts Expense is a permanent account.

T   F   20. Recording the recovery of a bad debt under the allowance method involves a credit to Allowance for Doubtful Accounts whether the recovery is for a debt written off in the current period or in a prior period.

PART II MATCHING

Please match each of the following terms with its definition.

a. aging the receivables
b. aging schedule
c. Allowance for Doubtful Accounts
d. allowance method
e. bad debts

f. balance sheet approach
g. contra account
h. direct write-off method
i. income statement approach
j. net receivables

_____ 1. A contra asset account used to record the estimated amount of bad debts.

_____ 2. A way of estimating bad debts by analyzing customers' accounts to see how long each has been outstanding.

_____ 3. Accounts that cannot be collected.

_____ 4. The balance of accounts receivable minus the estimated bad debts.

_____ 5. A form that groups receivables by age and shows an estimated rate expected to be uncollectible for each age group.

_____ 6. An account whose balance is opposite to the balance of a related account.

_____ 7. A method used to record bad debts whereby an estimate is made at the end of an accounting period of the total bad debts that are expected to come from credit sales of that period.

_____ 8. A method of estimating bad debts that is based on a percent of credit sales.

_____ 9. A method used to record bad debts whereby accounts are written off to Bad Debts Expense when it is decided that a specific customer's account cannot be collected.

_____ 10. A method of estimating bad debts that is based on aging the receivables.

PART III FILL IN THE BLANKS

Please complete each sentence with the correct word or words.

1. When an account is considered uncollectible, the balance of the account is _____ the books.

2. Under the direct write-off method, receivables are assumed to be _____ until one proves to be _____.

3. When an account is written off under the direct write-off method, _____ is debited and _____ is credited.

4. The direct write-off method is used mainly by _____ firms and smaller _____ businesses that have limited amounts of credit sales.

5. The accrual basis of accounting requires that the _____ from credit sales be recognized at the _____.

6. Sometimes an account will become uncollectible in a(n) _____ accounting period, so that a direct write-off of the account results in an improper _____ of expenses and revenue.

7. Under the allowance method, a(n) _____ of bad debts is made at the end of each accounting period.

8. Recording the estimated bad debts expense in the same period as the related sales results in a proper _____ of expenses and _____.

9. The actual amount of receivables expected to be collected is referred to as _____ receivables.

10. Estimates of bad debts are usually based on the _____ of the business.

11. When estimating bad debts, _____ trends should be considered.

12. A good economy usually means _____ bad debt losses than a bad economy.

13. Estimating bad debts by taking a percent of credit sales is called the _____ approach.

14. Estimating bad debts by aging the accounts receivable is called the _____ approach.

15. Recording the adjusting entry for bad debts using the allowance method requires a debit to _____ and a credit to _____.

16. The adjustment for bad debts is made first on the _____ along with other adjustments.

17. Allowance for Doubtful Accounts is a(n) _____ account to Accounts Receivable.

18. The _____ account is closed to the _____ account at the end of the accounting period.

19. Under the allowance method, a bad debt is written off with a(n) _____ to Accounts Receivable and a(n) _____ to Allowance for Doubtful Accounts.

20. When an account written off in a prior period is recovered under the direct write-off method, _____ is credited.

PART IV MULTIPLE CHOICE

Please circle the correct answer.

1. Under the direct write-off method,
   a. receivables are considered good until proven uncollectible.
   b. bad debts are estimated at the end of the accounting period.
   c. uncollectible accounts are written off to Allowance for Doubtful Accounts.
   d. bad debts are recognized only in the period in which the related sale was made.

2. Company A uses the direct write-off method. One of its customers is disabled and cannot pay an account. In recording the bad debt,
   a. Accounts Receivable is debited and Bad Debts Expense is credited.
   b. Bad Debts Expense is debited and Allowance for Doubtful Accounts is credited.
   c. Bad Debts Expense is debited and Accounts Receivable is credited.
   d. none of the above.

3. Company B records bad debts using the allowance method. Its adjusting entry at the end of the year is
   a. a debit to Allowance for Doubtful Accounts and a credit to Accounts Receivable.
   b. a debit to Bad Debts Expense and a credit to Allowance for Doubtful Accounts.
   c. a debit to Bad Debts Expense and a credit to Accounts Receivable.
   d. none of the above.

4. Company B estimates its bad debts using the percent of credit sales approach. At year-end, it has credit sales of $50,000, Accounts Receivable of $6,000, and Allowance for Doubtful Accounts of $100 (credit balance). It estimates that 1% of credit sales will be lost. Its debit to Bad Debts Expense is
   a. $500.
   b. $400.
   c. $600.
   d. $60.

5. Company C estimates its bad debts using the aging the receivables approach. At year-end, it has Accounts Receivable of $40,000, Allowance for Doubtful Accounts of $450 (debit balance), and credit sales of $390,000. Company C estimates that it will have $2,000 in bad debt losses. Its debit to Bad Debts Expense is
    a. $1,550.
    b. $2,000.
    c. $2,450.
    d. none of the above.

6. Allowance for Doubtful Accounts is
    a. a temporary account.
    b. an income statement account.
    c. an expense account.
    d. a contra asset account.

7. On the income statement, Bad Debts Expense is reported as
    a. a selling expense.
    b. other expense.
    c. a general expense.
    d. a cost of goods sold account.

8. Company D uses the direct write-off method for recording bad debts. The company wrote off a $500 account in December. In March of the following year, the customer paid the amount owed. In recording this transaction,
    a. Allowance for Doubtful Accounts is credited and Accounts Receivable is debited.
    b. Recovery of Bad Debts is credited and Accounts Receivable is debited.
    c. Bad Debts Expense is credited and Accounts Receivable is debited.
    d. Accounts Receivable is credited and Bad Debts Expense is debited.

9. Under the allowance method, if bad debt write-offs have used up the balance in Allowance for Doubtful Accounts, what account should be debited for any additional bad debt losses?
    a. Allowance for Doubtful Accounts
    b. Bad Debts Expense
    c. Accounts Receivable
    d. Other Expense

10. When a customer's account becomes uncollectible under the allowance method, the write-off of the bad debt involves the customer's subsidiary ledger account and
    a. two temporary accounts.
    b. one temporary account and one permanent account.
    c. two permanent accounts.
    d. none of the above.

PART V WRITING/SHORT ANSWER

1. **Reflect** Make a list, in words or simple phrases, of the most important and meaningful points in this chapter.

2. **Question** Think about the most confusing points or the material you do not understand in this chapter. Write down two or three questions that remain unanswered.

3. **Connect** Explain, in one or two sentences, the connection between the main points of this chapter and the major goals of the entire course.

4. **Summarize** Review this chapter's Joining the Pieces visual summary and explain the concept(s) illustrated in a few sentences.

WORKING PAPERS

SKILLS REVIEW

EXERCISE 14-1

General Journal Page 1

	Date		Account Title	P.R.	Debit	Credit	
1							1
2							2
3							3
4							4
5							5
6							6
7							7
8							8
9							9
10							10
11							11
12							12

EXERCISE 14-2

General Journal Page 1

		Date		Account Title	P.R.	Debit	Credit	
(a)	1							1
	2							2
	3							3
	4							4
	5							5
	6							6
	7							7
(b)	8							8
	9							9
	10							10
	11							11
	12							12
	13							13
	14							14
	15							15
	16							16

EXERCISE 14-3

General Journal

	Date		Account Title	P.R.	Debit	Credit	
1							1
2							2
3							3
4							4
5							5
6							6

EXERCISE 14-4

Balance	Estimated Uncollectible Rate	Estimated Uncollectible Amount
_____	_____	_____
_____	_____	_____
_____	_____	_____
_____	_____	_____
_____	_____	_____
_____	_____	_____
	Total	_____

General Journal

	Date		Account Title	P.R.	Debit	Credit	
1							1
2							2
3							3
4							4
5							5
6							6
7							7
8							8

EXERCISE 14-5

	Date	Account Title	P.R.	Debit	Credit	
1						1
2						2
3						3
4						4
5						5
6						6
7						7
8						8
9						9
10						10
11						11
12						12
13						13
14						14
15						15
16						16

EXERCISE 14-6

General Journal

	Date		Account Title	P.R.	Debit	Credit	
1							1
2							2
3							3
4							4
5							5
6							6
7							7
8							8
9							9
10							10
11							11
12							12
13							13
14							14
15							15
16							16
17							17
18							18
19							19
20							20
21							21
22							22
23							23
24							24
25							25
26							26
27							27
28							28
29							29
30							30
31							31
32							32

EXERCISE 14-7

General Journal

	Date	Account Title	P.R.	Debit	Credit	
1						1
2						2
3						3
4						4
5						5
6						6
7						7
8						8
9						9
10						10
11						11
12						12
13						13
14						14
15						15
16						16
17						17
18						18
19						19
20						20
21						21
22						22
23						23
24						24
25						25
26						26
27						27
28						28
29						29
30						30
31						31
32						32

Allowance Method   **General Journal**

	Date	Account Title	P.R.	Debit	Credit	
1						1
2						2
3						3
4						4
5						5
6						6
7						7
8						8
9						9
10						10
11						11
12						12
13						13
14						14
15						15
16						16
17						17
18						18
19						19
20						20
21						21
22						22
23						23
24						24
25						25
26						26
27						27
28						28
29						29
30						30
31						31
32						32

CASE PROBLEMS

PROBLEM 14-1A OR 14-1B

General Journal

	Date		Account Title	P.R.	Debit	Credit	
1							1
2							2
3							3
4							4
5							5
6							6
7							7
8							8
9							9
10							10
11							11
12							12
13							13
14							14
15							15
16							16
17							17
18							18
19							19
20							20
21							21
22							22
23							23
24							24
25							25
26							26
27							27
28							28
29							29
30							30
31							31
32							32

PROBLEM 14-1A OR 14-1B (continued)

ACCOUNT Bad Debts Expense

DATE		ITEM	P.R.	DEBIT	CREDIT	BALANCE	
						DEBIT	CREDIT

3.

General Journal

	Date		Account Title	P.R.	Debit	Credit	
1							1
2							2
3							3
4							4
5							5
6							6
7							7
8							8
9							9
10							10
11							11
12							12
13							13
14							14
15							15
16							16
17							17
18							18
19							19
20							20
21							21
22							22
23							23
24							24
25							25
26							26
27							27
28							28
29							29
30							30
31							31
32							32

1., 2., 4.

ACCOUNT Accounts Receivable   ACCOUNT NO. 112

DATE	ITEM	P.R.	DEBIT	CREDIT	BALANCE DEBIT	BALANCE CREDIT

ACCOUNT Allowance for Doubtful Accounts   ACCOUNT NO. 112.1

DATE	ITEM	P.R.	DEBIT	CREDIT	BALANCE DEBIT	BALANCE CREDIT

5.

PROBLEM 14-3A OR 14-3B

1.

Age Category	Balance	Estimated Uncollectible Rate	Estimated Uncollectible Amount
Total			

2.

General Journal

Page 1

	Date	Account Title	P.R.	Debit	Credit	
1						1
2						2
3						3
4						4
5						5
6						6

3.

This page intentionally left blank.

PROBLEM 14-4A OR 14-4B

2.

General Journal

	Date		Account Title	P.R.	Debit	Credit	
1							1
2							2
3							3
4							4
5							5
6							6
7							7
8							8
9							9
10							10
11							11
12							12
13							13
14							14
15							15
16							16
17							17
18							18
19							19
20							20
21							21
22							22
23							23
24							24
25							25
26							26
27							27
28							28
29							29
30							30
31							31
32							32

General Journal

	Date	Account Title	P.R.	Debit	Credit	
1						1
2						2
3						3
4						4
5						5
6						6
7						7
8						8
9						9
10						10
11						11
12						12
13						13
14						14
15						15
16						16
17						17
18						18
19						19
20						20
21						21
22						22
23						23
24						24
25						25
26						26
27						27
28						28
29						29
30						30
31						31
32						32

PROBLEM 14-4A OR 14-4B (continued)

1., 3.

ACCOUNT **Allowance for Doubtful Accounts**   ACCOUNT NO. 112.1

DATE	ITEM	P.R.	DEBIT	CREDIT	BALANCE DEBIT	BALANCE CREDIT

ACCOUNT **Income Summary**   ACCOUNT NO. 315

DATE	ITEM	P.R.	DEBIT	CREDIT	BALANCE DEBIT	BALANCE CREDIT

ACCOUNT **Bad Debts Expense**   ACCOUNT NO. 614

DATE	ITEM	P.R.	DEBIT	CREDIT	BALANCE DEBIT	BALANCE CREDIT

4.

PROBLEM 14-5A OR 14-5B

2.

General Journal

	Date		Account Title	P.R.	Debit	Credit	
1							1
2							2
3							3
4							4
5							5
6							6
7							7
8							8
9							9
10							10
11							11
12							12
13							13
14							14
15							15
16							16
17							17
18							18
19							19
20							20
21							21
22							22
23							23
24							24
25							25
26							26
27							27
28							28
29							29
30							30
31							31
32							32

General Journal

	Date		Account Title	P.R.	Debit	Credit	
1							1
2							2
3							3
4							4
5							5
6							6
7							7
8							8
9							9
10							10
11							11
12							12
13							13
14							14
15							15
16							16
17							17
18							18
19							19
20							20
21							21
22							22
23							23
24							24
25							25
26							26
27							27
28							28
29							29
30							30
31							31
32							32

1., 3.

ACCOUNT Accounts Receivable   ACCOUNT NO. 112

DATE		ITEM	P.R.	DEBIT	CREDIT	BALANCE	
						DEBIT	CREDIT

ACCOUNT Allowance for Doubtful Accounts   ACCOUNT NO. 112.1

DATE		ITEM	P.R.	DEBIT	CREDIT	BALANCE	
						DEBIT	CREDIT

ACCOUNT Notes Receivable   ACCOUNT NO. 113

DATE		ITEM	P.R.	DEBIT	CREDIT	BALANCE	
						DEBIT	CREDIT

PROBLEM 14-5A OR 14-5B (continued)

ACCOUNT Accounts Payable   ACCOUNT NO. 211

DATE	ITEM	P.R.	DEBIT	CREDIT	BALANCE DEBIT	BALANCE CREDIT

ACCOUNT Notes Payable   ACCOUNT NO. 212

DATE	ITEM	P.R.	DEBIT	CREDIT	BALANCE DEBIT	BALANCE CREDIT

4.

PROBLEM SOLVING

General Journal   Page 1

	Date		Account Title	P.R.	Debit	Credit	
1							1
2							2
3							3
4							4
5							5
6							6
7							7
8							8
9							9
10							10
11							11
12							12
13							13
14							14
15							15
16							16
17							17
18							18
19							19
20							20
21							21
22							22
23							23
24							24
25							25
26							26
27							27
28							28
29							29
30							30
31							31
32							32

Cash

Accounts Receivable

Notes Receivable

Sales

Bad Debts Expense

Interest Income

Recovery of Bad Debts

Income Summary

COMMUNICATIONS

ETHICS

This page intentionally left blank.

PRACTICE TEST ANSWERS

PART I

1. T
2. T
3. F
4. F
5. T
6. T
7. T
8. T
9. T
10. F
11. T
12. T
13. F
14. F
15. F
16. T
17. T
18. F
19. F
20. T

PART II

1. c
2. a
3. e
4. j
5. b
6. g
7. d
8. i
9. h
10. f

PART III

1. written off
2. good, uncollectible
3. Bad Debts Expense, Accounts Receivable
4. professional service, merchandising
5. revenue, time of sale
6. later, matching
7. estimate
8. matching, revenue
9. net
10. past experience
11. economic
12. lower
13. income statement
14. balance sheet
15. Bad Debts Expense, Allowance for Doubtful Accounts
16. work sheet
17. contra
18. Bad Debts Expense, Income Summary
19. credit, debit
20. Recovery of Bad Debts

PART IV

1. a
2. c
3. b
4. a
5. c
6. d
7. c
8. b
9. a
10. c

PART V

Answers will vary. Please discuss questions with your instructor. You can also discuss issues related to this chapter by logging onto the Paradigm Accounting Web Site at www.emcp.com and clicking on the discussion section.

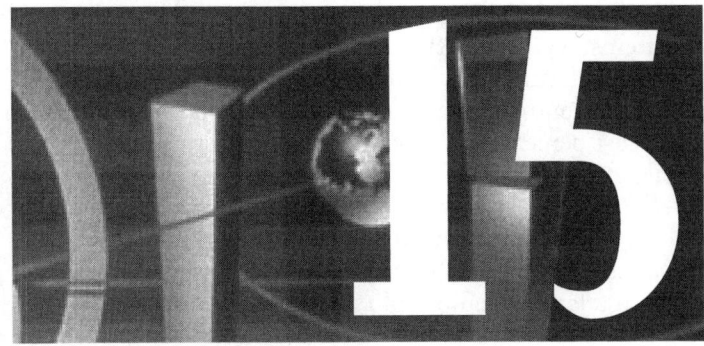

15 Accounting for Merchandise Inventory

CHAPTER SUMMARY

The term **merchandise inventory** is used to describe goods that are purchased for resale to customers in the normal course of business. Not included in merchandise are such things as plant assets that are being sold due to loss of usefulness or the purchase of a more efficient asset. Although such assets may be held for sale, they are not held for sale in the normal course of business.

The cost assigned to the ending inventory affects cost of goods sold. Cost of goods sold (an expense) affects the net income figure. Thus, an error in the cost of the ending inventory will cause an equal error in computing net income. If the cost assigned to the ending inventory is understated, the net income figure will be understated. On the other hand, if the cost assigned to the ending inventory is overstated, the net income figure will be overstated. This happens because the cost of the ending inventory is subtracted from the cost of goods available for sale to get cost of goods sold.

The first step in the **periodic inventory system** is taking a physical inventory. This usually involves a "hand count" of all items on hand. The count is recorded on an **inventory sheet**. Prices are multiplied by quantities to obtain the **extension**. Only goods owned are included in the count. Thus, goods held on **consignment** are excluded. The next step in the inventory process is assigning a cost (or value) to the counted units. If the merchandise on hand can be identified with a specific purchase, **specific identification** costing is possible. Specific identification costing involves multiplying the actual cost of an item by the number of items on hand.

Though specific identification gives an exact inventory cost, the method is often time consuming and costly. If inventories are very large, it may be impossible to identify the units on hand with a specific purchase. When inventory by specific identification is impossible or impractical, an assumed cost flow is used to assign a cost to the inventory. There are three common cost flows: the **first-in, first-out method (FIFO)**, the **last-in, first-out method (LIFO)**, and the **weighted-average method**.

Under FIFO, the latest costs are assigned to the ending inventory, and earlier costs flow, by the working of the cost of goods sold formula, into cost of goods sold. Under LIFO, earlier costs are assigned to the ending inventory, and later costs flow into cost of goods sold. Under the weighted-average method, an average cost per unit of merchandise is calculated by dividing the total cost of an item by the number of items available for sale. The unit cost is then multiplied by the units on hand to get an ending inventory cost. Whatever method is chosen, it must be kept unless circumstances dictate a real need for change. The principle of **consistency** applies.

A frequently used alternative to valuing inventories at cost is to compare the cost of inventory items with the replacement cost of the same items and to assign costs based on the lower figure. This is an application of the **lower of cost or market (LCM) rule**. The LCM rule should only be used when the replacement cost of inventory has fallen considerably below the original cost and the decline is expected to be permanent. Tax laws forbid the use of LCM when cost is determined by the LIFO method.

A physical inventory often involves a considerable investment of time and expense. Consequently, many businesses take a physical inventory only once a year. However, inventory figures are often needed more frequently. For example, some firms prepare **interim financial statements**. Thus, it is sometimes necessary to estimate the value of an ending inventory. Two common methods of estimating inventories are the gross profit method and the retail method. The **gross profit method** is based on the average rate of gross profit and is accomplished by subtracting an estimated cost of goods sold figure from the cost of goods available for sale. An estimated cost of goods sold is determined by reducing net sales by the average gross profit rate.

The **retail method** involves accumulating two sets of figures for the beginning inventory and the purchases during a period. One set shows the cost of such items, while the other set shows the retail price of the same items. An ending inventory at retail figure is determined by subtracting the net sales for a period from the goods available for sale at retail. The ending inventory at retail is then converted to cost by multiplying the inventory figure by a **cost percentage**. A cost percentage is obtained by dividing the goods available for sale at cost by the goods available for sale at retail price.

There are two principal types of inventory systems—the periodic system and the perpetual system. Under the periodic inventory system, no entry is made in the Merchandise Inventory account when merchandise is purchased or sold. Instead, the account is adjusted at the end of an accounting period to reflect the value of the latest inventory count. Businesses with a large inventory of relatively low unit cost items usually use the periodic system.

The **perpetual inventory system** involves the maintenance of inventory records that continuously disclose the amount of inventory. This system gives an inventory according to "the books." Thus, the perpetual system is often said to be a *book* or *running inventory*. Under this system, the Merchandise Inventory account is increased when merchandise is purchased. When merchandise is sold, the Merchandise Inventory account is decreased. Thus, the Merchandise Inventory account always reflects the amount of inventory. Businesses with a smaller inventory of higher unit cost items are more likely to use the perpetual system.

Since the perpetual inventory system involves maintaining **perpetual inventory records** that continuously disclose the amount of inventory on hand, journal entries are made to record the purchase and sale of merchandise. When merchandise is purchased, the cost of the purchase is debited to the Merchandise Inventory account and credited to either Cash or Accounts Payable. When merchandise is sold, two entries are needed. One transfers the cost of the merchandise sold from the Merchandise Inventory account to an account entitled Cost of Goods Sold. The second entry records the sale by debiting either Cash or Accounts Receivable and crediting Sales. If a difference is found between the perpetual records and a physical count, the **Inventory Short and Over account** is used in an adjusting entry.

PRACTICE TEST

PART I TRUE/FALSE

Please circle the correct answer.

T   F   1. Merchandise inventory includes anything that is sold by the business.

T   F   2. The merchandise inventory is often the largest current asset of a merchandising business.

T   F   3. Both the beginning and ending merchandise inventories are included on the income statement.

T   F   4. If ending merchandise inventory is understated, net income is overstated.

T   F   5. In the perpetual inventory system, debits are made directly to the Merchandise Inventory account when merchandise is purchased.

T   F   6. The periodic inventory system is ordinarily used by businesses that sell a high volume of low-cost items.

T   F   7. Businesses using a periodic inventory system maintain records that show a continuous count and value of the merchandise inventory.

T   F   8. A physical count of inventory is needed every year.

T   F   9. All merchandise owned by a business on the inventory date should be included on the inventory sheets.

T   F   10. The specific identification method of assigning costs to inventory is usually used by businesses having a high volume of low-cost items for sale.

T   F   11. The FIFO cost flow method assumes that the oldest units in inventory are sold first.

T   F   12. LIFO cost flow is the exact opposite of FIFO.

T   F   13. The LIFO method of assigning costs to inventory is popular when the inflation rate is high.

T   F   14. Lower of cost or market should be used to value inventories only when the cost of an inventory is substantially less than the market value.

T   F   15. The gross profit method of estimating inventories requires data on both the cost and retail prices of inventory items.

PART II MATCHING

Please match each of the following terms with its definition.

a. cost of goods sold
b. cost percentage
c. first-in, first-out method
d. gross profit method
e. gross profit percentage
f. inventory sheet
g. last-in, first-out method
h. lower of cost or market rule

i. merchandise inventory
j. periodic inventory system
k. perpetual inventory system
l. retail method
m. specific identification method
n. taking a physical inventory
o. weighted-average method

_____ 1. Goods held for sale to customers in the normal course of business activities.

_____ 2. Hand counting merchandise.

_____ 3. Method in which the cost of merchandise on hand is compared with its replacement cost and the lower of the two is used in valuing the inventory.

_____ 4. Method that assumes that the first goods bought are the first goods sold.

_____ 5. Method in which costs are assigned to an inventory based on the weighted average cost of units.

_____ 6. The relationship between gross profit and sales expressed as a percent.

_____ 7. System in which the Merchandise Inventory account shows the value of the most recent inventory count and no entries are made for purchases and sales of goods during the accounting period.

_____ 8. A method of estimating inventories in which an estimated gross profit is found and then an estimated cost of goods sold is subtracted from the goods available for sale in order to calculate the estimated ending inventory.

_____ 9. An expense arrived at by adding purchases to beginning inventory and subtracting ending inventory.

_____ 10. System in which accounting records are continuously updated to show the amount of inventory on hand.

_____ 11. The form used when taking a physical inventory count.

_____ 12. Method in which costs are assigned to inventory based on specific invoice prices.

_____ 13. The cost flow method that assumes that the last units purchased are the first ones sold.

_____ 14. A method of estimating inventories in which the estimated ending inventory at retail prices is reduced to cost using the cost percentage.

_____ 15. The relationship of cost to retail price obtained by dividing goods available for sale at cost by goods available for sale at retail.

Please complete each sentence with the correct word or words.

1. Both the _____ and _____ merchandise inventory balances are used in the computation of cost of goods sold.

2. The two types of inventory systems are the _____, in which the inventory is adjusted at the end of each accounting period to reflect the new balance on hand, and the _____, in which entries are made in the inventory account throughout the accounting period to reflect each purchase and each sale of goods.

3. All merchandise owned by a business on the inventory date should be _____ in the inventory count.

4. Merchandise accepted on consignment should be _____ from the inventory count.

5. After merchandise has been counted, the next step is to assign a(n) _____ to the inventory items.

6. When actual invoice prices are used to value the items purchased on those invoices, the company is using the _____ method.

7. The first-in, first-out method assumes that the _____ goods purchased were the first goods sold and the _____ goods purchased are in inventory.

8. The last-in, first-out method assumes that the last goods purchased were the _____ goods sold.

9. A weighted average is calculated by dividing the total _____ of the units available for sale by the total _____ of units available.

10. If inventory costs were to remain constant over time, all inventory costing methods would result in the _____ dollar value for inventory.

11. A higher value for ending inventory results in _____ net income for the period.

12. In a period of rising prices, the _____ inventory cost flow method will result in the lowest net income for the period.

13. The lower of cost or market rule requires a comparison of the _____ of merchandise on hand with the _____ of the merchandise.

14. When the lower of cost or market rule is used, the inventory is valued at _____ if the replacement cost is lower than the actual cost and the decline is expected to be _____.

15. According to the income tax laws, the lower of cost or market rule cannot be used with the _____ cost flow method.

16. Some businesses do not stop to count inventory every month in order to prepare interim financial statements, so they need some means of _____ inventory amounts.

17. The method of estimating inventory that uses a slightly modified formula for cost of goods sold is the _____ method.

18. In the gross profit method, an estimated cost of goods sold is subtracted from _____ to arrive at an estimated _____.

19. The retail method requires that records be available for inventory items at both their _____ and _____ prices.

20. A perpetual inventory system keeps the records necessary to reveal inventory _____ due to theft and breakage, which are concealed by the periodic inventory system.

Please circle the correct answer.

1. Cost of goods available for sale is computed by
   a. adding net purchases to ending merchandise inventory.
   b. adding net purchases to beginning merchandise inventory.
   c. adding beginning and ending merchandise inventory.
   d. none of the above.

2. Cost of goods sold is computed by
   a. subtracting ending merchandise inventory from goods available for sale.
   b. subtracting ending merchandise inventory from gross profit.
   c. subtracting beginning merchandise inventory from gross profit.
   d. none of the above.

3. An error in the ending balance of merchandise inventory will cause
   a. an equal error in total operating expenses.
   b. an equal error in goods available for sale.
   c. an equal error in net income.
   d. none of the above.

4. A physical count of inventory should include
   a. goods accepted on consignment.
   b. goods sold but not yet delivered.
   c. goods that are owned but not yet ready for sale.
   d. all of the above should be excluded from inventory.

5. The FIFO cost flow method assumes that
   a. the first goods purchased were the first goods sold.
   b. the first goods purchased are still in inventory.
   c. there is no way to tell which goods are still in inventory.
   d. the first goods purchased set the cost that is used for all computations of cost of goods sold.

6. The LIFO cost flow method
   a. follows the physical flow of goods sold.
   b. transfers the earliest costs to cost of goods sold first.
   c. results in a higher net income in periods of rising prices.
   d. results in a lower net income in periods of rising prices.

7. The use of FIFO cost flow results in
   a. the most current costs being assigned to inventory.
   b. the most current costs being assigned to cost of goods sold.
   c. lower inventory values in periods of rising prices.
   d. a lower net income in periods of rising prices.

8. The lower of cost or market rule should be used when
   a. none of the other cost flow methods are used.
   b. market value is substantially higher than cost.
   c. market value is substantially lower than cost and the decline is expected to be permanent.
   d. market value is known but cost is not known.

9. In order to use the gross profit method to estimate the ending inventory, the following information must be available
   a. cost of goods sold and beginning inventory.
   b. sales, gross profit rate, beginning inventory, and net purchases.
   c. sales, cost of goods sold, and beginning inventory.
   d. sales, cost of goods sold, and net purchases.

10. In order to use the retail method to estimate the ending inventory, the following information must be available or must be calculated.
   a. beginning inventory and net purchases at both cost and retail.
   b. sales for the period.
   c. the cost percentage.
   d. all of the above.

PART V WRITING/SHORT ANSWER

1. **Reflect** Make a list, in words or simple phrases, of the most important and meaningful points in this chapter.

2. **Question** Think about the most confusing points or the material you do not understand in this chapter. Write down two or three questions that remain unanswered.

3. **Connect** Explain, in one or two sentences, the connection between the main points of this chapter and the major goals of the entire course.

4. **Summarize** Review this chapter's Joining the Pieces visual summary and explain the concept(s) illustrated in a few sentences.

This page intentionally left blank.

WORKING PAPERS

CASE PROBLEMS

EXERCISE 15-1

EXERCISE 15-2

(a) _____

(b) _____

(c) _____

(d) _____

EXERCISE 15-3

	Company A	Company B	Company C
Cost of goods sold:			
Beginning merchandise inventory	_____	_____	_____
Add: Net purchases of merchandise	_____	_____	_____
Cost of goods available for sale	_____	_____	_____
Less: Ending merchandise inventory	_____	_____	_____
Cost of goods sold	_____	_____	_____

EXERCISE 15-4

Ending inventory calculated under:

(a)   Specific identification method: _____

_____

_____

(b)   FIFO method: _____

_____

_____

(c)   LIFO method: _____

_____

_____

(d)   Weighted-average method: _____

_____

_____

_____

_____

_____

_____

_____

_____

_____

EXERCISE 15-5

EXERCISE 15-6

Item	Cost	Market	LCM
1	_____	_____	_____
2	_____	_____	_____
3	_____	_____	_____
4	_____	_____	_____
Totals	_____	_____	_____

(a) LCM item by item _____

(b) LCM entire inventory _____

EXERCISE 15-7

EXERCISE 15-8

	Cost	Retail

EXERCISE 15-9

General Journal

	Date	Account Title	P.R.	Debit	Credit	
1						1
2						2
3						3
4						4
5						5
6						6
7						7
8						8
9						9
10						10
11						11
12						12
13						13
14						14
15						15
16						16
17						17
18						18
19						19
20						20
21						21
22						22
23						23
24						24
25						25
26						26
27						27
28						28
29						29
30						30
31						31
32						32

This page intentionally left blank.

CASE PROBLEMS

PROBLEM 15-1A OR 15-1B

1. (a) _____
   (b) _____
   (c) _____

2. (a) _____
   (b) _____
   (c) _____

Use space below and on the next page for calculations.

PROBLEM 15-2A OR 15-2B

ENDING INVENTORY	Units	Unit Cost	Unit Market	FIFO (1) End Inv. FIFO	FIFO (1) FIFO Total Cost	MARKET (2) End. Inv. Market	MARKET (2) Market Total Cost	LCM (3) Lower of Cost or Market	LCM (3) LCM Total Cost
Product A									
Product B									
Product C									

1. _____

2. _____

3. _____

This page intentionally left blank.

PROBLEM 15-3A OR 15-3B

1.

Sales _____

Less: Sales returns and allowances _____

Sales discounts _____

Net sales _____

Average gross profit rate _____

Estimated gross profit _____

Net sales _____

Less: Estimated gross profit _____

Estimated cost of goods sold _____

Beginning merchandise inventory _____

Add: Purchases _____

Less: Purchases returns and allowances _____

Purchases discounts _____

Net purchases _____

Cost of goods available for sale _____

Less: Estimated cost of goods sold _____

Estimated cost of ending inventory _____

2.

PROBLEM 15-4A OR 15-4B

	Cost	Retail
Merchandise inventory, June 1	_____	_____
Net purchases during June	_____	_____
Goods available for sale	_____	_____
Less: Net sales during June	_____	_____
Estimated inventory at retail	_____	_____

Cost percentage:

	Cost	Retail
	_____	_____
	_____	_____
Estimated inventory at cost	_____	_____

This page intentionally left blank.

PROBLEM 15-5A OR 15-5B

1., 2.

Inventory Record

Item _____   Stock Number _____

Department _____   Reorder Point _____

Date	Received			Sold			Balance		
	UNITS	PRICE	AMOUNT	UNITS	PRICE	AMOUNT	UNITS	PRICE	AMOUNT

2.

General Journal

	Date		Account Title	P.R.	Debit	Credit	
1							1
2							2
3							3
4							4
5							5
6							6
7							7
8							8
9							9
10							10
11							11
12							12
13							13
14							14
15							15
16							16
17							17
18							18
19							19
20							20
21							21
22							22
23							23
24							24
25							25
26							26
27							27
28							28
29							29
30							30
31							31
32							32

PROBLEM 15-6A OR 15-6B

1.

General Journal

Page 1

	Date		Account Title	P.R.	Debit	Credit	
1							1
2							2
3							3
4							4
5							5
6							6
7							7
8							8

(a) applies to rows 1–3; (b) applies to rows 5–8.

2. _____

3. _____

This page intentionally left blank.

PROBLEM SOLVING

	PERIODIC LIFO		
	Units	**Unit Price**	**Total**

Inventory Record

Item _____   Stock Number _____

Department _____   Reorder Point _____

Date	Received			Sold			Balance		
	UNITS	PRICE	AMOUNT	UNITS	PRICE	AMOUNT	UNITS	PRICE	AMOUNT

Summary: Perpetual LIFO ending inventory _____

Periodic LIFO ending inventory _____

Change in ending inventory _____

COMMUNICATIONS

ETHICS

This page intentionally left blank.

PRACTICE TEST ANSWERS

PART I

1. F
2. T
3. T
4. F
5. T
6. T
7. F
8. T
9. T
10. F
11. T
12. T
13. T
14. F
15. F

PART II

1. i
2. n
3. h
4. c
5. o
6. e
7. j
8. d
9. a
10. k
11. f
12. m
13. g
14. l
15. b

PART III

1. beginning, ending
2. periodic, perpetual
3. included

4. excluded
5. value
6. specific identification
7. first, last
8. first
9. cost, number
10. same
11. higher
12. LIFO
13. cost, replacement cost
14. market, permanent
15. LIFO
16. estimating
17. gross profit
18. goods available for sale, ending inventory
19. cost, retail
20. losses

PART IV

1. b
2. a
3. c
4. c
5. a
6. d
7. a
8. c
9. b
10. d

PART V

Answers will vary. Please discuss questions with your instructor. You can also discuss issues related to this chapter by logging onto the Paradigm Accounting Web Site at www.emcp.com and clicking on the discussion section.

Accounting for Plant Assets and Depreciation

CHAPTER SUMMARY

Current assets are assets that will be sold, used up, or turned into cash within one accounting cycle. **Plant assets** are assets that: (1) have a useful life of more than one year, (2) are acquired for use in the operation of the business, (3) are not intended for resale to customers in the normal course of business, and (4) are **tangible** (you can touch them). Examples of plant assets include buildings, land, furniture, equipment, and machinery. Other terms used to describe plant assets include **long-term assets**, **fixed assets**, **capital assets**, and **property, plant, and equipment**.

    Intangible assets and **natural resources** are also long-term assets. Intangible assets lack physical substance but do benefit a business because they provide legal rights. Examples of intangible assets include patents, copyrights, trademarks, and franchises. Natural resources (often called **wasting assets**) are assets that are acquired for the purpose of removing or extracting natural resources, such as timber, coal, gold, gas, and oil.

    When a plant asset is purchased, an asset account is debited for the cost of the asset and either Accounts Payable, Notes Payable, or Cash is credited, depending on whether the purchase was on account, in exchange for a promissory note, or for cash.

    The cost of a plant asset includes all expenditures necessary to actually acquire the asset and get it into operation. For example, the cost of a new microcomputer would include not only the purchase price but also sales taxes (if any), freight charges, installation charges, and fees paid to train employees how to use the computer. However, the cost of a plant asset does not include expenditures for repairs when the asset is damaged by vandalism or careless handling before it goes into use. Such expenditures are debited to expense accounts. The **Land Improvement** account is a specific type of plant asset.

    Plant assets are purchased for the use they provide in operating a business and earning revenue. However, all plant assets—with the exception of land—either wear out with the passage of time, become obsolete with new technology, or become inadequate to meet expanded needs. Since plant assets lose their usefulness, a part of their cost should be allocated to each accounting period in which the assets are used. The process of allocating the cost of a plant asset over its expected useful life is referred to as **depreciation**, and the amount allocated is called **depreciation expense**. The process of allocating the cost of an intangible asset over its expected useful life is referred to as **amortization**. And the process of allocating the cost of a natural resource over its expected useful life is referred to as **depletion**.

    Depreciation is recorded by debiting a depreciation expense account and crediting an **accumulated depreciation** account. The depreciation expense account is temporary and is thus closed to the Income Summary account. The accumulated depreciation account, on the other hand, is a permanent account and will remain open to accumulate depreciation charges over the life of the related plant asset.

    Three factors are needed to compute depreciation: (1) the original cost of the asset, (2) the estimated salvage value of the asset, and (3) the estimated useful life of the asset. The original cost of a plant asset is the recorded cost, which includes the purchase price plus any additional expenditures necessary to acquire the asset and get it into operation. The estimated **salvage value** of a plant asset is the expected value of the asset at the end of its productive life. The **estimated useful life** of a plant asset is the estimated length of its usefulness to the business that acquired it. The length of usefulness can be measured in terms of time, such as years, or in terms of units of output, such as miles driven.

There are various methods of figuring depreciation. The principal of **consistency**—keeping one method—applies. Three common methods are: (1) the straight-line method, (2) the units-of-production method, and (3) the double declining-balance method. The **straight-line method** is simple to use and results in an equal amount of depreciation expense over each year in the life of a plant asset. Straight-line depreciation is computed using the following formula:

$$\frac{C - S}{L}$$

where C = cost of the asset, S = estimated salvage value of the asset, and L = estimated useful life of the asset. The **straight line rate** is the percent of annual depreciation. Depreciation is summarized in a **depreciation schedule**.

The **units-of-production method** uses an estimate of the output of an asset. With this method, the life of the asset is usually stated in terms of miles driven, hours of operation, or units produced. A rate is obtained by dividing the estimated life into the cost of the asset minus its salvage value. The result is a constant rate that is applied to actual usage in the current and later accounting periods.

The **double declining-balance method** results in greater depreciation being charged during the earlier years of a plant asset's life and less depreciation as the asset ages. This **accelerated method of depreciation** is appropriate for assets whose productivity is greater during the earlier years or in cases where technology will probably make an asset inadequate before its physical life is over.

Some expenditures benefit only the current period. These are called **revenue expenditures**. Other expenditures add value to an asset or extend its life. These are called **capital expenditures**. Capital expenditures that add value are **additions** or **betterments**. A capital expenditure that prolongs life is an **extraordinary repair**.

When an asset is no longer useful, it should be sold, traded, or discarded. The first step in recording the disposal of a plant asset is to update depreciation. Updating depreciation involves recording the depreciation expense for the time between the date on which depreciation was last recorded and the disposal date.

If an asset is sold for more than its **book value**, there is a gain; if an asset is sold for less than its book value, there is a loss; if an asset is sold for exactly book value, there is no gain or loss.

Often, plant assets are traded in for other plant assets. If an asset is traded in for a similar asset and a difference (**boot**) is paid, special rules come into play. For financial reporting purposes, a gain cannot be recognized if the amount received in a trade is more than book value, but a loss can be recognized if the amount received in a trade is less than book value. For federal income tax purposes, neither gains nor losses can be recognized when an asset is traded for a similar asset and a difference is paid. When a gain or loss is not recognized, the cost of the asset acquired is determined as follows:

	Book value of asset being traded
+	Difference paid (boot)
=	Cost of new asset

An intangible asset should be amortized (written off) over its expected useful life. A business must decide how long an intangible asset will be of benefit. A patent, for example, has a legal life of 17 years. However, the cost may be written off over a shorter period (but not a longer period) if it is believed that the patent will not benefit the business for its full legal life. According to accounting pronouncements, intangible assets should be written off over a reasonable period of time, not to exceed 40 years.

As we have noted already, the expense that results from the consumption or exhaustion of natural resources is called *depletion*. The calculation of depletion is similar to the calculation of depreciation under the units-of-production method. The cost of the asset is divided by the estimated output. The rate obtained is applied to the actual output from the asset.

PART I TRUE/FALSE

Please circle the correct answer.

T   F   1. Plant assets have a useful life of more than one year and are intended for use in the normal operations of the business.

T   F   2. An example of an intangible asset is a patent.

T   F   3. The cost of a plant asset is its invoice price only.

T   F   4. The normal cost of getting a plant asset ready for use includes any repairs as a result of accidental damage to the asset while it is being installed.

T   F   5. When dividing the purchase price between land and a building bought for a lump sum, the usual practice is to debit only a small part of the cost to the Land account because land cannot be depreciated.

T   F   6. The cost of a new building being constructed includes all construction costs plus architect's fees, insurance during construction, and all other normal and necessary costs.

T   F   7. A plant asset is depreciated in order to allocate the cost of the asset over the period of its expected useful life.

T   F   8. The accumulated depreciation account is a temporary account.

T   F   9. Businesses often estimate salvage value based on past experience with similar assets.

T   F   10. Useful life can be expressed in years or in terms of units of production.

T   F   11. The straight-line method of depreciation results in an equal depreciation charge for each unit of output.

T   F   12. Book value and market value are the same.

T   F   13. Depreciation is figured only to the nearest whole month.

T   F   14. Accelerated depreciation methods are not acceptable for financial reporting purposes.

T   F   15. An easy way to compute the double declining-balance rate is to divide 100% by the useful life of the asset and then multiply that figure by 2.

T   F   16. Salvage value is not considered in computing the depreciation rate used in double declining-balance depreciation.

T   F   17. Maintenance expenditures for a plant asset that benefit only the current period are called capital expenditures and are recorded in the asset account.

T   F   18. The first step in recording the disposal of a plant asset is to bring the depreciation up to date.

T   F   19. Book value is used in determining any gain or loss on disposal of plant assets.

T   F   20. When a plant asset is traded for a similar plant asset, federal income tax law requires recognition of any gain or loss.

PART II MATCHING

Please match each of the following terms with its definition.

a. accelerated depreciation method
b. amortization
c. book value
d. boot
e. capital expenditures
f. cost of a plant asset
g. depletion
h. depreciation
i. intangible assets
j. natural resources
k. plant assets
l. revenue expenditures
m. straight-line method
n. units-of-production method

_____ 1. The difference between the trade-in allowance being given for an old plant asset and the price of the new similar asset, which is paid in cash or on credit.

_____ 2. The depreciation method that allocates the same amount of depreciation to each period of a plant asset's useful life.

_____ 3. A depreciation method that results in greater depreciation being charged during the earlier years of a plant asset's useful life.

_____ 4. The allocation of the cost of an intangible asset over its expected useful life.

_____ 5. Assets such as timber, oil, and copper that are acquired for the purpose of removal or extraction.

_____ 6. The process of allocating the cost of a plant asset over its expected useful life.

_____ 7. Assets that have a useful life of more than one year, are acquired for use in a business, and are not intended for resale to customers in the normal course of business operations.

_____ 8. The process of allocating the cost of a natural resource over its expected useful life.

_____ 9. The purchase price of a plant asset and any normal amounts spent to get the plant asset ready for its intended use.

_____ 10. The cost of a plant asset minus its accumulated depreciation.

_____ 11. Maintenance expenditures for a plant asset that benefit only the current period.

_____ 12. A depreciation method that allocates the cost of a plant asset by using a constant rate per unit of output.

_____ 13. Assets that have no physical substance, such as patents or copyrights.

_____ 14. Expenditures that add to a plant asset's efficiency or capacity.

PART III FILL IN THE BLANKS

Please complete each sentence with the correct word or words.

1. Patents, copyrights, and trademarks are examples of _____ assets.

2. Trucks, desks and chairs, computers, and store fixtures used in a business are examples of _____ assets.

3. Timber, oil, and iron ore are examples of _____.

4. The cost of a plant asset includes all _____ expenditures necessary to acquire the asset and get it ready for use.

5. When land and a building are acquired in the same purchase, the cost must be _____ between the two assets.

6. The process of allocating the cost of a plant asset over its expected useful life is called _____.

7. Depreciation expense is a(n) _____ account that is closed to _____ at the end of the accounting period.

8. Accumulated depreciation is a(n) _____ account that is found in the _____ section of the balance sheet.

9. The _____ of a plant asset is the number of years the asset is expected to remain useful.

10. The _____ of a plant asset is the amount the asset is expected to be worth at the end of its productive life.

11. To calculate straight-line depreciation, subtract the _____ of the plant asset from the _____ and divide the remainder by the _____.

12. The book value of a plant asset is the _____ minus the _____.

13. To calculate units-of-production depreciation, subtract the salvage value of the plant asset from the _____ and divide the remainder by the estimated _____.

14. Double declining-balance depreciation is a form of _____ depreciation.

15. When a plant asset is sold at a loss, the loss is recorded in a(n) _____ account entitled _____.

16. The accounting method of recording the trade of a plant asset for a similar asset requires recognition of a(n) _____ but no recognition of a(n) _____ on the trade.

17. The income tax method of recording the trade of a plant asset for a similar asset does not permit recognition of either _____ or _____.

18. In the income tax method of recording exchanges of similar plant assets, the new asset is valued at the _____ of the old asset plus the _____ paid.

19. When disposing of a plant asset, it is necessary to debit the _____ account for the amount of depreciation taken over the asset's useful life.

PART IV MULTIPLE CHOICE

Please circle the correct answer.

1. Plant assets are assets that
   a. have a useful life of more than one year.
   b. are acquired for use in the operation of the business.
   c. are not intended for resale to customers in the normal course of business.
   d. all of the above.

2. In the purchase of a plant asset, the asset account is debited for
   a. the cost of the asset plus all normal costs of getting the asset ready for use.
   b. the cost of the asset only.
   c. the cost of the asset plus all costs related to the asset up until the time it is ready for use.
   d. the cost of the asset minus any trade-in allowance.

3. The purpose of recording depreciation is
   a. to record the wear and tear on the asset.
   b. to record the decline in market value as the asset gets older.
   c. to record a share of the cost of the asset in each period benefited by the use of the asset.
   d. all of the above.

4. When depreciation is recorded,
   a. the depreciation expense account is credited and the accumulated depreciation account is debited.
   b. the depreciation expense account is debited and the accumulated depreciation account is credited.
   c. the asset account is debited and the depreciation expense account is credited.
   d. the asset account is credited and the depreciation expense account is debited.

5. When an asset has been held for less than a year, depreciation is computed for
   a. the whole year.
   b. the whole year if the asset was purchased before July 1 and not at all if the asset was purchased on or after July 1.
   c. the part of the year that the asset was held, figured to the nearest whole month.
   d. none of the above.

6. Which of the following depreciation methods does not consider salvage value in the computation?
   a. straight-line
   b. units-of-production
   c. double declining-balance
   d. all of the above.

7. An example of a capital expenditure is
   a. a new motor for the company's delivery truck.
   b. a tune-up for the company car.
   c. repairs on the assistant's computer.
   d. steam-cleaning the company's carpet.

8. An example of a revenue expenditure is
   a. a new transmission for the company's car.
   b. a disk drive for the company's computer.
   c. an oil change for the company's truck.
   d. a new compressor for the company's air conditioner.

9. When equipment is sold for cash at a gain, the journal entry will
   a. debit Cash and Accumulated Depreciation—Equipment and credit Equipment and Gain on Disposal of Plant Assets.
   b. debit Cash and credit Equipment and Gain on Disposal of Plant Assets.
   c. debit Cash and credit Equipment and Sales Revenue.
   d. none of the above.

PART V WRITING/SHORT ANSWER

1. **Reflect** Make a list, in words or simple phrases, of the most important and meaningful points in this chapter.

2. **Question** Think about the most confusing points or the material you do not understand in this chapter. Write down two or three questions that remain unanswered.

3. **Connect** Explain, in one or two sentences, the connection between the main points of this chapter and the major goals of the entire course.

4. **Summarize** Review this chapter's Joining the Pieces visual summary and explain the concept(s) illustrated in a few sentences.

WORKING PAPERS

SKILLS REVIEW

EXERCISE 16-1

_____
_____
_____
_____
_____
_____

General Journal   Page 1

	Date		Account Title	P.R.	Debit	Credit	
1							1
2							2
3							3
4							4
5							5
6							6
7							7
8							8

EXERCISE 16-2

(a) Straight-line method

Year	Depreciation Expense
20X1	_____
20X2	_____
20X3	_____

(b) Double declining-balance method

Year	Depreciation Expense
20X1	_____
20X2	_____
20X3	_____

EXERCISE 16-3

(a) Straight-line method

Year	Depreciation Expense
20X1	
20X2	
20X3	

(b) Double declining-balance method

Year	Depreciation Expense
20X1	
20X2	
20X3	

EXERCISE 16-4

Year	Depreciation Expense
Year 1	
Year 2	
Year 3	

EXERCISE 16-5

General Journal

Page 1

	Date	Account Title	P.R.	Debit	Credit	
1						1
2						2
3						3
4						4
5						5
6						6
7						7
8						8
9						9
10						10
11						11
12						12
13						13
14						14
15						15

EXERCISE 16-6

General Journal

Page 1

	Date	Account Title	P.R.	Debit	Credit	
1						1
2						2
3						3
4						4
5						5
6						6
7						7
8						8
9						9
10						10
11						11
12						12
13						13
14						14

EXERCISE 16-7

General Journal

Page 1

	Date	Account Title	P.R.	Debit	Credit	
1						1
2						2
3						3
4						4
5						5
6						6
7						7
8						8
9						9
10						10
11						11
12						12
13						13
14						14
15						15
16						16

EXERCISE 16-8

General Journal

	Date		Account Title	P.R.	Debit	Credit	
1							1
2							2
3							3
4							4
5							5
6							6
7							7
8							8
9							9
10							10
11							11
12							12

EXERCISE 16-9

General Journal

Page 1

	Date		Account Title	P.R.	Debit	Credit	
1							1
2							2
3							3
4							4
5							5
6							6
7							7
8							8
9							9
10							10
11							11

CASE PROBLEMS

PROBLEM 16-1A OR 16-1B

(a)   Straight-line method

Year	Depreciation Expense	Accumulated Depreciation	Book Value End of Year
1	_____	_____	_____
2	_____	_____	_____
3	_____	_____	_____
4	_____	_____	_____
5	_____	_____	_____

(b)   Double declining-balance method

Year	Depreciation Expense	Accumulated Depreciation	Book Value End of Year
1	_____	_____	_____
2	_____	_____	_____
3	_____	_____	_____
4	_____	_____	_____
5	_____	_____	_____

This page intentionally left blank.

PROBLEM 16-2A OR 16-2B

(a)   Straight-line method

Year	Depreciation Expense	Accumulated Depreciation	Book Value End of Year
1	_____	_____	_____
2	_____	_____	_____
3	_____	_____	_____
4	_____	_____	_____
5	_____	_____	_____
6	_____	_____	_____

(b)   Double declining-balance method

Year	Depreciation Expense	Accumulated Depreciation	Book Value End of Year
1	_____	_____	_____
2	_____	_____	_____
3	_____	_____	_____
4	_____	_____	_____
5	_____	_____	_____

This page intentionally left blank.

PROBLEM 16-3A OR 16-3B

General Journal

Page 1

	Date	Account Title	P.R.	Debit	Credit	
1						1
2						2
3						3
4						4
5						5
6						6
7						7
8						8
9						9
10						10
11						11
12						12
13						13
14						14
15						15
16						16
17						17
18						18
19						19
20						20
21						21
22						22
23						23
24						24
25						25
26						26
27						27
28						28
29						29
30						30
31						31
32						32
33						33
34						34
35						35

General Journal

	Date		Account Title	P.R.	Debit	Credit	
1							1
2							2
3							3
4							4
5							5
6							6
7							7
8							8
9							9
10							10
11							11
12							12
13							13
14							14
15							15
16							16
17							17
18							18
19							19
20							20
21							21
22							22
23							23
24							24
25							25
26							26
27							27
28							28
29							29
30							30
31							31
32							32
33							33
34							34
35							35

General Journal

Page 1

	Date	Account Title	P.R.	Debit	Credit	
1						1
2						2
3						3
4						4
5						5
6						6
7						7
8						8
9						9
10						10
11						11
12						12
13						13
14						14
15						15
16						16
17						17
18						18
19						19
20						20
21						21
22						22
23						23
24						24
25						25
26						26
27						27
28						28
29						29
30						30
31						31
32						32
33						33
34						34
35						35

This page intentionally left blank.

CHALLENGE PROBLEMS

PROBLEM SOLVING

Year	Depreciation Expense
20X1	_____
20X2	_____
20X3	_____
	_____
20X4	_____

This page intentionally left blank.

COMMUNICATIONS

ETHICS

This page intentionally left blank.

PART I

1. T
2. T
3. F
4. F
5. F
6. T
7. T
8. F
9. T
10. T
11. F
12. F
13. T
14. F
15. T
16. T
17. F
18. T
19. T
20. F

PART II

1. d
2. m
3. a
4. b
5. j
6. h
7. k
8. g
9. f
10. c
11. l
12. n
13. i
14. e

PART III

1. intangible
2. plant
3. natural resources
4. normal
5. divided
6. depreciation
7. temporary, Income Summary
8. permanent, Plant Assets
9. estimated useful life
10. salvage value
11. salvage value, cost, estimated useful life
12. cost, accumulated depreciation
13. cost, units of output
14. accelerated
15. expense, Loss on Disposal of Plant Assets
16. loss, gain
17. losses, gains
18. book value, boot
19. accumulated depreciation

PART IV

1. d
2. a
3. c
4. b
5. c
6. c
7. a
8. c
9. a

PART V

Answers will vary. Please discuss questions with your instructor. You can also discuss issues related to this chapter by logging onto the Paradigm Accounting Web Site at www.emcp.com and clicking on the discussion section.

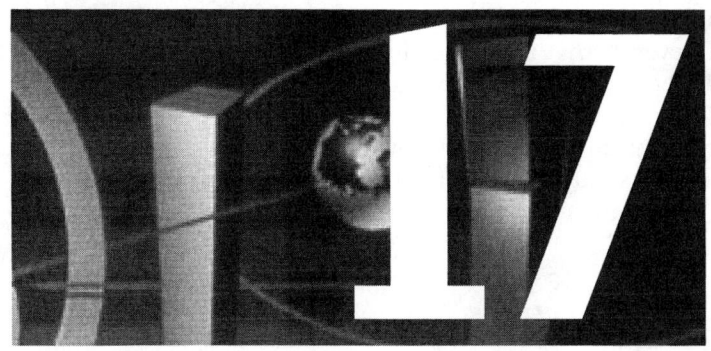

17 Accounting for Accruals and Deferrals

CHAPTER SUMMARY

In the **cash basis**, an expense is recorded when paid, and revenue when received. In the **accrual basis**, an expense is recorded when it is incurred, and revenue is recorded when earned. The accrual basis requires adjusting entries.

Adjusting entries are made at the end of an accounting period to apply the **matching principle** to revenue and expenses and to more accurately state the amount of assets and liabilities. Most adjusting entries can be grouped into two categories: accruals and deferrals.

An **accrual** is the accumulation of an expense or revenue over a period of time. At the end of an accounting period, there are usually some revenue or expense items that have accrued but have not been recorded. In order to show the proper amount of revenue and expenses, adjusting entries should be made for all accruals.

A **deferral** is the advance payment of an expense that benefits more than one accounting period or the advance receipt of revenue that will not be fully earned at the end of an accounting period. Adjusting entries should be made for deferrals to allocate the appropriate amount of expenses or revenue to the appropriate accounting period.

Accrued expenses represent both an expense and a liability. Thus, accrued expenses can also be referred to as **accrued liabilities**. A common example of an accrued expense is unpaid salaries at the end of an accounting period. An adjusting entry must be made to debit the Salaries Expense account and credit the Salaries Payable account. This has the effect of recording all salaries incurred in a period and recognizing the liability for unpaid salaries. All accrued expenses involve a debit to an expense account and a credit to a liability account.

Accrued revenue represents both an asset and revenue. Thus, accrued revenue can also be referred to as **accrued assets**. Accrued revenue occurs when revenue has been earned but not collected at the time the accounting period ends. The adjusting entry for accrued revenue requires a debit to an asset account (such as Accounts Receivable, Rent Receivable, Interest Receivable, etc.) and a credit to a revenue account.

When an accrued expense is paid in the next accounting period—or when accrued revenue is received in the next accounting period—the entry must be split between the part of the accrual that pertains to the previous accounting period and the part that pertains to the current accounting period. Some accountants, however, do not like to split an entry between two accounting periods. In Chapter 10 we discussed a technique known as **reversing entries** that allows the accountant to make routine entries as if an accrual had not taken place. A reversing entry is made as of the first day of the next accounting period and is the exact reverse of the adjusting entry for the accrual.

A **deferred expense** is an advance payment for goods or services that benefits more than one accounting period. Deferred expenses are also called **prepaid expenses** or **deferred charges**.

Prepaid expenses can be accounted for in two ways. The prepayment can be recorded (1) as an asset or (2) as an expense. Both methods yield identical results, but the end-of-period adjusting entry depends on how the prepayment was first recorded.

Deferred revenue is the advance receipt of revenue that will not be fully earned until a later period. Common examples of deferred revenue include sales of season tickets by an athletic team, subscriptions received in advance by a magazine, and rent collected at the beginning of a lease period.

Revenue that is deferred for a shorter period (less than a year) is referred to as **unearned revenue** and is listed on the balance sheet as a current liability. Revenue that is deferred for a longer period (in excess of a year) is referred to as **deferred credits** and is reported on the balance sheet under the heading Deferred Credits.

Deferred revenue can be accounted for in two ways. The advance receipt can be recorded (1) as a liability or (2) as revenue. Both methods yield identical results, but the end-of-period adjusting entry depends on the initial recording.

PART I TRUE/FALSE

Please circle the correct answer.

T F 1. The matching principle states that all transactions should be recorded at cost.

T F 2. To apply the matching principle, most businesses use the accrual basis of accounting.

T F 3. Adjusting entries are made at the end of the accounting period to correct mistakes in the records.

T F 4. Accrued expenses are expenses that have accumulated over time and have not yet been recorded.

T F 5. An accrued expense means that there is an accrued liability for the payment, but the payment has not yet been made.

T F 6. To record an accrued expense, the expense account is credited and the liability account is debited.

T F 7. Accrued revenues are revenues that have been collected but have not yet been earned.

T F 8. To record an accrued revenue, an asset account is debited and a revenue account is credited.

T F 9. All accruals can be reversed at the beginning of the next accounting period.

T F 10. A reversing entry is one that exactly reverses an adjusting entry.

T F 11. A deferral is a prepayment of an expense or an advanced collection of revenue.

T F 12. Deferred expenses include such items as accrued interest and accrued salaries.

T F 13. A deferred expense can be initially recorded as either an asset or an expense.

T F 14. If a deferred expense has been recorded as an asset, the adjustment must transfer the unexpired portion to an expense account.

T F 15. Deferred revenue can be initially recorded as either an asset or a liability.

T F 16. Adjusting entries for deferred expenses that have been initially recorded as assets can be reversed.

T F 17. Deferred revenue is revenue that has been collected in advance.

T F 18. Deferred revenue can be recorded as revenue or as a liability.

T F 19. If deferred revenue has been recorded as revenue and adjusted at the end of the period, the adjusting entry can be reversed.

T F 20. The adjusting entries for deferrals depend on how the initial transactions were recorded.

PART II MATCHING

Please match each of the following terms with its definition.

a. accrual
b. accrued asset
c. accrued expense
d. accrued liability
e. accrued revenue
f. adjusting entries
g. closing entries
h. deferral

i. deferred charge
j. deferred credits
k. deferred expense
l. deferred revenue
m. prepaid expense
n. reversing entries
o. unearned revenue

_____ 1. An expense incurred but not yet recorded.

_____ 2. Revenue that has been collected but not yet earned; also called unearned revenue or deferred credits.

_____ 3. Another name for deferred revenue or unearned revenue that is used for amounts that will not be earned for more than one year.

_____ 4. Journal entries made at the end of an accounting period to bring certain accounts up to date.

_____ 5. The liability that results from accrued expenses.

_____ 6. Another name for deferred revenue or deferred credits.

_____ 7. A synonym for prepaid expense or deferred charge.

_____ 8. An advance payment of an expense or an advance receipt of revenue that will benefit more than one accounting period.

_____ 9. An accumulation of expense or revenue over time.

_____ 10. Revenue that has been earned but not yet collected.

_____ 11. Another name for accrued revenue.

_____ 12. An advance payment for goods or services that will benefit one year or less.

_____ 13. A prepaid expense that will benefit a period of longer than a year.

_____ 14. Entries made at the beginning of an accounting period to undo adjusting entries made at the end of the prior period.

_____ 15. Entries made at the end of an accounting period to transfer the balances of the temporary accounts into the owner's capital account.

PART III FILL IN THE BLANKS

Please complete each sentence with the correct word or words.

1. The accrual basis of accounting recognizes revenue when _____ and expenses when _____.

2. A(n) _____ is an expense or revenue that has been incurred or earned even though it has not been recorded.

3. A(n) _____ is an expense or revenue that has not been incurred or earned even though it has been recorded.

4. Unpaid or unrecorded interest expense is an example of a(n) _____ expense.

5. When an adjusting entry is recorded for an accrued expense, the _____ account is debited and the _____ account is credited.

6. Accruals can always be _____ at the beginning of the following accounting period.

7. Supplies and prepaid insurance are example of _____ expenses.

8. The adjusting entry for a deferral depends on how the item was _____ when the original transaction occurred.

9. The adjusting entry for a deferred expense that was originally recorded as an asset debits the expired portion of the asset to a(n) _____ account.

10. Adjusting entries for deferred expenses that were originally recorded as assets cannot be _____.

11. A deferred expense can be recorded originally as a(n) _____ or as a(n) _____.

12. Deferred revenue can be recorded originally as _____ or as a(n) _____.

13. Adjusting entries for deferred revenue recorded originally as revenue _____ be reversed.

14. An accrual is the opposite of a(n) _____.

15. Adjusting entries are needed in order to recognize revenue and expenses in the proper period according to the rules of the _____ basis of accounting.

PART IV MULTIPLE CHOICE

Please circle the correct answer.

1. An accrued expense is also an accrued
   a. asset.
   b. liability.
   c. revenue.
   d. none of the above.

2. Accrued revenue is also an accrued
   a. asset.
   b. liability.
   c. expense.
   d. none of the above.

3. In recording accrued revenue,
   a. a revenue account is debited and an asset account is credited.
   b. an asset account is debited and a revenue account is credited.
   c. a liability account is debited and an asset account is credited.
   d. an asset account is debited and a liability account is credited.

4. Reversing entries are
   a. always optional.
   b. always possible for accruals.
   c. possible for some deferrals.
   d. all of the above.

5. If a deferred expense is recorded as an asset, the adjusting entry
   a. will put the unexpired portion into an asset account.
   b. will record the payment.
   c. will put the expired portion into an expense account.
   d. could be reversed.

6. If a deferred expense is recorded as an expense, the adjusting entry
   a. will put the unexpired portion into an asset account.
   b. will record the payment.
   c. will put the expired portion into an expense account.
   d. could not be reversed.

7. If deferred revenue is recorded as revenue, the adjusting entry
   a. will record the collection.
   b. will put the unearned portion into a liability account.
   c. will put the earned portion into a revenue account.
   d. should not be reversed.

8. If deferred revenue is recorded as a liability, the adjusting entry
   a. will record the collection.
   b. will put the unearned portion into a liability account.
   c. will put the earned portion into a revenue account.
   d. may be reversed.

9. The purpose of reversing entries is
   a. to avoid splitting later routine entries between two accounting periods.
   b. to offset all adjusting entries.
   c. to avoid future adjusting entries.
   d. all of the above.

10. An accrual is the exact opposite of
    a. an adjustment.
    b. a deferral.
    c. a reversing entry.
    d. a closing entry.

PART V WRITING/SHORT ANSWER

1. **Reflect** Make a list, in words or simple phrases, of the most important and meaningful points in this chapter.

2. **Question** Think about the most confusing points or the material you do not understand in this chapter. Write down two or three questions that remain unanswered.

3. **Connect** Explain, in one or two sentences, the connection between the main points of this chapter and the major goals of the entire course.

4. **Summarize** Review this chapter's Joining the Pieces visual summary and explain the concept(s) illustrated in a few sentences.

WORKING PAPERS

SKILLS REVIEW

EXERCISE 17-1

1.

General Journal

Page 1

	Date		Account Title	P.R.	Debit	Credit	
1							1
2							2
3							3
4							4
5							5

2.

General Journal

Page 1

	Date		Account Title	P.R.	Debit	Credit	
1							1
2							2
3							3
4							4
5							5

3.

General Journal

Page 1

	Date		Account Title	P.R.	Debit	Credit	
1							1
2							2
3							3
4							4
5							5

4.

General Journal

Page 1

	Date		Account Title	P.R.	Debit	Credit	
1							1
2							2
3							3
4							4
5							5

EXERCISE 17-2

(a) _____

(b) _____

(c) _____

EXERCISE 17-3

General Journal   Page 1

		Date	Account Title	P.R.	Debit	Credit	
1.	1		Adjusting Entries				1
	2						2
	3						3
	4						4
2.	5						5
	6						6
	7						7
	8						8
	9						9
	10		Reversing Entries				10
3.	11						11
	12						12
	13						13
4.	14						14
	15						15
	16						16
	17						17
	18						18

EXERCISE 17-4

General Journal Page 1

	Date		Account Title	P.R.	Debit	Credit	
1			Adjusting Entries				1
2							2
3							3
4							4
5							5
6							6
7							7
8							8
9							9
10			Reversing Entries				10
11							11
12							12
13							13
14							14
15							15
16							16
17							17
18							18

1. (line 2)

2. (line 5)

3. (line 11)

4. (line 14)

EXERCISE 17-5

General Journal

Page 1

	Date		Account Title	P.R.	Debit	Credit	
1			Adjusting Entries				1
2							2
3							3
4							4
5							5
6							6
7							7
8							8
9							9
10			Reversing Entries				10
11							11
12							12
13							13

1.

2.

3.

EXERCISE 17-6

General Journal

Page 1

	Date		Account Title	P.R.	Debit	Credit	
1			Adjusting Entries				1
2							2
3							3
4							4
5							5
6							6
7							7
8							8
9							9
10			Reversing Entries				10
11							11
12							12
13							13

1.

2.

3.

CASE PROBLEMS

PROBLEM 17-1A OR 17-1B

General Journal   Page 1

	Date		Account Title	P.R.	Debit	Credit	
1			Adjusting Entries				1
2							2
3							3
4							4
5							5
6							6
7							7
8							8
9							9
10							10
11			Reversing Entries				11
12							12
13							13
14							14
15							15
16							16
17							17
18							18
19							19
20							20
21							21
22							22
23							23
24							24
25							25
26							26
27							27
28							28
29							29
30							30

1. (a)

(b)

(c)

2.

3.

This page intentionally left blank.

General Journal

	Date	Account Title	P.R.	Debit	Credit	
1						1
2						2
3						3
4						4
5						5
6						6
7						7
8						8
9						9
10						10
11						11
12						12
13						13
14						14
15						15
16						16
17						17
18						18
19						19
20						20
21						21
22						22
23						23
24						24
25						25
26						26
27						27
28						28
29						29
30						30
31						31
32						32

This page intentionally left blank.

PROBLEM 17-3A OR 17-3B

1., 2.   **General Journal**   Page 1

	Date		Account Title	P.R.	Debit	Credit	
1							1
2							2
3							3
4							4
5							5
6							6
7							7
8							8
9							9
10							10
11							11
12							12
13							13
14							14
15							15
16							16
17							17
18							18
19							19
20							20
21							21
22							22
23							23
24							24
25							25
26							26
27							27
28							28
29							29
30							30
31							31
32							32

This page intentionally left blank.

1., 2. **General Journal** Page 1

	Date	Account Title	P.R.	Debit	Credit	
1		Adjusting Entries				1
2						2
3						3
4						4
5						5
6						6
7						7
8						8
9						9
10						10
11						11
12						12
13						13
14						14
15						15
16						16
17		Reversing Entries				17
18						18
19						19
20						20
21						21
22						22
23						23
24						24
25						25
26						26
27						27
28						28
29						29
30						30
31						31
32						32

This page intentionally left blank.

PROBLEM 17-5A OR 17-5B

General Journal

Page 1

	Date	Account Title	P.R.	Debit	Credit	
1						1
2						2
3						3
4						4
5						5
6						6
7						7
8						8
9						9
10						10
11						11
12						12
13						13
14						14
15						15
16						16
17						17
18						18
19						19
20						20
21						21
22						22
23						23
24						24
25						25
26						26
27						27
28						28
29						29
30						30
31						31
32						32

Study Guide and Working Papers • Chapter 17

705

This page intentionally left blank.

CHALLENGE PROBLEMS

PROBLEM SOLVING

1. Balance of Rent Income account before adjustment:

_____

_____

_____

_____

Balance of Insurance Expense account before adjustment:

_____

_____

_____

_____

2.

General Journal

Page 1

	Date		Account Title	P.R.	Debit	Credit	
1			Adjusting Entries				1
2							2
3							3
4							4
5							5
6							6
7							7
8							8
9							9
10							10
11							11
12							12
13							13
14							14
15							15
16							16

This page intentionally left blank.

COMMUNICATIONS

_____

_____

_____

_____

_____

_____

_____

_____

_____

_____

_____

_____

_____

_____

_____

_____

_____

_____

_____

_____

ETHICS

_____

_____

_____

_____

_____

_____

_____

_____

_____

_____

_____

_____

_____

_____

_____

_____

_____

_____

This page intentionally left blank.

PRACTICE TEST ANSWERS

PART I

1. F
2. T
3. F
4. T
5. T
6. F
7. F
8. T
9. T
10. T
11. T
12. F
13. T
14. F
15. F
16. F
17. T
18. T
19. T
20. T

PART II

1. c
2. l
3. j
4. f
5. d
6. o
7. k
8. h
9. a
10. e
11. b
12. m
13. i
14. n
15. g

PART III

1. earned, incurred
2. accrual
3. deferral
4. accrued
5. expense, liability
6. reversed
7. deferred
8. recorded
9. expense
10. reversed
11. asset, expense
12. revenue, liability
13. can
14. deferral
15. accrual

PART IV

1. b
2. a
3. b
4. d
5. c
6. a
7. b
8. c
9. a
10. b

PART V

Answers will vary. Please discuss questions with your instructor. You can also discuss issues related to this chapter by logging onto the Paradigm Accounting Web Site at www.emcp.com and clicking on the discussion section.

Comprehensive Review Problem 4

WORKING PAPERS

2.

	Date	Account Title	P.R.	Debit	Credit	
1						1
2						2
3						3
4						4
5						5
6						6
7						7
8						8
9						9
10						10
11						11
12						12
13						13
14						14
15						15
16						16
17						17
18						18
19						19
20						20
21						21
22						22
23						23
24						24
25						25
26						26
27						27
28						28
29						29
30						30
31						31
32						32

	Date	Account Title	P.R.	Debit	Credit	
1						1
2						2
3						3
4						4
5						5
6						6
7						7
8						8
9						9
10						10
11						11
12						12
13						13
14						14
15						15
16						16
17						17
18						18
19						19
20						20
21						21
22						22
23						23
24						24
25						25
26						26
27						27
28						28
29						29
30						30
31						31
32						32
33						33
34						34
35						35

	Date		Account Title	P.R.	Debit	Credit	
1							1
2							2
3							3
4							4
5							5
6							6
7							7
8							8
9							9
10							10
11							11
12							12
13							13
14							14
15							15
16							16
17							17
18							18
19							19
20							20
21							21
22							22
23							23
24							24
25							25
26							26
27							27
28							28
29							29
30							30
31							31
32							32
33							33
34							34
35							35

Cash Payments Journal

Date	Ck. No.	Account Debited	P.R.	General Dr.	Accounts Payable Dr.	Purchases Discounts Cr.	Cash Cr.

1., 2.

ACCOUNT Allowance for Doubtful Accounts   ACCOUNT NO. 112.1

DATE		ITEM	P.R.	DEBIT	CREDIT	BALANCE	
						DEBIT	CREDIT

1., 2., 3.

ACCOUNT Accounts Payable   ACCOUNT NO. 211

DATE		ITEM	P.R.	DEBIT	CREDIT	BALANCE	
						DEBIT	CREDIT

18 Accounting for Partnerships

CHAPTER SUMMARY

A **partnership** is a voluntary association of persons entered into with the objective of earning a profit. By law, a partnership must have at least two persons, but there is no maximum limit on the number of partners in a firm.

There are certain advantages and disadvantages of operating as a partnership. The advantages are:

1. Ease of formation
2. Combined experience and talent
3. Combined resources
4. Better credit rating

The disadvantages of a partnership are:

1. Unlimited liability
2. Mutual agency
3. Limited life
4. Division of authority

Although a written agreement is not required by law, all matters of importance to the partnership should be clearly expressed in written form. This written agreement is referred to as the **articles of partnership** or the **partnership agreement**.

Most of the day-to-day accounting for a partnership is the same as that studied earlier for a sole proprietorship. The same journals and ledgers used by a sole proprietorship can be used by a partnership. It is in the area of formation and income division that partnership accounting differs from proprietorship accounting. In a sole proprietorship, there will be a single capital account and a single drawing account for the owner in the ledger. In a partnership, the ledger contains a capital account and a drawing account for each partner.

The closing process for a partnership is basically the same as that for a sole proprietorship. However, the net income (or net loss) for the firm is split among the partners according to their **distributive shares**, which is usually set forth in the partnership agreement.

A partnership is usually formed by two or more persons investing cash or assets in a business. It is not necessary for each partner to invest the same amount of assets. In fact, it is not necessary for all partners to make an investment; some partners may be admitted to a firm because of special skills or special knowledge.

The net income of a partnership belongs to the partners, and they are free to make any division of earnings they choose. As noted already, the division is usually set forth in the articles of partnership. If the articles are silent as to the division of earnings, the law presumes an equal division. If the articles provide for a division of earnings but are silent on losses, the law generally presumes that losses will be shared in the same ratio as earnings. Profit distributions may include a **salary allowance** and/or an **interest allowance**.

Because a partnership is an association of persons, any change in its ownership results in the dissolution of the partnership agreement, and a new agreement must be formed if the business is going to continue. Among other causes, a partnership can be dissolved by a partner's death, disability, **bankruptcy**, or retirement. A partnership is also dissolved if a new partner is admitted to the firm.

According to the Uniform Partnership Act, a partner can sell his or her interest in a firm even if the other partners object. However, the person who buys the interest cannot have a voice in the firm unless admitted to the firm by all the original partners.

When a new partner invests in a partnership, three outcomes are possible: **goodwill** to the partnership; a **bonus to the new partner**; or a **bonus to the existing partners**.

Since a partnership is created voluntarily, it can be terminated at any time the partners choose. The termination process, known as **liquidation**, involves selling all noncash assets (realization), paying all debts to creditors, and dividing any remaining cash among the partners. Any gain or loss resulting from the sale of noncash assets is divided among the partners according to their distributive shares. The final distribution of cash, however, is made to the partners according to the balances in their capital accounts. The steps can be outlined in a **liquidation schedule**.

PRACTICE TEST

PART I TRUE/FALSE

Please circle the correct answer.

T F 1. A partnership is an association of two or more persons who co-own a business for profit.

T F 2. One of the advantages of a partnership is unlimited liability.

T F 3. Mutual agency means that each partner can enter into binding contracts in the name of the partnership.

T F 4. It is always necessary to have a written partnership agreement.

T F 5. Recording most routine transactions in a partnership differs from recording such transactions in a sole proprietorship.

T F 6. The entries for recording the initial investments in a partnership are very much like those made in a sole proprietorship; the difference is that there is a capital account for each partner.

T F 7. It is always necessary for partners to make equal investments when beginning a business.

T F 8. When partners fail to agree on an earnings distribution, the law requires an equal division.

T F 9. Partners can agree to any means of earnings distribution that they choose.

T F 10. A partner is an employee of the partnership and, therefore, draws a salary.

T F 11. The distributive shares specified in the partnership agreement must be followed to determine the amount debited or credited to each partner's capital account when Income Summary is closed.

T F 12. The distribution of earnings to the partners in the closing process involves the payment of cash to each partner.

T F 13. The financial statements for a partnership show a capital account for each partner.

T F 14. When a new partner is admitted or when a partner withdraws, the old partnership terminates and a new agreement must be made.

T F 15. Most accountants recommend recording goodwill on the partnership books.

T F 16. A partner must have the approval of all other partners before withdrawing.

T F 17. Terminating a business and selling and distributing all assets is called liquidation.

T F 18. Realization means converting noncash assets into cash.

T F 19. After the creditors are paid, any remaining cash in the liquidated partnership is divided among the partners according to their distributive shares.

T F 20. One advantage of a partnership is that the combined resources of two or more partners often make the new business stronger financially than individual proprietorships would be.

PART II MATCHING

Please match each of the following terms with its definition.

a. articles of partnership
b. distributive share
c. goodwill
d. limited life
e. liquidation

f. mutual agency
g. partner
h. partnership
i. realization
j. unlimited liability

_____ 1. One of the owners of a partnership.

_____ 2. Each partner is individually liable for the debts of the firm.

_____ 3. An association of two or more persons who co-own a business for profit.

_____ 4. Each partner can enter into binding contracts in the name of the partnership.

_____ 5. A partnership is dissolved when any partner ceases to be a member of the firm.

_____ 6. A legally enforceable contract setting forth the agreement to form a partnership.

_____ 7. The share of net income or net loss received by each partner.

_____ 8. An intangible asset made up of such favorable factors as superior management skills, excellent location, superior product line, or solid reputation.

_____ 9. Ceasing business, selling assets, paying creditors, and distributing the remaining cash to the partners.

_____ 10. Converting noncash assets into cash.

PART III FILL IN THE BLANKS

Please complete each sentence with the correct word or words.

1. Legally, there cannot be a partnership with fewer than _____ partners.

2. The most common type of business partnership is a(n) _____ organization.

3. A partnership is a(n) _____ association.

4. A partnership is _____ whenever a partner ceases to be a member of the firm.

5. It is good business practice to express all terms of the partnership agreement in _____.

6. The ledger of a partnership contains a(n) _____ account and a(n) _____ account for each partner.

7. When the partners cannot agree on income distribution, the law will divide it _____.

8. If the partnership agreement contains instructions for dividing income but does not mention losses, losses will be divided the _____ way.

9. To recognize investment in the firm, the partnership agreement can provide for _____ on capital balances.

10. When distributing income according to the ratio of capital invested, divide each _____ investment by the _____ investment to get the ratio for each partner.

11. Step three in the closing process is to close _____ to the partners' _____ accounts.

12. Distribution of earnings at the end of the period _____ a distribution of cash.

13. The balance sheet of a partnership will show a separate _____ account for each partner.

14. A new partner can be admitted to a firm only with the consent of _____ existing partners.

15. When a new partner receives more or less interest in a partnership than the amount of assets contributed, _____ may be recognized.

16. An alternative to recognizing goodwill is to record the investment of a new partner by the _____ method.

17. A partner may _____ from a partnership at any time.

18. The process of ending a partnership and paying out all the assets is called _____.

19. Before liquidation, the books of the partnership should be _____ and _____.

20. In the event of liquidation, any cash remaining after paying creditors is divided among the partners according to their _____.

PART IV MULTIPLE CHOICE

Please circle the correct answer.

1. Which of the following is a partnership?
   a. a group of persons who start a nonprofit neighborhood improvement association
   b. a business that provides services
   c. a voluntary association of persons entered into with the objective of earning a profit
   d. none of the above.

2. An advantage of a partnership is
   a. unlimited liability.
   b. limited life.
   c. mutual agency.
   d. ease of formation.

3. A disadvantage of a partnership is
   a. unlimited liability.
   b. ease of formation.
   c. combined talent and experience.
   d. combined resources.

4. In a partnership, net income or net loss will be divided
   a. equally.
   b. any way the partners agree.
   c. according to the provisions of the Uniform Partnership Act.
   d. according to a ratio of capital balances.

5. When the books of a partnership are closed, the usual closing routine is followed except that
   a. each partner's share of the net income or net loss must be determined before closing the Income Summary account.
   b. no adjusting entries are needed.
   c. it is not necessary to close the partners' drawing accounts.
   d. none of the above.

6. If John Smith is admitted to a partnership and his capital account is credited for more than the amount of the assets he is investing,
   a. he may be giving a bonus to the old partners.
   b. he may be paying extra for goodwill.
   c. he may be receiving a bonus from the old partners.
   d. none of the above.

7. If Mary Jones is admitted to a partnership and her capital account is credited for less than the amount of the assets she is investing,
   a. she may be giving a bonus to the old partners.
   b. she may be receiving a bonus from the old partners.
   c. she may be bringing goodwill into the firm.
   d. none of the above.

8. A partner may withdraw from a firm
   a. only with the consent of all partners.
   b. only with the vote of the majority of partners.
   c. only at the end of a year.
   d. at any time.

9. The first step in liquidating a partnership is
   a. to adjust and close the books.
   b. to sell the noncash assets.
   c. to pay the creditors.
   d. to pay the partners.

10. Converting all noncash assets into cash is the process of
    a. liquidation.
    b. realization.
    c. collection.
    d. recognition.

PART V WRITING/SHORT ANSWER

1. **Reflect** Make a list, in words or simple phrases, of the most important and meaningful points in this chapter.

2. **Question** Think about the most confusing points or the material you do not understand in this chapter. Write down two or three questions that remain unanswered.

3. **Connect** Explain, in one or two sentences, the connection between the main points of this chapter and the major goals of the entire course.

4. **Summarize** Review this chapter's Joining the Pieces visual summary and explain the concept(s) illustrated in a few sentences.

SKILLS REVIEW

EXERCISE 18-1

General Journal   Page 1

	Date	Account Title	P.R.	Debit	Credit	
1						1
2						2
3						3
4						4
5						5
6						6
7						7
8						8
9						9
10						10
11						11
12						12
13						13

EXERCISE 18-2

(a) Net income of $72,000

    (1) Ratio of original capital investments:

    (2) Ratio of 2:3:

(b) Net loss of $22,000

    (1) Ratio of original capital investments:

_____

_____

_____

    (2) Ratio of 2:3:

_____

_____

_____

_____

EXERCISE 18-3

(a) Excess divided equally	Kean	Garza	Total

(b) Excess divided in 4:1 ratio	Kean	Garza	Total

(c) Excess divided equally	Kean	Garza	Total

EXERCISE 18-4

	Date		Account Title	P.R.	Debit	Credit	
1			Closing Entries				1
2							2
3							3
4							4
5							5
6							6
7							7
8							8
9							9
10							10
11							11
12							12
13							13
14							14
15							15
16							16
17							17
18							18
19							19
20							20
21							21
22							22
23							23
24							24

EXERCISE 18-5

<table>
<tr><td colspan="7" align="center">Motley and Drew
Statement of Owners' Equity
For Year Ended December 31, 20X1</td></tr>
<tr><td></td><td colspan="2" align="center">Motley</td><td colspan="2" align="center">Drew</td><td colspan="2" align="center">Total</td></tr>
<tr><td></td><td></td><td></td><td></td><td></td><td></td><td></td></tr>
<tr><td></td><td></td><td></td><td></td><td></td><td></td><td></td></tr>
<tr><td></td><td></td><td></td><td></td><td></td><td></td><td></td></tr>
<tr><td></td><td></td><td></td><td></td><td></td><td></td><td></td></tr>
<tr><td></td><td></td><td></td><td></td><td></td><td></td><td></td></tr>
<tr><td></td><td></td><td></td><td></td><td></td><td></td><td></td></tr>
<tr><td></td><td></td><td></td><td></td><td></td><td></td><td></td></tr>
<tr><td></td><td></td><td></td><td></td><td></td><td></td><td></td></tr>
</table>

EXERCISE 18-6

General Journal

Page 1

	Date	Account Title	P.R.	Debit	Credit	
1						1
2						2
3						3
4						4
5						5
6						6
7						7
8						8
9						9
10						10
11						11
12						12
13						13
14						14
15						15
16						16
17						17
18						18
19						19
20						20

EXERCISE 18-7

General Journal

Page 1

		Date	Account Title	P.R.	Debit	Credit	
(a)	1						1
	2						2
	3						3
(b)	4						4
	5						5
	6						6
(c)	7						7
	8						8
	9						9
	10						10
	11						11
	12						12

EXERCISE 18-8

General Journal

Page 1

	Date	Account Title	P.R.	Debit	Credit	
1						1
2						2
3						3
4						4
5						5
6						6
7						7
8						8

EXERCISE 18-9

General Journal

Page 1

	Date		Account Title	P.R.	Debit	Credit	
1							1
2							2
3							3
4							4
5							5
6							6
7							7
8							8
9							9
10							10
11							11
12							12
13							13
14							14
15							15
16							16
17							17
18							18
19							19
20							20

PROBLEM 18-1A OR 18-1B

General Journal

Page 1

	Date		Account Title	P.R.	Debit	Credit	
1							1
2							2
3							3
4							4
5							5
6							6
7							7
8							8
9							9
10							10
11							11
12							12
13							13
14							14
15							15
16							16
17							17

This page intentionally left blank.

General Journal

	Date		Account Title	P.R.	Debit	Credit	
1							1
2							2
3							3
4							4
5							5
6							6
7							7
8							8
9							9
10							10
11							11
12							12
13							13
14							14
15							15
16							16
17							17
18							18
19							19
20							20
21							21
22							22
23							23
24							24
25							25
26							26
27							27
28							28
29							29
30							30
31							31
32							32

This page intentionally left blank.

PROBLEM 18-3A OR 18-3B

(a) Original capital investments:

_____

_____

_____

_____

(b) 3:2 ratio:

_____

_____

_____

_____

(c) _____ _____ _____   **Total**

(d) _____ _____ _____   **Total**

(e) _____ _____ _____   **Total**

(f) _____ _____ _____ **Total**

PROBLEM 18-4A OR 18-4B

1.

General Journal

Page 1

	Date	Account Title	P.R.	Debit	Credit	
1						1
2						2
3						3
4						4
5						5
6						6
7						7
8						8
9						9
10						10
11						11
12						12
13						13
14						14
15						15
16						16
17						17
18						18
19						19
20						20
21						21
22						22

2.

			Total

This page intentionally left blank.

PROBLEM 18-5A OR 18-5B

1.

Liquidation Schedule

	Cash	+	Noncash Assets	=	Liabilities	+	Capital ______	+	Capital ______

2.

General Journal Page 1

	Date		Account Title	P.R.	Debit	Credit	
1							1
2							2
3							3
4							4
5							5
6							6
7							7
8							8
9							9
10							10
11							11
12							12
13							13
14							14

This page intentionally left blank.

PROBLEM 18-6A OR 18-6B

1.

Liquidation Schedule

	Cash	+	Noncash Assets	=	Liabilities	+	Capital	+	

2.

General Journal

Page 1

	Date	Account Title	P.R.	Debit	Credit	
1						1
2						2
3						3
4						4
5						5
6						6
7						7
8						8
9						9
10						10
11						11
12						12
13						13
14						14

This page intentionally left blank.

CHALLENGE PROBLEMS

PROBLEM SOLVING

	Myers	Gibbs	Total	Net Income

This page intentionally left blank.

COMMUNICATIONS

_____

_____

_____

_____

_____

_____

_____

_____

_____

_____

_____

_____

_____

_____

_____

_____

_____

_____

ETHICS

_____

_____

_____

_____

_____

_____

_____

_____

_____

_____

_____

_____

_____

_____

_____

_____

_____

_____

_____

_____

This page intentionally left blank.

PRACTICE TEST ANSWERS

PART I

1. T
2. F
3. T
4. F
5. F
6. T
7. F
8. T
9. T
10. F
11. T
12. F
13. T
14. T
15. F
16. F
17. T
18. T
19. F
20. T

PART II

1. g
2. j
3. h
4. f
5. d
6. a
7. b
8. c
9. e
10. i

PART III

1. two
2. service
3. voluntary
4. dissolved
5. writing
6. capital, drawing
7. equally
8. same
9. interest
10. partner's, total
11. Income Summary, capital
12. is not
13. capital
14. all
15. goodwill
16. bonus
17. withdraw
18. liquidation
19. adjusted, closed
20. capital balances

PART IV

1. c
2. d
3. a
4. b
5. a
6. c
7. a
8. d
9. a
10. b

PART V

Answers will vary. Please discuss questions with your instructor. You can also discuss issues related to this chapter by logging onto the Paradigm Accounting Web Site at www.emcp.com and clicking on the discussion section.